Praise for *Some Science Adventures with Real Magic*

Telepathy, psychokinesis, remote viewing, clairvoyance and so forth are terms assigned to "exotic" phenomena of human consciousness that are as old as the hills. Even so, these have remained unexplainable by the modern sciences that have dwelt too long within the assumption that our familiar three-dimensional matter and physicality is all that exists.

As it is turning out in our immediate times, however, that "scientific" assumption is undergoing some significant jolts at its own cutting edges - with, for example: the discovery of so-called "dark" or "exotic" matter and energy that interpenetrate our own physicality; and the increasing probability of ten or more dimensions that also might interface with what has fondly been referred to as our atomic-matter-only universe.

As awesome as these cutting-edge discoveries are, the official conventional sciences in general have not yet supplied their meaningful implications to consciousness itself, much less to "exotic" forms of it.

However, the authors of this marvelous and astonishing book have been busy filling in this "exotic" gap in which they present more than enough scientific "subtle energy" evidence to choke several battalions of nay-sayers.

This terrific book clearly signals a new dawn of consciousness enhancement and unfolding.

- Ingo Swann
Artist, author and psychic extraordinaire

In this new book Dr. Tiller works his Magic in bringing us a new advance in science, in understandable language. James Conant said, 'by definition science moves ahead as a biped with a step in empirical research leading to, and often requiring, a step of revising conceptual schemes.' The history of science has revealed a common inclination, even among great scientists, to refuse to look at new research if it is in conflict with the prevailing paradigm. Real science requires theoretical revisions, sometimes even a new world view. If vested interests prevail, the advance of science is detained, and the pioneer may lose credibility, reputation and funding. Only the brave move ahead, as Dr. Tiller has done in this great work. He has addressed the new paradigm issue, conducted extensive and thoroughly scientific research, and integrated his findings with a theoretical framework adequate to the requirements of the data presented. This is real science! We join Dr. Tiller in challenging "scientists" and all thinkers, to examine the strong empirical foundations of these experiments and to reflect upon the new paradigms these data require. As we absorb the implications of this research we may have to move 'Intentionality' to the head of the list of factors influencing our personal lives and the destiny of the planet.

- Herbert Bruce Puryear, Ph. D.
Author, Psychologist, President of The Logos Center, Scottsdale, AZ

A plethora of books has been published in recent years questioning the validity of mainstream paradigms concerning time, space, and energy. However, few of them command the authority reflected in *Some Science Adventures with Real Magic*. Its authors have focused their research on human intention, a quality typically overlooked, even by other pioneers in this field. Tiller, Dibble, and Fandel describe instrumentation that can quantify the results of intention when it is directed towards influencing physical and organic phenomena. Finally, this book presents a summary of successful replications in other laboratories, making a persuasive case that human consciousness must be taken into account when constructing a viable worldview for the 21st century. In a world whose available resources are heading toward exhaustion, Tiller and his colleagues offer a technology that is corrective as well as sustainable, practical as well as visionary, provocative as well as inspirational. This book could not have arrived at a more suitable time, and its message could change the direction of history.

- Stanley Krippner, Ph.D.
Author & Professor of Psychology Saybrook Graduate School and Research Center

How healing happens is a great mystery. From cut knees to major health crises, we all have a stake in its outcome. Today, there are many new approaches to stimulating a healing response, including an increasing interest in the powers of our minds and the use of biofields and subtle energies. Unfortunately, science has often lagged behind public interest in these provocative treatment approaches. Fortunately, we have the numerous theoretical and experimental contributions of William Tiller, who is bridging the gap between mainstream science and the frontiers of knowledge about healing and the nature of reality in which it is embedded.

- Marilyn Schlitz, Ph.D.
V.P. for Research and Education at the Institute of Noetic Sciences
& Senior Scientist at the Complementary Medicine Research Institute of the
California Pacific Medical Center

It is spectacular. The consequences of the discoveries, described in this book, are far reaching and revolutionary. They are creating the foundation of the new science of the twenty-first century, in which the anomalies of the paranormal, of Eastern medicine, and of subtle energy will transform present science and begin to integrate it with an understanding of consciousness and spirit. It is an important work.

- Claude Swanson, Ph.D.
Physicist and author: *The Synchronized Universe*

William A. Tiller and his scientific co-adventurers take the reader to the very heart of a quest that significantly and convincingly expands the legitimate terrain of science. They expand the purview of scientific theory by widening the range of the empirically-given manifold of fact that constitutes the raw material of science through rigorous experimentation and quantitative demonstration firmly based on the scientific method.

The most important contribution they make to science is the categorical expansion of the domain of physical science. They demonstrate that human consciousness, hitherto considered "non-physical", can and does play a significant role not only in the manifest expression of nature but also as an integral constituent of physical reality.

Some Science Adventures with Real Magic presents a new paradigm of science in which the magical wonder of the universe disclosed to human consciousness is, in fact, the logical order of the cosmos interwoven with human consciousness. This is a science book with real magic that both stimulates our scientific imagination and satisfies our demand for scientific rigor.

- Yasuhiko Genku Kimura
Author: *The Book of Balance* and *Think Kosmically, Act Globally*
& Editor, *VIA: The Journal of Integral Thinking for Visionary Action*

At last! Most of us have long awaited "simple" discussions of some of the most intriguing issues from modern physics and consciousness. Just as he does in lectures, Professor Tiller has now provided the abundant wisdom of modern science in terms that demystify the remarkable magic of discovery. The exciting field of psychoenergetics is now revealed as the science of the twenty-first century.

C. Norman Shealy, M.D. Ph.D.
President, Holos University Graduate Seminary
Founding President, American Holistic Medical Association
Author: *Youthful Aging - Secret of the Fountain*

We are on the verge of a major shift in science, in which consciousness takes its place as a major factor in how the world behaves. This change will affect every facet of our lives. For a closer look at how the transitions will unfold, *Some Science Adventures with Real Magic* is an illumination.

- Larry Dossey, M.D.
Author: *The Extraordinary Healing Power of Ordinary Things* and *Healing Words*

"Subtle energy medicine" has become a popular but confusing buzzword because it covers time tested ancient approaches and therapies as well as a host of spurious devices and products offered by entrepreneurs, charlatans and well meaning but often misguided zealots. A major impediment to progress in this area has been the lack of scientific studies to support various claims and a paucity of knowledge about the mechanisms of action that might mediate any beneficial effects. This book provides a major breakthrough by demonstrating how human intention can robustly affect physical properties ranging from the pH of water and the activity of enzymes to the maturation of fruit fly larvae and how this energy can be stored on a low-tech electronic device to produce the same results at different locations and at other times. More importantly, it explains how these "real magic" results are attained based on precepts of quantum mechanics, thermodynamics, solid-state physics and electromagnetism that for the first time are clarified in a comprehensive but understandable fashion.

At the core of this emerging paradigm shift of "subtle energy medicine" is a growing recognition of how stress, emotions, a strong faith and intentionality can significantly affect physical and mental health, quality of life and everything around us. This can no longer be disregarded in scientific studies that ignore the variations in "objectivity" of different researchers. From a more practical perspective, this book can teach individuals how to use their own intentionality to promote health and achieve higher states of consciousness, creativity and intuition. The body is its own best pharmacy and the authors provide important insights into how to tap into the vast innate potential for self healing that resides in all of us.

Paul J. Rosch, M.D., F.A.C.P.
President, The American Institute of Stress
& Clinical Professor of Medicine and Psychiatry, New York Medical College

Some
Science
Adventures
with
Real
Magic

by

William A Tiller, Ph.D.
Walter E. Dibble, Jr., Ph.D.
J. Gregory Fandel

Library of Congress Cataloging-in-Publication Data

Tiller, William A.
  Some science adventures with real magic / William A Tiller, Walter E. Dibble, Jr.,
J. Gregory Fandel.— 1st ed.
      p. cm.
  ISBN 1-929331-11-8 (alk. paper)
  1. Parapsychology and science. I. Dibble, Walter E., 1946- II. Fandel, J. Gregory,
1951- III. Title.
  BF1045.S33T55 2005
  133.8'01'5—dc22
                                        2005007170

SAN 299-4038

PAVIOR

Printed in the United States of America

"Any sufficiently advanced technology is indistinguishable from magic."

Arthur C. Clarke, *Technology and the Future*
Harper, 1972

"The only way to discover the limits of the possible is to go beyond them into the impossible."

Arthur C. Clarke, *Technology and the Future*
Harper, 1972

"Any scientific data or personal observations that cannot be explained by the prevailing paradigm must be considered as magic - until an expanded paradigm accepts their lawfulness as an important part of nature's manifest expressions."

William A. Tiller
June 2004

Contents

Preface

The title of this book proclaims an important aspect of what this book is about. Our research work, procedures and experimental data is sufficiently beyond the common worldview and conventional paradigm that most people would consider it as "magic". However, it is fully lawful and consistent with an expanded paradigm, wherein it is just a higher level of physics, that is unfolding at this time to allow all of humanity to attain a higher level of beingness in our near future!

If we look at what science has accomplished in the past four centuries, perhaps the most important accomplishment is that it has taught us *how to do careful science in the simplest case*, where forces between objects in spacetime are either very local or very weak (these are gravity, electromagnetism (EM), the weak nuclear and the strong nuclear force). Thus, we are perhaps ready to tackle the other level of physical reality, which is at a higher electromagnetic inner symmetry level wherein everything is strongly connected to everything else (both local and non-local). Here, the biofields of the investigators react with the phenomenon being investigated. This book is at the fulcrum of such a change for science and thus for humanity.

Our conventional science has taught us that a quantitative relationship exists between mass and energy; that energy occurs in only discrete units so that all the basic processes of this cognitive domain (that we experience with our primary five physical senses) are quantized; and that the coordinates, distance and time, (that we utilize as a reference frame for viewing nature) are relativistically coupled via the velocity of EM light, c. Thus, at least macroscopically, establishment science tells us that our atom/molecule world is constrained to exist in the U(1) EM inner symmetry state where $E = mc^2$, $v \leq c$, the physical vacuum is empty, human consciousness cannot significantly influence physical phenomena, no significant connectivity exists between humans, and this worldview will forever describe nature's behavior. Unfortunately for establishment science, our psychoenergetics research of the past 35 years shows this worldview to be very, very wrong!

This book provides the reader with many things:

1.   It gathers in one place all of the key, robust, experimental psychoenergetics observations made by the Tiller group over the past 35 years and encapsulates them into four tables;

2.   It provides a description of a successful replication experiment at remote sites, run by other investigators in the U.S. and Europe, for the earlier intention imprinted electrical device (IIED) experiment with $\Delta pH = +1$ pH units (measurement accuracy of $\sim \pm 0.01$ pH units);

3.   It confirms that a **necessary** precursor for successful psychoenergetics experiments is the development of a higher electromagnetic (EM) gauge symmetry state than our normal U(1) state in the experimental space. Thus, human intention can lift our normal inner symmetry state of a macroscopic space above our normal U(1) level to ~ the SU(2) level where strong connectivity occurs between humans and also between objects;

4.   It reveals that the human acupuncture meridian/chakra system appears to be at a higher (~SU(2)) EM gauge state than our normal U(1) level so that, on the higher side, the main energy form of this level becomes modulated with information from the intention level of self and, on the lower side, has the thermodynamic capability to drive all processes at the atom/molecule level of the physical body and in the world outside of the physical body. This is how "sacred" spaces were created by humans in the olden days;

5.   It reveals that the physical vacuum is not empty **at this higher EM gauge symmetry level**, but rather, here the physical level processes appear to be magnetic monopole-related traveling at $v \geq c$ and, under the proper conditions, can couple strongly to the atom/molecule level so that our digital instruments reveal a sum of contributions from the two unique levels of physical reality;

6.   It describes a method/procedure (patent pending) for experimentally measuring the elevated gauge symmetry state functioning in an IIED-conditioned space in practical energy units. Thus, now we not only have a consciousness-stimulated device (an IIED) for the conditioning of a macroscopic space, and all the equipment therein, from the U(1) inner symmetry state to the SU(2) inner symmetry state, but we have also created a new type of device that actually **measures** the degree of elevation of the inner symmetry level of such a conditioned space above the U(1) level in electron volts (eV);

7.   It reveals the presence of an entirely new energy in nature, that appears to function via the movement of magnetic charge (monopoles) in the vacuum level of physical reality,

which produces very long range information entanglement between different sites of the same overall experimental system and

8.   It uses all of the experimental data to theoretically formulate a new reference frame (RF) for viewing nature which allows relatively easy coexistence of both our conventional spacetime science **and** all psychoenergetic phenomena with their new science plus consciousness, intention, emotion, mind and spirit.

In this book, using almost no mathematical aids, we have summarized the key experimental findings of our two earlier books and have outlined our more recent results on the successful replication experiments at several laboratories in the U.S. and Europe. Together, this large body of experimental data forms a firm foundation upon which we lay out a greatly expanded paradigm for future science wherein human consciousness can play a significant role in the manifested expressions of nature and in the technologies that might thereby be created.

This book is meant for a general readership and all possible steps have been taken to make it user friendly. However, both the experimental research findings and the new concepts needed to be assimilated are at considerable variance with our day-to-day, present cognitive world so some stretch of self is required for easy assimilation.

Chapter 1 tells the story of how this research got started and the key experimental findings from both the 1970 to 1997 period and the 1997 to 2000 period. These important findings have been summarized in two tables that will be utilized in Chapter 3 to help formulate the theoretical model we use for assessing this data. Chapter 2 describes the protocols and experimental findings for the two-year long remote-sites experiment wherein we show successful replicability of one of our Chapter 1 target experiments at four U.S. laboratories and two European laboratories. Chapter 2 also presents the important findings carried out on humans in the Payson laboratory during this same time period. Two additional tables of key experimental findings are summarized there for use in Chapter 3. Chapter 3 is where the background and key postulates are made for a new theory of reality, both the physical reality and the larger reality. In this chapter, a new reference frame is presented for the viewing of nature and for expanding the present quantum mechanical paradigm to include human consciousness as an important factor in physics considerations.

Chapter 4 describes the physics involved in the creation of our new magnetoelectrochemical potential energy detector for the hydrated proton. This detector allows one to measure the degree of conditioning of a space and its equipment above the U(1) level. Chapter 5 describes our growth in understanding of the two other characteristic features we have come to recognize as being associated with a "conditioned" space. These are (1) large magnitude, global oscillations of a wide variety of material property measurements and (2) information entanglement between both local and non-local measurement stations in the overall experimental system (even when they are 6,000 miles apart) and between humans and such measurement stations.

Chapter 6 qualitatively applies the theory of Chapter 3 to provide an explanation of eight different psychoenergetic processes (remote viewing, local and distant healing etc.,) and thereby shows that all psychoenergetic phenomena can be straightforwardly included in a description of nature's manifold expressions. Chapter 7 is the closing chapter and deals with the philosophical aspects of this new worldview as applied to humanity, science and technology.

The path ahead will be a great new adventure for all of us as we unfold in our beingness to build our inner sensory systems, infrastructures and capabilities to balance our outer actions on both this planet and others in the not too distant future.

First, we would like to acknowledge, and express our deepest appreciation for, the financial support of Lynn ("Buck") Charlson and Wayne Jonas, via Ditron, LLC and the Samueli Institute for Information Biology, respectively.

Next, we owe a considerable debt to a number of individuals for making this a more successful book. First, to Ed Mitchell, Suzanne Mendelssohn and Kim Jobst for each agreeing to read the manuscript in its final form before writing a section of the "foreward" for this book. Second, to Larry Dossey, Yasuhiko Kimura, Stan Krippner, Herbert Puryear, Paul Rosch, Marilyn Schlitz, Norm Shealy, Ingo Swann and Claude Swanson for each reading the manuscript and writing important and useful personal opinions concerning the quality and importance of this book for leading and supporting the important human inner transformation that is now occurring around our planet. Finally, we thank the fourth member of our team, Jean Tiller, for her nurturing of the team concept and for her personal contributions to its strength.

William A. Tiller

March 1, 2005

Foreward

The most challenging problem of modern science is to understand and model the many facets of consciousness in a manner acceptable to scientific scrutiny. It has been obvious to serious students of consciousness phenomena for several decades that mind is causal with regard to creating physical effects both within and external to the body. However, to apply the understanding from physics, chemistry and mathematics to this problem in an acceptably rigorous manner, other than simple statistical analysis of data, has been a daunting challenge for decades. In this breakthrough book, Tiller, Dibble and Fandel provide both experimental evidence and theoretical structure that represent important new insights and evidence into these illusive natural properties of well-trained minds. A central concept is *intentionality*, that illusive aspect of mind that suggests proactive association between mind and the environment. By demonstrating that intentionality can be stored in physical devices, transported to remote locations, and used to cause an alteration in the properties of physical matter, they have made a major scientific breakthrough that will have not only technological applications, but also provide a path for research into deeper aspects of the consciousness enigma.

-Edgar Mitchell, Sc.D.
Author, Astronaut & Founder, Institute of Noetic Sciences

In his preface to this book, Dr. Tiller makes clear "that human consciousness, under the proper conditions, can **robustly** influence physical phenomena in inorganic, organic and living materials". Whilst writing this book, he served as a founding influence in the creation of a global team of healers joined in distance healing of the 6-year-old son of a British MD. In the conception and the carrying out of the "Healing Hugo Experiment (HHE)", for which Dr. Tiller contributed a tutorial for team members, it has been abundantly and consistently demonstrated that human consciousness can **robustly** impact on physical phenomena to the extent of (1) contributing measurably to the will to live, (2) removal of pain beyond any expectation of the medical profession, (3) last minute cancellation of surgery strongly urged by surgeon who, on the basis of healing results, chose to change his mind and (4) correction of several gross bone impairments in the hip and back of Hugo.

While I find the Tiller team's replicable and **replicated** experiments all riveting, the ones I most heartily recommend to the reader are those which demonstrate the difference that specific intentions make in experimentation wherein all other variables remain the same. These experiments alone are, in my view, sufficient to transform the face of science for **all** time to come. It is also worthwhile to study what Dr. Tiller has to say about his personal experiments with the HeartMath techniques. Anyone uninformed about how our own consciousness can impact strongly on our own bodies, or who has ever doubted that this is so, will find in these descriptions compelling reasons to believe otherwise.

For those interested in Einstein and in the unification of both relativity and quantum mechanics, a topic that eluded Einstein for the 30 years that he devoted to it, Dr. Tiller says "Einstein quantified the relationship between mass and energy. Now it is time to do the same for the relationship between energy and consciousness, this latter process will change us greatly". Certainly, this is the big change in direction that lies ahead for science **in our lifetime**. We may expect an immense evolutionary leap forward for all humankind to result from this.

- Suzanne Mendelssohn, Ph.D.
Psychic and healer extraordinaire

As a physician I can not overstate the importance of this book. Let me tell you why, by beginning with a series of questions, just a few of the many, many questions that arise spontaneously as I begin to ponder the implications of what this book is saying.

What is intention? Where and how does it arise? What conditions intention? What determines its strength, its effects, its influences, its nature? What does intention do and how does it do it? Imagine that intention affects everything; not only what is done and how it is done but also the one doing the intending as well as every one and everything in immediate, intermediate and even far distant environments. It is important also to remember that one can equally substitute thought and feeling for the word intention, although there are, as the book articulates very real differences in the effects of so called automatic, ordinary thoughts and those that arise from a state of focused meditation leading to a clearly intended outcome or state. The implications of such a reality are so far reaching, and so profound as to be impossible to apprehend with the ordinary mind, with our ordinary thought and perception, for such a state of affairs, if true, would affect every aspect not only of science, but life as we know it. This is particularly important when considering negative thoughts and feelings, feelings of low self-worth and self-deprecation as well as negative intentions towards people and things around one. These too have measurable consequences most importantly for the one intending them as well as for those to whom they are directed. There are laws that govern these things, best encapsulated in the aphorism "what goes around, comes around". The evidence that heart-felt, loving and positive intentions or thoughts have significant physiological effects is easily seen in examining the effects of such states on heart rate variability and cardiac function. Heart-felt in such contexts assumes its rightful sense and meaning.

This book brings together evidence from painstaking experiments, conducted by committed, courageous and serious scientists, over a period of over 35 years, on and with living organisms and systems as well as inanimate objects, and processes. It is a work of such profound significance that it is difficult to overstate its importance. Its relevance at this time in world history is vital and critical. As a doctor it is evident to me that this is work that has stunning implications for science, for medicine, for healing and for the entire edifice of human life and relationship, indeed for all life and matter in and on our planet and beyond.

Such work does not emerge often in any epoch. When it does it and its originators are usually denigrated publicly and professionally. Professor and Mrs. Tiller, Dr. Dibble and Mr. Fandel, and their work are no exception. As with every encounter with what are for the time in which they originate, new, complex, and subtle phenomena, these heroic human beings have been tried, tried and tried again by professional and other critics and the media . Ultimately as a result, they are all stronger, more alert, and if anything more conscious than before they began. In this context I am moved to suggest that *"Some Science Adventures with Real Magic"* is a work that *must* be read, somehow and in some form or another by many, many people world wide. It is a book that if not required reading or too complex to read for many people (quite probably the majority), is nevertheless one which should inform the development of curricula for every school, every college, every university; in fact every one and anyone committed to understanding the nature of cause and effect and how one can positively and creatively influence this for the good of all. It should be part of the core subject matter in every theological school, every seminary and every religious institution, because it is the book that makes it abundantly clear that every aspect of life impinges on every other; not just as a casual intellectual comment. In short this is a book that makes it abundantly clear that every thought, every feeling and every action can and does affect everything else. As a doctor I explore this with my patients in many different ways. To have a work to which I can refer people to see that there is evidence for this is very good news.

What this work demonstrates is that intention is a process which can be cultivated, nurtured, concentrated, directed and measured. It is a tool, a process and a state more paradoxically powerful than almost any other in life, for it is something that we can become conscious of, that we can have control over and that we can use both for an infinity of reasons and in an infinity of ways. For years it has been customary to believe that mental state or consciousness cannot significantly affect physical phenomena, experimental space or experimental outcomes. This is now quite clearly no longer the case. Increasingly it is known that the observer affects the observed, that the participants in any experiment are integral to the effects observed and any consequent outcomes. This book demonstrates that human consciousness can and does influence and impact upon physical phenomena in all realms from the inorganic to the living.

When these ideas began to emerge they seemed so obvious to me. As a medical student the reason seemed so simple. It appeared self-evident that every thought, every feeling, every personal state, however mundane or spiritually elevated is accompanied by a complex matrix of physiological and biochemical interactions and states, and that as a result, no matter how weak, every single one would have its own field. When I enquired of myself what gives rise to these states and processes the question led naturally to asking what gives rise to the first thought or feeling, the first perception. Is it the result of a biochemical process and if so what gives rise to that? Where and or what is the energetic beginning? This leads inevitably to the question as to which came first, the chicken or the egg, or what matters, mind or matter?! It is obvious from the results of the experiments included in this book that Mind reigns supreme. However one seeks to answer the question, it is nevertheless an inescapable fact that complex biochemical interactions, states and processes are involved and that these involve atoms and molecules, particles and fields. This being the case there will be an interaction between all things. What came as a surprise to many is just how strong that can be, even though the measurable strength with current devices is so weak. Yet despite this, and this is particularly important in healing, is how it can be manipulated and just how serious the potential impact can be. This being the case, remote viewing, prayer, healing at a distance and many psychic phenomena can be shown to have a scientific reality, becoming explicable, becoming concrete rather than fantasy, and as such they become gifts for humanity.

Furthermore then, it is no longer acceptable to hide behind ones thoughts, to deny responsibility in any community for one's own state and spiritual integrity, and its impact on what happens psychically and physically. In medicine and healing, in all human relationship the importance of this is readily apparent, for it brings home so very forcibly the importance of mental state, and of attitude. This book goes on to show how such intention can be imprinted into very simple devices, and that such devices, and such intention, can influence matter at every level. Such imprinting requires self discipline and ability. If there is now scientific proof to underpin the experience, then there is also a language and an emergent methodology with which to take further the understanding of spiritual phenomena and perhaps most important of all, a way in which to prove God and the crucial significance of Love.

Kim A Jobst, MA DM MRCP MFHom
& Editor-in-Chief, *The Journal of Alternative and Complementary Medicine*

Chapter 1

Introduction

The reference frame (R.F) that we in our Payson lab use to analyze and understand our inner world is called "reciprocal spacetime", another 4-dimensional construct that is a frequency domain. Thus, together with spacetime (our outer world) we use a single, duplex reference frame for analyzing and understanding a united, inner and outer worldview of nature's manifold expressions.

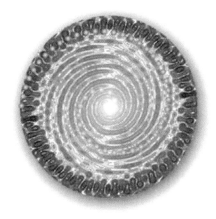

How this psychoenergetics adventure began

This story actually began about forty years ago in the summer of 1964. My wife, Jean, and I, along with our two small children, Andrea (6) and Jeff (4), were driving our Ford Fairlane across the country from Pennsylvania to California. I had resigned from my job of 9 years as a research scientist at Westinghouse Research laboratories, on the east side of greater Pittsburgh, and was taking up a new position as a tenured, full professor of Materials Science at Stanford University. I was thirty-four at the time and thought of myself as a scientist/business man who was a world-class expert on the science of crystallization. It was the beginning of a great, new adventure for all of us!

One day, while the kids were resting quietly in the back seat, Jean turned to me and said "Bill, when we get to California, let's try and pull together the spiritual side of our lives". I said "sure, let's do that". We had already been exploring the works of Edgar Cayce and had had a long-standing but casual and accepting interest in the psychic domain of human experience. Jean had grown up living across the street from a United Church of Canada (the closest analogy would be the Methodist church in the U.S.) and activities there were an important part of her early life. I, on the other hand, although very interested in "human fruits of the spirit", had a low tolerance for organized religion.

The way this joint decision unfolded in California was to get involved in some of the A.R.E.'s activities (Association for Research and Enlightenment, the Edgar Cayce organization). This introduced us to serious meditation practice and to study-group activities on two of Cayce's books "Search for God, Books 1 and 2". Concurrently, we found a Religious Science church in the Palo Alto area that we enjoyed attending. I took to meditation like a duck to water, while Jean not quite so quickly. We soon built this practice to a daily routine of ~1 hour duration. Meditation, centering ourselves daily in the spirit domain of reality allowed us to experience and explore both inner and outer realms of human awareness in a very balanced way. It greatly enriched our life and we both loved the time devoted to this practice. From this practice, both Jean and I developed a sense of communion with, and subtle guidance from, the "unseen". For me, I learned to rapidly oscillate (timeshare) between a state of being sharply focused on an item of particular interest and on a state of being open, receptive and loving to everything in the environment of the moment. It greatly aided me in my technical consulting practice and in my role as Department Chairman of Materials Science that I accepted in 1966 (due to an unforeseen illness to the long-time incumbent of that post at Stanford).

Although the late 1960's were turbulent years for academia in Northern California, they were also the years that Jean and I became avocationally exposed to many psychics and to many interesting psychic phenomena. These years might be labeled the "learning discernment" years for us. As the 60's came to an end, I received a Guggenheim Fellowship for a sabbatical year of study at Oxford University in England and, just before leaving the U.S. with my family, I purchased a copy of a fascinating new book that had just appeared, "Psychic Discoveries behind the Iron Curtain",[1] to read on the plane.

Our previous half-decade of personal exploration of this general topic area had prepared us to be able to accept the reality and viability of such psychoenergetic phenomena but not the scope and richness of the Russian technical explorations. At some deep level of self I knew that these writings were largely truthful, but I couldn't conceive of how the universe might be constructed to allow this crazy-seeming kind of "stuff" to naturally coexist with the orderly scientific phenomena that I was dealing with daily in my Stanford laboratories.

This puzzled me to such a degree that I largely abandoned what I planned to work on during this sabbatical stay in England (however, I did pursue and complete that work during the 1980's). I decided to use my mediation practice time to seek an answer to the question "how might our universe be constructed so that a natural expansion of our conventional scientific constructs would allow this strange class of psychoenergetic phenomena to become both sane and rational within a larger conceptual framework?

What assumed rigid constraints of our conventional worldview could possibly be relaxed to allow these two sets of experimental data to comfortably coexist?"

The procedure I followed on a daily basis was to hold both this general question and more specific detailed questions (like a "brick" in my open palms) during Jean's and my daily meditation - like a supplicant asking for guidance from the "unseen". By the end of the hour, I would usually have some intuitive measure of seeming enlightenment concerning the detailed questions. These, Jean and I would discuss after the meditation period and then I would work with them in my office for most of the day to see if they violated any rock-solid experimental data as distinct from our present interpretation of such data. Her unprofessional intuitions on such matters were importantly helpful. It was like trying to assemble an amazingly large and complex jigsaw puzzle with the boundaries between the individual pieces being allowed to be a little fuzzy. After six months of this daily routine a "working hypothesis model" had formed in my conscious brain that, although quite radical, might be useful, testable and possibly even correct! The overall conceptual picture that had begun to form in my mind was that illustrated in Figure 1.1. It had a distinctly theosophical flavor - probably from some of the books I had been reading around that time. Probably the most important part of this structure is that it was multidimensional; well beyond spacetime.

By this time, I had reached the irrevocable conclusion that it was extremely important for both humanity and future science that some competent U.S. investigator make a long-term, serious commitment to both experimentally and theoretically investigate psychoenergetic phenomena from a science perspective. Of course, this was a study area that was a total anathema to current and past science. This is because all science to date has worked under the implicit assumption that no qualities of human consciousness and intention can significantly influence well-designed experiments into physical reality. By this time I realized that the fragmentary experimental data from psychoenergetic studies, conducted at various locations in the world over the previous two centuries, overwhelmingly showed that this implicit assumption was very, very wrong!

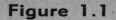

Figure 1.1

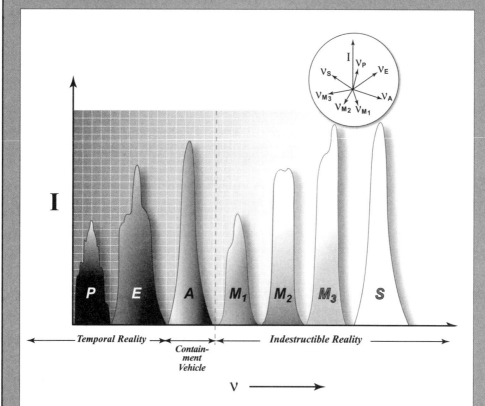

My first multidimensional representation of uniquely different bands of reality in spectral terms. (I = Intensity, ν = Frequency, P = Physical, E = Etheric, A = Astral, M_1 = Instinctive Mind, M_2 = Intellectual Mind, M_3 = Spiritual Mind & S = Spirit)

Through intuitive guidance from the "unseen", my first psychoenergetic model of the universe emerged from meditation. The overall conceptual picture had begun to form in my mind. Probably the most important part of this structure is that it was multi-dimensional; well beyond spacetime.

Before returning to the U.S., I decided that I could not avoid taking up this challenge and must begin leading a dual-path type of life wherein I would professionally continue my conventional science as a Stanford professor and, simultaneously, begin an avocational life-path of serious research in the area of psychoenergetics studies. In order to gain a block of time for the avocational research, I felt it was necessary for me to give up all my professional power positions, (1) the chairmanship position in my Stanford department, (2) my U.S. government committee memberships and (3) my technical societies committee memberships. My uses for this avocational block of time were threefold and all were equally important: (1) the continued experiential development of self via "inner" practices, (2) theoretical modeling of a multidimensional universe that allowed both conventional science and psychoenergetic science to easily coexist and (3) design and conduct of experiments to both test the theory and to push the envelope of our understanding. My ultimate goal was to build a robust and reliable bridge of scientific understanding that would, on one end, seamlessly join with conventional scientific understanding; would straightforwardly project through the various subtle domains of reality in the middle; and would be firmly planted in the bedrock of spirit at the other end. I was substantially supported in this by my wife, Jean, and substantially opposed in this by most, but not all, of my Stanford colleagues.

This psychoenergetics adventure was a joint adventure between Jean and myself. I was the very visible member of the team "trodding the boards of the world stage" so-to-speak while Jean made sure that everything ran smoothly at home. She served the daily needs of our two children and her husband, maintained a beautiful home, served as a cook and gracious hostess for many, many meals and meetings in our home for visitors, friends and acquaintances from both our conventional and unconventional worlds, arranged most of the social activities of our overly-busy life and yet still managed to strongly participate in the spiritual core of our unfolding adventure. Although I get most of the credit for this work, it could not have been accomplished without such a supportive and contributing partner!

During the 1970's I lectured widely on the topics of both psychoenergetics and conventional materials science. During this early period, I became a founding director of both (1) the Academy of Parapsychology and Medicine and (2) the Institute of Noetic Science, and began to also write scientific papers in the area of psychoenergetics. A reference list of these early psychoenergetic publications is provided in Appendix I-A for those who might be interested in learning what types of areas we had begun to investigate. Almost none of these journals are front-line scientific journals because the editors of such journals "were sure that their readership would not be interested in such material". By 1992, I had fulfilled my obligation to my main conventional science field by writing and publishing two books as a 40-year long investigation of the science of crystallization[2] and thus felt free to more strongly pursue my psychoenergetics studies. In 1992, I gave up my academic teaching duties to become a Professor Emeritus of Materials Science. I continued having conventional science Ph.D. students until ~2000 but began writing my first psychoenergetics book in 1992 based upon some of the papers in Appendix I-A and upon my ~50 years perspective on this field. This first book "Science and Human Transformation: Subtle Energies, Intentionality and Consciousness" was published in 1997[3] and provided some important conclusions for this present book. Some of the figures from that book will appear later without detailed captions but with a code (SHT 15, for example, referring to page 15 of the above book).

Defining the whole person

By this time, Figure 1.1 had transformed to Figure 1.2 and I had come to believe that we are all spirits having a physical experience as we ride the "river of life" together and, to effectively have this experience, we needed a suitable structural interface with the spacetime world. To make this more tangible, I came to believe that the whole person is much more than they appear to be. As a metaphor for the whole person, I like to visualize a sphere comprised of three concentric zones that are *at least* weakly coupled to each other (see Figure 1.3).

The outermost zone consists of two concentric layers of very different kinds of materials. This I call the personality self. The middle zone consists of three concentric layers, each constructed from three still different kinds of materials. I call this the soul

Figure 1.2 (SHT 56)

Figure 1.1 transformed to Figure 1.2 and I had come to believe that we are all spirits having a physical experience as we ride the "river of life" together and, to effectively have this experience, we needed a suitable structural interface with the spacetime world.

Here, the physical is spacetime while the conjugate physical is inverse space time; together, they form a unique member of an 8-space. This duplex space is imbedded in the domain of emotion, a 9-space, which in-turn is imbedded in the domain of mind, a 10-space. This 10-dimensional construct forms "the world of appearances", our relative universe, over which we have dominion. All of this is imbedded in still higher dimensions, 11 and above, the domain of spirit which forms the absolute universe.

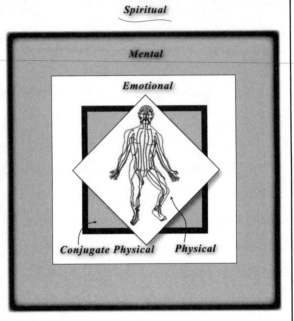

Spiritual

Mental

Emotional

Conjugate Physical   *Physical*

Figure 1.3

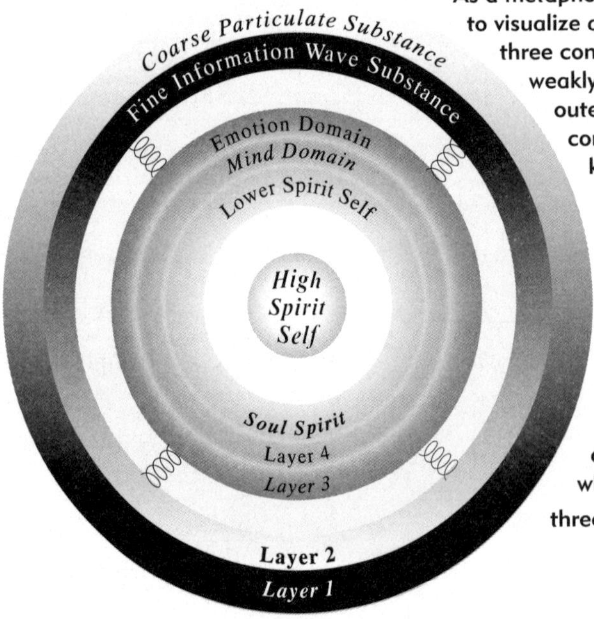

As a metaphor for the whole person, I like to visualize a sphere comprised of three concentric zones that are *at least* weakly coupled to each other. The outermost zone consists of two concentric layers of very different kinds of materials. This I call the personality self. The middle zone consists of three concentric layers, each constructed from three still different kinds of materials. I call this the soul self. The third, and inner zone, I call the high spirit self or the "God Self", whichever label one wishes to use. Thus, the whole person is made up of three very different selves!

Coarse Particulate Substance
Fine Information Wave Substance
Emotion Domain
Mind Domain
Lower Spirit Self

High Spirit Self

Soul Spirit
Layer 4
Layer 3
Layer 2
Layer 1

self. The third, and inner zone, I call the high spirit self or the "God Self", whichever label one wishes to use. Thus, the whole person is made up of three very different selves!

In the personality self, the outermost layer of material interfaces, via our five-physical senses neural circuitry, with what we call the outer world - the earth, our solar system, the cosmos. We have developed, over time, a successful reference frame (R.F.) for analyzing and understanding this outer world - we call that R.F. spacetime, a 4-dimensional construct.

With the adjacent layer in the personality self, via a yet unspecified sensory system but which is probably the acupuncture meridian/chakra system, we interface with the soul self. The R.F. that we in our Payson lab use to analyze and understand this inner world is called "reciprocal spacetime", another 4-dimensional construct but which is a frequency domain. Thus, together we use a single, duplex R.F. for analyzing and understanding a united, inner and outer worldview of nature's manifold expressions. Because these two, 4-dimensional subspaces of the unique 8-dimensional R.F. are reciprocals of each other, mathematics requires a unique and quantitative connection between the different materials in the two layers of the personality self.

With this unique 8-dimensional R.F., one is automatically led to simultaneous particle-type behavior in one sub-space connected to wave-type behavior in the other. This type of wave/particle behavior is a cornerstone of present quantum mechanics. In addition, this reference frame shows that a unique connectivity exists between any two points in one subspace via the totality of the other subspace and vice versa. The degree or magnitude of that connectivity, in turn, depends upon the activation of a particular energy that is thought to come from the soul self body.

As we all know, although our collective personality selves are all stewards of the earth, our personality selves have only a brief temporal existence.

The soul self, consisting of the still higher dimensional domains of emotion, mind and an aspect of spirit, is the entity that is importantly evolving in this overall process. It is much more durable than the personality self and is the repository of all the key experiences from a long succession of personality selves. When the various outer world classrooms have little more to teach the soul self, it graduates and transfers all of its essential information to the God Self. In this way the God Self is thought to keep expanding.

The personality self body is thought to be an evolved form of a basic animal species appropriate to the planet, in our case from the chimpanzee/ape family. In this way, it provides the well-developed 5-physical senses infrastructure needed to interface with spacetime. Interaction with the soul self genetically alters this personality self body making it an increasingly resonant vehicle for the soul self to interface with the spacetime world. However, at all stages of this complex uplift process, vestiges of the basic animal instincts and drives are present to varying degrees in the personality self. Thus, the personality self has a basically independent will and emotional structure from the soul self but can entrain to that of the soul self with ever-increasing degrees of coherence. It is interesting that such a model would make the Darwinian evolutionists correct (with respect to the personality self body) and the creationists correct (with respect to the soul self body).

As to the God Self, when I was considerably younger I had many wonderful theories about God. Now that I am older, and perhaps more awake, I realize that my personality self is not sufficiently conscious to even begin to seriously understand what that concept means!

Of course, this overall construct looks like a type of two-stage stepdown transformer/transducer between what we call God and one of God's inventions "spacetime nature perturbed by free-will humans". Consciousness exists at each stage with much more existing at the soul level than at the personality self level and, when a particular personality self breaks down and dies, consciousness continues in the frequency domains of the soul self and the high self. Our working hypothesis concerning what is meant by the term "consciousness" is that it is a byproduct, or emergent property, of spirit entering dense matter.

All of this metaphor is useful to our understanding of nature, but very little of it has been proven in a way that is satisfactory to science. Thus, let us now put on our "science" hat and return to a discussion of our experimental observations.

What important experimental findings were generated via the "Science and Human Transformation" study?

1. In a dual camera, rigid tripod mounting with a single shutter release switch experiment, wherein one camera was a normal, unsensitized camera while the other was sensitized by lengthy exposure to the biofield of a very special person, pictures were taken that appeared normal for the unsensitized camera but strikingly anomalous for the biofield-sensitized camera. In particular, often (1) normally opaque human bodies, revealed by the unsensitized camera, were semi-transparent to reveal objects on the wall behind such bodies, by the sensitized camera or (2) normal pictures of light wells and chairs in a room, revealed by the unsensitized camera, contained waving streamers or ribbons of light from the light wells and rising plumes of light from the chairs in the photos from the sensitized camera. Further, in a single sensitized camera on the tripod experiment, with the plastic lens cap still covering the lens, relatively bright and detailed pictures of the room appeared on the photos.

In all of this, the intention held by this very special person was just "to reveal God's Universe".

2. With a uniquely designed and constructed, high voltage AC gas-discharge device, (see Figure 1.4) set at an applied voltage several percent below the system electrical breakdown voltage and with a current pulse detector set to a level slightly higher than that which allows any microavalanche pulse to be recorded, we conducted a "poised-system" experiment. This poised system would exhibit zero recorded counts for many hours to many days. Even when a human stood close to the equipment intending nothing, there was still zero counts registered. However, (1) if the human placed their hands around (but not touching) the gas discharge device and *intended* to increase the counting rate, within a few minutes flashes of light appeared in the device concurrent with pulses of sound heralding electron microavalanche collisions with the electrode surfaces and tens of thousands of counts registered on the detector, and (2) with exactly the same human/device geometry as in (1) but the human now concentrating on a set of simple arithmetic sums like 2+2=4, 3+3=6, 4+4=8,……..48+48=96, etc. there was a *zero count* condition recorded. Further, with a human lying in a large, electrically-grounded Faraday cage, located ~15 feet away from the gas-discharge device that was itself surrounded by a small, electrically-grounded Faraday cage, and focusing their *intention* on the device to cause it to count, large bursts of counts occurred in the device (many thousands).

3.　　In a specially designed copper wall environment, utilizing four, 7 foot square copper sheets arranged in a cubic type of geometry but with two opposing side faces missing (see Figure 1.5), some human biofield effects were studied by Elmer Green and his associates.[4] Each copper panel was connected through a high input impedance electrometer to a common electrical ground in order to record electric voltage effects associated with a human sitting ~centered in this ~8 foot room, within a laboratory space, that had one copper wall in front (F) and one behind (B), one above (U) and one below (D). An additional electrode was attached to the subject's earlobe so that five independent and simultaneous recordings of voltage were being made.

Normal biofield humans and biofield-special humans were investigated in this unique experimental set-up. The biofield-special subjects were further classified into two groups (1) those that were energy projectors (healers, Qigong masters, etc.) and (2) those that were information receivers (remote viewers, clairvoyants, etc.). It was found that members of the energy projector group sometimes generated anomalously large voltage pulses that appeared on the ear electrode (with correlated smaller voltage pulses appearing on each of the copper walls). Instead of the typical ~10-15 millivolt baseline with ~1 millivolt ripple, the earlobe voltage often plunged to ~-30 to -300 volts and then recovered to baseline in ~0.5 to ~10 seconds. This is an astoundingly large voltage pulse, ~100,000 times normal!

For one healer, in a single 30 minute simulated healing session that took place inside this special environment, 15 of these anomalously large voltage bursts were recorded. A mathematical analysis of this data (based upon a subtle energy to electric dipole transduction postulate) showed that, in 13 of the 15 bursts, the spatial origin of the primary biofield pulses from the healer was the lower abdomen, front side of the body

Figure 1.4 (SHT 7-12)

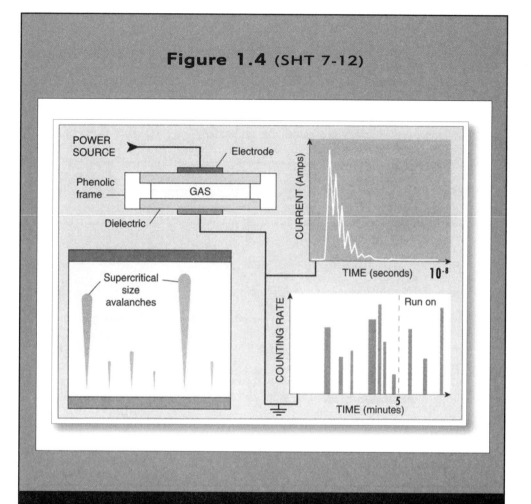

Even when a human stood close to the equipment intending nothing, there was still zero counts registered. However, (1) if the human placed their hands around (but not touching) the gas discharge device and *intended* to increase the counting rate, within a few minutes flashes of light appeared in the device concurrent with pulses of sound heralding electron microavalanche collisions with the electrode surfaces and tens of thousands of counts registered on the detector, and (2) with exactly the same human/device geometry as in (1) but the human now concentrating on a set of simple arithmetic sums like 2+2=4, 3+3=6, 4+4=8,........48+48=96, etc. there was a zero count condition recorded.

(second chakra location). For the other two cases, a second simultaneous burst origin was located in the head with the electrically negative end of the dipole closest to the ear and the electrically positive end closest to the upper copper wall.

It was theoretically predicted that, for the 13 main pulses, the electric dipole was ~5 feet in length and probably was associated with charge transfer along the acupuncture meridian that extends from the foot to the clavicle. Further, the amount of electric charge transfer needed to produce the required effect was extremely small and well within the known capacity of a human's acupuncture meridian/chakra system. [5]

4. Inner self-management at mental and emotional levels is crucially important for human capability development and a variety of procedures exist for pursuing such a goal; three of these are (1) yoga is the most well known practice and, here, one focuses on the mind in order to *still* the mind and thus come into communion with the deeper aspects of self, (2) Qigong is less well known but is quite powerful for the development of one's subtle energy infrastructure; here, one focuses on the "dan tien" point (second chakra region) in order to still the mind and (3) HeartMath is an even less well known procedure and here one focuses on the heart (heart chakra) in order to still the mind. In all cases, experienced practitioners gain great inner stability at mental and emotional levels and manifest very special human biofield capabilities.

Personal experiments with the HeartMath technique involved (1) consciously disengaging the mental and emotional reactions to either external or internal events and then shifting the center of attention from the brain and the emotions to the physical area of the heart while intentionally focusing on someone or something to love and/or sincerely appreciate and (2) simultaneously recording one's electrocardiogram (EKG) and converting that data into heart rate variability (HRV). At the electrophysiology level, the experimental data shows that there is an abrupt shift from a fairly erratic HRV-plot with time to an almost pure sine-wave type of HRV-plot with time indicating a special type of entrainment of heart and brain (see Figure 1.6). If one is simultaneously measuring body respiration and pulse transit time for blood flow from the heart to the finger tips, one also notices that these rhythms also entrain to the new HRV rhythm; that is, the electrophysiological

Figure 1.5 (SHT 15-16)

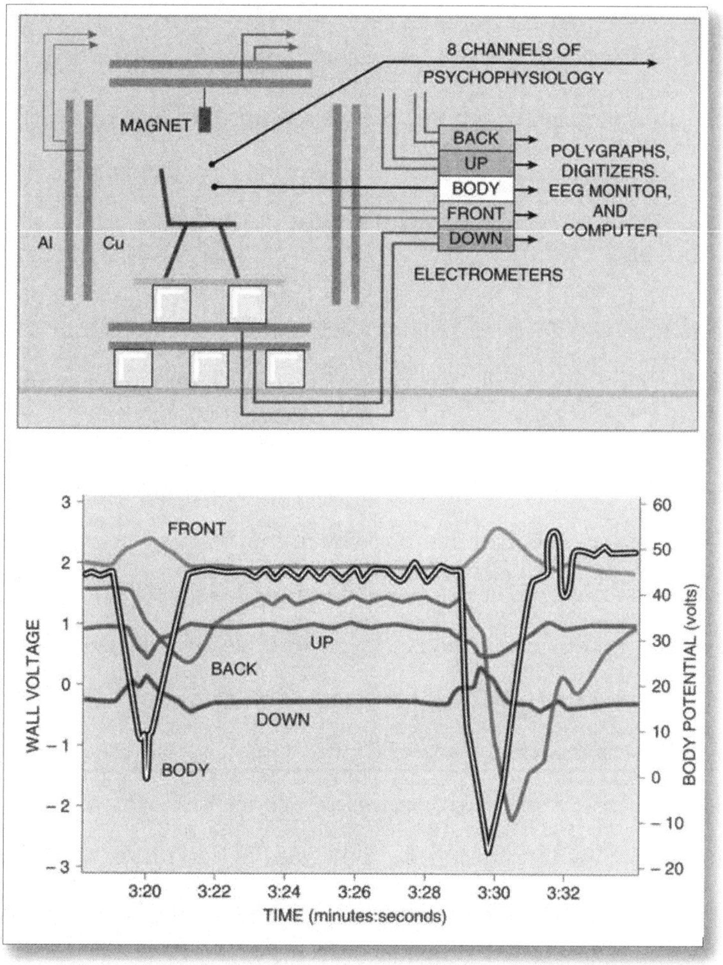

It was found that members of the energy projector group sometimes generated anomalously large voltage pulses that appeared on the ear electrode (with correlated smaller voltage pulses appearing on each of the copper walls). Instead of the typical ~10-15 millivolt baseline with ~1 millivolt ripple, the earlobe voltage often plunged to ~-30 to -300 volts and then recovered to baseline in ~0.5 to ~10 seconds. This is an astoundingly large voltage pulse, ~100,000 times normal!

state of the body is becoming coherent. With some small amount of practice with this technique, one begins to notice that important body chemicals begin to change. The DHEA levels increase while the choline levels decrease indicating a much healthier state for the body. For moderate to long-time practitioners of this technique one experimentally observes that, when in this "entrainment" mode or the "coherence" mode of heart function, the individual can *intend* to interact with an aqueous solution of DNA in a vessel several feet away from the body and can cause the DNA to unwind or to wind more tightly by choice. Ultraviolet absorption spectra of the water confirm such results.

5.   In experiments with young children (ages ~7-15), as detectors of subtle energy, it was learned that most, if not all, have a visual capacity to register both conventional electrical plus magnetic fields and subtle energy fields. In a "Punch and Judy" type of viewing box containing separated electrode plates or separated magnetic poles, they observed (1) colored and straight line patterns in the air gap between the plates which changed abruptly in form at unique electric field strengths on any given day for one subject and (2) the patterns were all curved and changed abruptly in form at unique magnetic field strengths on any given day for a single subject. Thus, these are subjective observations that change somewhat from day to day and from subject to subject.

Utilizing an early-on "mirror principle" concept, that is proposed to operate between the coarse physical realm and the conjugate physical realm (see Figure 1.2), it was speculated that the children were responding to this subtle realm light in order to detect these patterns, and they lost the ability when adults (most of whom could not see such patterns) told them to put away such imaginative nonsense and grow up - the imagined patterns are not real. Both a telescope experiment and a prism experiment were designed to test this "mirror principle" concept with the children. Normal light slows down and converges or diverges when it passes through a glass lens, depending on the type of lens (converging or diverging) while, via this mirror principle, the subtle realm light should speed up on passing through a glass lens or prism. Thus, via observations of these patterns by children through a simple telescope, instead of a magnified and inverted image as one would see with normal light, the children should see a demagnified, erect image with the

Figure 1.6 (SHT 220-221)

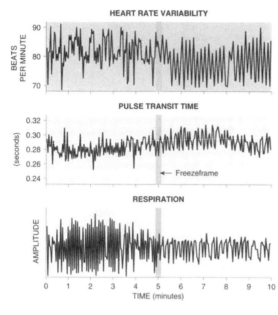

A column of entrained state data for each measurement plus the EEG data showing all lined up at the baroreflex frequency

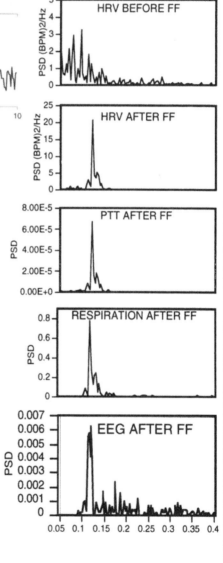

HeartMath experiments involved shifting the center of attention from the brain and emotions to the physical area of the heart while intentionally focusing on someone or something to love and/or sincerely appreciate and simultaneously recording one's EKG and converting that data into heart rate variability (HRV). The DHEA levels increase while the choline levels decrease indicating a much healthier state for the body. When in this mode of heart function, the individual can <u>intend</u> to interact with an aqueous solution of DNA in a vessel several feet away from the body and can cause the DNA to unwind or to wind more tightly by choice.

subtle domain light. The latter is what the children's data showed. Likewise, with the prism experiment, with the prism in a strong electric field that is perpendicular to the light beam passing into the prism (see Figure 1.7), normal light bends towards the base of the prism to give the Newton spectrum while this other type of light should bend in the opposite direction, relative to the straight-through path of the light beam, to yield a subtle realm spectrum. The children's data yielded the detection of both spectra.

6.   Experiments on some subtle properties of materials plus human body polarities were conducted with a professional dowser using various types of hand-held dowsing wands that could clearly discriminate five different modes of motion; (a) horizontal and vertical oscillations and (b) clockwise circular, counterclockwise circular and oscillatory circular. The type of wand motion was able to distinguish both bipolar and unipolar human energy fields (biofields) as well as bipolar, unipolar and oscillating polarity materials. Although the various modes of wand motion differed slightly for different wand-holders when one tested a large variety of different materials, there was no doubting that a strong physiological effect was felt with some materials (some quite positive and physically strengthening and some quite negative and physically debilitating). Different energy circuits of the body, with some materials, would appear to stop functioning until restored by holding some very different material. It became very clear that certain body circuits required subtle energy flow to occur only in a particular direction for a sense of physical well-being and physical strength to exist in the body.

Some theoretical deductions, from these experimental findings

1.   From experiment 1, one can deduce that the biofield of some humans emits/ contains certain subtle substances/radiations that (a) can pass through materials normally considered to be opaque to EM radiations, (b) generate or illuminate patches of subtle substance in the environment that are normally transparent to EM radiation and (c) cause this new information to register at some level of the film and transfer that information to the silver halide layer of the film so that it can be revealed by the normal film development

Figure 1.7 (SHT 29-30)

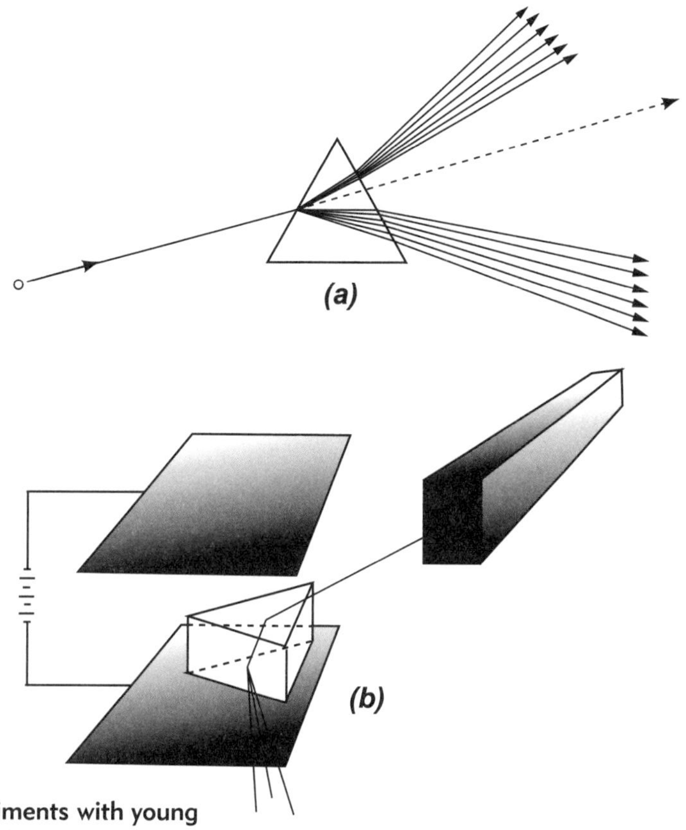

(a)

(b)

In experiments with young children (ages ~7-15), as detectors of subtle energy, it was learned that most, if not all, have a visual capacity to register both conventional electrical plus magnetic fields and subtle energy fields. The children were responding to this subtle realm light in order to detect these patterns and they lost the ability when adults (most of whom could not see such patterns) told them to put away such imaginative nonsense and grow up - the imagined patterns are not real.

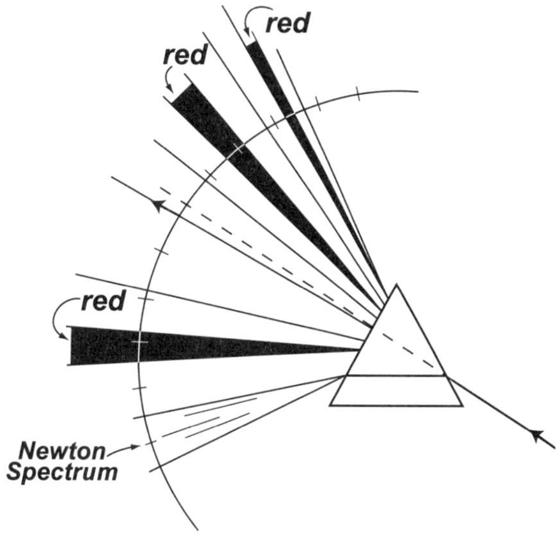

red

red

red

Newton Spectrum

process. Further, whatever quality is transferred from the biofield of this special individual to the sensitized camera, it slowly decays over a ~1-2 hour period so that the sensitization state of the camera is lost. Resensitization of the camera is readily restored by reintroducing it to the individual's biofield.

2. As in experiment 1, here we deduce that an energy substance emitted by the human, in response to their intention, interacts with electron avalanches in the layer of gas buried in the device. A friend, who was a good clairvoyant, observed the process and stated that something akin to ectoplasm (a word from two centuries ago) appeared to flow out of the human's solar plexus into the device and, as it flowed so, flashes of light and electron counts were registered. She also stated that, simultaneously, thin beams of light projected from both the forehead and throat centers of the humans into the device. From the experimental data it is also clear that, via *intention*, these energy emissions from the human body could be directed *away* from the gas discharge device so that zero counts were observed.

3. See Figure 1.8

4. From the studies at the Institute of HeartMath, we deduce that inner self-management exercises using a heart focus and heart rate variability measurement leads to profound electrophysiological entrainment of the body at the Baroreflex frequency (~0.14 hertz) where the heart communicates with and influences the brain. During this state, beneficial chemicals are manufactured and debilitating chemicals eliminated. In this special state of partial coherence, the human's intention also allows psychokinetic action to occur in media outside the body.

5. From experiment 5 we learn that young children exhibit many psychoenergetic capacities that we wean out of them around the time of puberty so that they can conform to the expectations of our "normal" society. As children, they appear to exhibit the

Figure 1.8 (SHT 18)

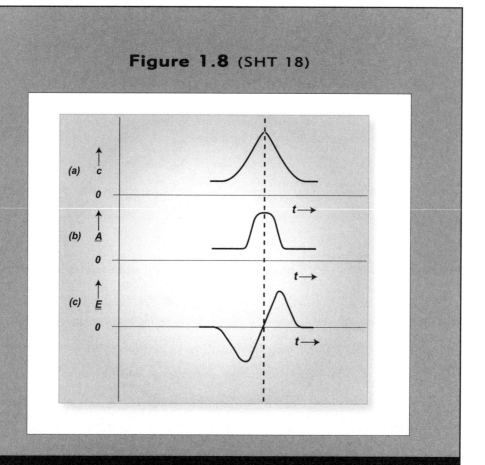

3.   From experiment 3, we deduce that a subtle energy projection occurs from the solar plexus chakra of the healer that is not directly observable by conventional techniques. However, if one postulates that transduction of this pulse to a magnetic vector potential pulse (a known potential in currently understood electrodynamics) occurs, then this creates a bipolar (in time) electric field pulse (see Figure 1.8) which, in turn, generates the electric dipole force accounting quantitatively for the phenomenon. Here, one sees that an electrical characteristic of the acupuncture meridian/chakra system of the body is intimately involved. Of course, many will presume that the electrical aspects of the model is the primary cause rather than a secondary cause.

[(a) primary pulse, (b) transduced pulse, (c) electric field pulse.]

capacity to visually perceive both normal EM light phenomena and a more subtle light-generated set of phenomena that manifests in a special type of "mirror" relationship to normal light phenomena. In this, since EM light travels at $v < c$ in air ($v = c$ in vacuum) and slows down while passing through denser media, the subtle domain light, traveling in the same collective light beam, appears to speed up while passing through denser media. Thus, we are dealing with a superluminal class of photons that appear to behave in a type of "mirror image" (not a simple reflection image) type of relationship to EM light.

6. From Nørretrander's book[6] we learn that the information channel capacity of the unconscious brain is ~50 million bits per second for the five accepted physical senses while the information channel capacity for the conscious part of the brain is *less than 50 bits per second*. We also learn that the unconscious processes manipulate and edit this incoming information in order to send kernels of such processed information to the conscious brain. However, it only sends kernels with the type of information that it knows the conscious brain will consider to be *meaningful*. In this regard, all sorts of dowsing wand, pendulum, etc., types of activity can be considered to be biomechanical transducers whereby the unconscious attempts to communicate with the conscious aspects of the brain. Of course, dreams are another channel for unconscious/conscious communication provided that the conscious brain considers the information to be meaningful and thus, in a discriminating fashion, makes serious attempts to interpret it.

Experiment 6 is just such an example of biomechanical transducer action revealing subtle energy functioning in both materials and humans. Further, it shows us that disciplined subtle energy flow circuits exist in humans that are extremely important to human health and to conscious/unconscious functioning. These findings have been summarized in Table 1.1 for further use in Chapter 3 where we fashion a work-in-progress theoretical model to account for all of our experimental data.

What came next?

Research funds for our psychoenergetics studies were always very difficult to find. In the mid-70's, a Swiss company's CEO arranged a $100,000 grant for WAT and

Table 1.1
Summary of Key Experimental Findings from "Science and Human Transformation"

1.   A highly developed human biofield can alter the properties of materials and the functioning of devices so as to reveal deeper levels of nature not anticipated from our normal every-day observations. The radiations from such levels of nature pass through materials that are optically opaque to EM radiations in the visible range.

2.   Non-EM emissions from the biofields of normal humans, when modulated by their attention and directed intention, can enhance or not enhance electron microavalanches in a simple gas discharge device depending upon the actual focus of the human's intention.

3.   Some humans emit bursts of subtle energy from various body chakras and, via a subtle energy/electrical energy conversion process involving the acupuncture meridian system, large voltage pulses appear both on the body and at sites remote to the body.

4.   When focusing on the heart with loving intent, the human EKG becomes harmonic at the baroreflex frequency, 0.14 hertz, where the heart entrains the brain and simultaneously all the other major electrophysiological systems of the body. In this heart entrainment mode of functioning, body chemical production becomes healthier and focused intent can psychokinetically influence molecular structures both inside and outside of the body.

5.   Most young children perceive both EM and subtle energies. Lens and prism experiments indicate that the latter travel at velocities , $v > c$, the EM light velocity, and speed up on entering denser matter.

6.   Dowsing is a natural human body response mechanism, for those who give it meaning, wherein the unconscious communicates valuable information to the conscious via involuntary small muscle movements or the creation of localized heat patterns.

eventually led to the gas discharge study and Figure 1.5. Unfortunately, this didn't help him politically within his own company and, in the outer world, he paid a price for this action. However in his inner world, we like to think that he benefited from this action. In the mid-1990's, at the behest of a friend, WAT was invited to consult with a wealthy Minnesota man on his own psychoenergetics experimental and theoretical work that he had been privately funding at his Lake Zumbra research facility. As a result of this, in 1996 he invited WAT to submit a 3-year psychoenergetics research proposal that involved fairly substantial funding. This research program began January 1, 1997, and focused on the use of intention imprinted electrical devices (IIEDs) to significantly influence specific target experiments utilizing inorganic and organic materials and, for the latter, both in vitro and in vivo experiments were carefully designed. The primary thrust of this new work was to provide a serious test of the long-held, unstated assumption of science that "no human qualities of consciousness, intention, emotion, mind or spirit can significantly influence a well-designed target experiment in physical reality".

To conduct the experimental side of this work, WAT first sought out and enlisted the aid of one of his former Stanford Ph.D. students, Dr. Walter Dibble, Jr., a geochemist. Serendipitously, a postdoctoral Ph.D. biologist, Dr. Michael Kohane, appeared at WAT's Stanford office looking for a new experimental research opportunity. These two plus WAT initiated the experiments at Stanford but, within 6-9 months moved the experimental portion of the work to the Minnesota facility at Lake Zumbra. In 1998, Gregory Fandel joined the group to assist Walter with his portion of the project. All the wonderful outcomes of this research have been documented in a number of published scientific papers (see Appendix I-B) and in a book by Dibble, Kohane and WAT entitled "Conscious Acts of Creation: The Emergence of a New Physics".[7] Some of the figures from this book will appear later without detailed captions but with the code (CAC 84-87) for example. Before considering the important experimental findings of this study, I think that the further unfoldment of the technical aspects of this story is best served by pausing briefly to learn something about Walter's and Greg's inner path development in this unfolding process, just as I did for myself, and somewhat for Jean, a little earlier.

Walter's and Greg's inner path unfoldment

Walter's interest in metaphysics began as a teenager living in Southern California. Both he and his mother were looking for alternatives to conventional religious paths and, in the turbulent 60's, their joint interest and search led them to the specific path of "Self Realization Fellowship" (SRF) founded by Paramahansa Yogananda. Walt and his mother were both initiated into Kriya Yoga in the mid-1960's.

Unbeknown to most of his friends and colleagues at both high school and college, at the University of California at Riverside, Walt explored the SRF spiritual path via reading and meditation practice. Many mystical experiences resulted from his relatively isolated practice in this regard during the 60's. In contrast, the 1970's was a time to focus on seemingly more "serious" academic work as a Geochemistry Ph.D. student at Stanford where WAT became his thesis advisor as he pursued a long term personal interest in the science behind crystal growth processes. The coincidence of our interests, both academic and spiritual, were not lost on him and, together, we embarked upon a joint path of discovery that continues today. This seeming coincidence has been remarkably fruitful for both of us.

The San Francisco Bay Area was a hotbed of "new age" mysticism in the 70's and 80's with a seemingly never-ending stream of Indian Gurus visiting the region, some to stay. One day, while listening to a radio program Walt heard an Indian Swami discourse on meditation with a perspective that appeared somewhat at odds with what Walt had learned from SRF. Since this program was followed by several weeks of frequent personal mystical experiences by Walt, he paid attention and many years later actually met Swami Muktananda, the radio program speaker, at his Ashram in Oakland.

In the years that followed, he renewed his abiding interest in the practices of Indian spirituality and this continues today. He was to learn from the power of mantra and chanting (Siddha Yoga) that there is no substitute for actually and regularly *performing* such practices, as distinct from merely supporting them intellectually. He learned from these experiences to both expect and enjoy the unexpected, something that is imperative for his performing much of the experimental work described in this book. For all of us, just when one thinks that you finally understand what is going on, a new set of confounding experimental data appears!

Greg's inner journey, like Walter's, began when he was a teenager. Introduction to Transcendental Meditation (T.M.) by his mother at the age of 18 calmed his life appreciably and opened his perspective to tremendous new ways of looking at the world - something vastly beyond outer appearances. Following his heart's wisdom and his own intuition soon became infinitely more important and promising to him than his former purely intellectual procedures.

In the early 1970's, he met an 80 year old Yogi, in Berkeley California, Mr. Chen, who thoroughly embodied the essence of Eastern Philosophy and was dedicated to spreading the Buddha's Dharma to the West. It eventually dawned on Greg that this great soul was in conscious meditation all the time and that he continually lived in a state of sublime peace and serenity. Greg took this as a model to follow. For him, the path of T.M. led first to "est" followed by the Church of Religious Science and eventually to Siddha Yoga in 1986 - quite a journey from his initial Roman Catholic upbringing.

One day, while in deep meditation, some inner wisdom suggested that he was not living the life he deeply wanted and that changes were required. In the spring of 1998 he quit a job of nine years that wasn't synchronous with this new dedication and took four months to relax, pray and request of the universe that a suitable opportunity might come his way wherein his inner world view and his outer world talents might be mutually satisfied and put to good use in the world.

Almost simultaneously, a friend from the Minnesota Siddha Yoga Meditation Center, one Walter Dibble, asked him if he would like to embark on a new adventure by working with Walter and myself in our psychoenergetics research program. Karma, fate, destiny, what was it? He sensed that his years of inner focus, via meditation and contemplation, were beginning to materialize and that a tangible spacetime opportunity had finally come. The physical universe was calling and he was joyfully ready to dive in and become a coherent, contributing partner to the new science/spirit "field" that Bill, Jean and Walter were creating. One of the many fruits of that joint enterprise to appear on the physical plane is this present book.

Figure 1.9 (CAC 84-87)

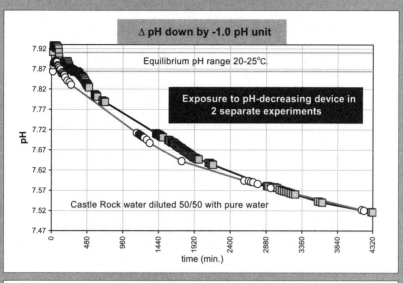

Δ pH down by -1.0 pH unit

Equilibrium pH range 20-25°C.

Exposure to pH-decreasing device in 2 separate experiments

Castle Rock water diluted 50/50 with pure water

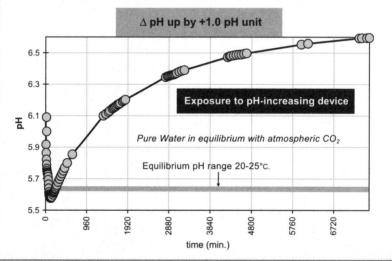

Δ pH up by +1.0 pH unit

Exposure to pH-increasing device

Pure Water in equilibrium with atmospheric CO_2

Equilibrium pH range 20-25°C.

Four accomplished meditators from a deep, collective meditation state, and perhaps with some unseen assistance, were able to imbed a specific target experiment <u>intention</u> into a simple, low tech, electronic device and then have that device (a) condition the space over time to what appears to be a higher symmetry state in nature and (b) to tune that space so that the prime directive imprint intention becomes ~fully manifested in the experimental results gathered from that specific target experiment.

What important experimental findings were generated via the "Conscious Acts of Creation" study?

1. That 4 accomplished meditators from a deep, collective meditation state, and perhaps with some unseen assistance, were able to imbed a specific target experiment *intention* into a simple, low tech, electronic device and then have that device act as a surrogate in a laboratory space, wherein the specific target experiment is set up, to do the following: (a) condition the space over time to what appears to be a higher symmetry state in nature and (b) to tune that space so that the prime directive imprint intention becomes ~fully manifested in the experimental results gathered from that specific target experiment.

2. We noticed that, taking two physically identical devices, one imprinted with a specific intention statement (IIED) and one not imprinted at all (UED), both in the electrically "off" state and separated by ~100 meters, a strange thing happened. In less than ~a week, the unimprinted device (UED) acquired the specific imprint of the IIED.

3. We found that, by wrapping the two devices in aluminum foil and placing them in separate, electrically-grounded, Faraday cages (FC), that the UED did not noticeably pick up the IIED's imprint over ~a 3-month period. Further, the IIED itself appeared to maintain a useful imprint charge intensity over ~a 3-month period.

4. Our four initial target experiments and their results were:
(a) **IIED-1**: to increase the pH of purified water (ASTM-I) *above* that of the standard theoretical value (water temperature and air CO_2 content-determined) by $\Delta pH = 1.0$ pH units with no chemical additions to the air or water. Our pH measurement accuracy was ~± 0.01 pH unit. It was successfully accomplished.
(b) **IIED-2**: to decrease the pH of the same class of pure water *below* that of the theoretical value by $\Delta pH = 1.0$ pH units with no chemical additions and the same experimental accuracy. It was successfully accomplished (See Figure 1.9).
(c) **IIED-3**: to increase the thermodynamic activity of a specific liver enzyme, alkaline phosphatase (ALP) by a significant amount, as determined by a standard colorimetric procedure. In a side-by-side, four treatment variations experiment, (i) a test tube of ALP in a dish of water exposed to the environment, (ii) the same as (i) but inside an electrically-grounded FC, (iii) the same as (ii) but also containing a UED (turned on) and (iv) the same as (ii) but also containing IIED-3 (turned on). The differences found for any pair were statistically significant at p<0.001 and percent differences in the

Figure 1.10 (CAC 151)

IIED-4: to significantly increase the adenosine triphosphate (ATP) to adenosine diphosphate (ADP) ratio in the cells of developing fruit fly larvae so that they become more fit and exhibit a significantly reduced larval development time to the adult fly stage.

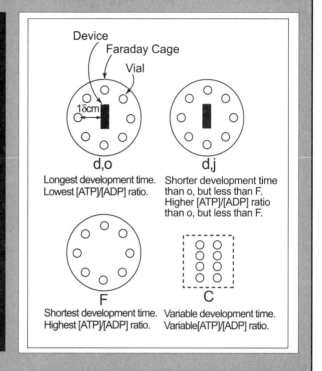

d,o
Longest development time. Lowest [ATP]/[ADP] ratio.

d,j
Shorter development time than o, but less than F. Higher [ATP]/[ADP] ratio than o, but less than F.

F
Shortest development time. Highest [ATP]/[ADP] ratio.

C
Variable development time. Variable[ATP]/[ADP] ratio.

Figure 1.11 (CAC 173)

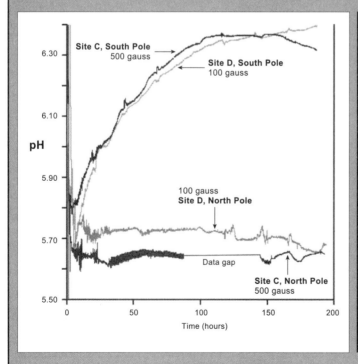

Experimental signatures associated with the IIED-conditioning of various Minnesota laboratory spaces showed up in a large DC magnetic field polarity effect on the pH of purified water.

15% - 25% range. This was particularly true for the IIED/UED pair, which showed the largest difference.

(d) **IIED-4**: to significantly increase the adenosine triphosphate (ATP) to adenosine diphosphate (ADP) ratio in the cells of developing fruit fly larvae so that they become more fit and exhibit a significantly reduced larval development time to the adult fly stage. Again, the same four, side-by-side, treatment variations as with the liver enzyme study were carried out (see Figure 1.10). All pair result differences were statistically significant at the $p < 0.001$ level with percent differences in the ~10%-20% range for the ATP/ADP ratio and with a maximum reduction in larval development time, $T_{1/2}$ of ~25%.

5. It was found that this space conditioning to a higher symmetry state was a necessary precursor for obtaining the robust target experiments result of 4, above. It was further found that, when the degree of conditioning reached a sufficiently high level, the IIED could be *removed from that space* and the space would maintain its high level of conditioning for a very long time (over a year at least).

6. Three characteristic experimental signatures associated with the IIED-conditioning of various Minnesota laboratory spaces were (i) a large DC magnetic field polarity effect on the pH of purified water was observed (see Figure 1.11). Such an effect did not occur in an unconditioned, non-IIED-treated space, (ii) *depending upon the rate of temperature change in the room* as a trigger, temporal oscillations appeared in the amplitude of a variety of measured parameters; such qualities as pH and electrical conductivity of water, air and water temperature, etc. The magnitudes of these oscillation amplitudes were ~100 to 1000 times larger than our measurement accuracy (see Figure 1.12). Further, they were global throughout the room (as distinct from only local) and the various wave components making up the wave patterns for these different measurements had exactly the same fundamental frequency plus higher harmonic frequencies and (iii) for two different laboratories ~100 to 1000 feet apart, when a pH-oscillation pattern is created in one laboratory (unconditioned), a highly correlated pH-oscillation pattern is created in the other laboratory provided it has been IIED-conditioned. However, a very poorly correlated pH-pattern appeared in the other laboratory if it was unconditioned.

7. Three experiments carried out in a highly conditioned laboratory space were very revealing. These were (i) the amplitude of air temperature oscillations measured at 6" intervals from a "source" and over an 11 foot distance were not significantly altered when a strong fan was directed at them, (ii) the spatial oscillation amplitude profile in a radial direction from this "source" exhibited a very anomalous shape (see Figure 1.13), (iii) when the supposed "source" of these oscillations was removed, the oscillation amplitudes did not collapse but only slowly decayed to small values over

Figure 1.12 (CAC 175)

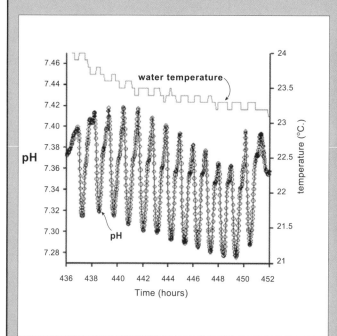

The magnitudes of these oscillation amplitudes were ~100 to 1000 times larger than our measurement accuracy. Further, they were global throughout the room (as distinct from only local) and the various wave components making up the wave patterns for these different measurements had exactly the same fundamental frequency plus higher harmonic frequencies.

Figure 1.13 (CAC 200)

The amplitude of air temperature oscillations measured at 6" intervals from a "source" and over an 11 foot distance were not significantly altered when a strong fan was directed at them; the spatial oscillation amplitude profile in a radial direction from this "source" exhibited a very anomalous shape.

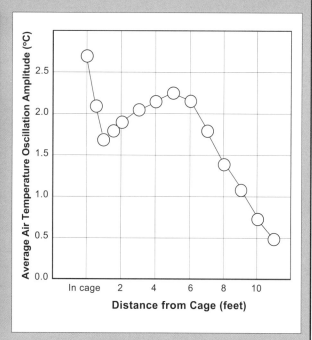

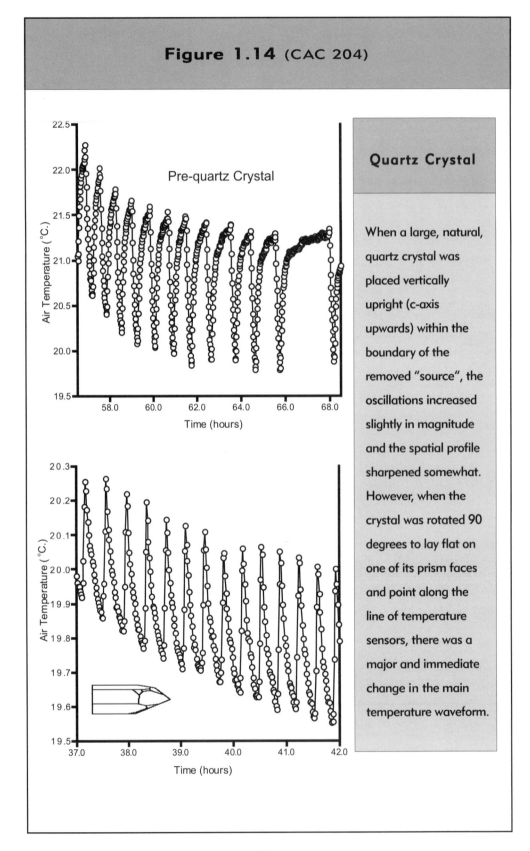

Figure 1.14 (CAC 204)

Pre-quartz Crystal

Quartz Crystal

When a large, natural, quartz crystal was placed vertically upright (c-axis upwards) within the boundary of the removed "source", the oscillations increased slightly in magnitude and the spatial profile sharpened somewhat. However, when the crystal was rotated 90 degrees to lay flat on one of its prism faces and point along the line of temperature sensors, there was a major and immediate change in the main temperature waveform.

several weeks and (iv) when a large, natural, quartz crystal was placed vertically upright (c-axis upwards) within the boundary of the removed "source", the oscillation amplitude profile increased slightly in magnitude and the spatial profile sharpened somewhat. However, when the crystal was rotated 90 degrees to lay flat on one of its prism faces and point along the line of temperature sensors, there was a major and immediate change in the main temperature waveform. Abruptly, the wave shape inverted, its fundamental frequency more than doubled and its amplitude decreased by about a factor of 3 to 4 (see Figure 1.14).

8. Several secondary, but nonetheless important, observations were also made. Perhaps first among these was the recurring observation that changing to a new piece of equipment, or adding a new material, to a target experiment generally produced an instant response in the oscillation patterns which then slowly (often over ~1-2 weeks) returned to its original pattern. Second, we observed a variety of anomalous time-dependent behaviors in our electrical monitoring and recording equipment that looked very much like temporary electric circuit instabilities. And third, we tended to see signs of experimenter effect wherein, the more positive and enthusiastic was the experimenter about the work, the better did the equipment perform and the larger was the effect size of the results.

Some theoretical deductions from these experimental findings

Experiments 1 and 4 above show that human consciousness, in the form of specific intentions, can have a robust effect on physical material property measurements for at least some inorganic and organic materials both in vitro and in vivo. A necessary requirement for this to happen is that the IIED must first "condition" the space to some higher level of reality wherein thermodynamic processes appear to exhibit more degrees of freedom that in normal, every-day reality. The IIEDs, themselves, seem to have acquired a kind of intelligence, at least sufficient to fulfill their own intention statement and no other, to act in this higher level of reality so as to produce new interactions in physical processes that allowed the intention statement to be fulfilled.

The underlying point of these results is that we humans must now accept the fact that nature allows the following type of reaction equation to occur

$$\textbf{Mass} \rightleftarrows \textbf{Energy} \rightleftarrows \textbf{Consciousness} \qquad (1.1)$$

More than a half century ago, Einstein quantified the connection between the first two terms of this equation and our abundant experimental data shows that there *is* a firm connection between the last two terms.

Experiments 2 and 3 above show that an IIED, in the electrically "off" state and unconnected to any electrical power source, can still broadcast information through some presently unknown channel of communication in nature to surrounding materials and somehow imprint them with this information. By wrapping the IIED in aluminum foil and storing it in an electrically-grounded Faraday cage, the rate of transfer of such information is significantly reduced.

From experiment 5 above, one sees that IIEDs, with repeated reimprinting, can raise the state of conditioning in a laboratory space, beyond the level where the state is kinetically metastable and will slowly decay after IIED removal, to a kinetically stable level from which it does not appear to decay even when all IIEDs have been removed from the space. It is almost as if some type of thermodynamic phase transformation has occurred which, even if metastable, exhibits such a large activation barrier for phase change that the kinetics of the reverse reaction is insignificantly small.

From experiment 6(i) above, one sees that, although a DC magnetic field polarity effect on pH is not allowed in our normal reality because the magnetic force is known to be proportional to the spatial gradient of the *square* of the magnetic field strength, $\underline{H}$, so the sign of $\underline{H}$ is irrelevant. However, in an IIED-conditioned space, we observe such a polarity effect and, to account for such an effect, one must propose that we are somehow accessing a magnetic monopole quality. The world governments via many very competent experimenters, have spent billions of dollars unsuccessfully looking for magnetic monopoles in our normal reality. Thus, we can conclude that they are not accessible from that level of reality. This supports the view that an IIED-conditioned space is at some higher symmetry state in nature.

Our normal reality readily accesses electric monopoles (single charges of + or - sign), electric dipoles (two bonded, opposite sign, electric charges at some separation distance) and magnetic dipoles (proposed to arise from spinning electric charges or orbiting electric charges). This electrodynamics is fully described by the well-known Maxwell's equations.

From experiment 6(ii), property oscillations of such a global nature are not observed in normal physical reality so they tend to again support the view that an IIED-conditioned space is at some higher symmetry state in nature that has a basic property of macroscopic coherence and this is what is driving all of these temporal oscillations.

The result of experiment 6(iii) is consistent with experimental observation 2, above, wherein an IIED, itself, is at this proposed higher symmetry state in nature so it is easy to understand how this proposed new energy field can communicate in a high correlation fashion with an already IIED-conditioned space but not so readily with one that has not been conditioned.

From experiments 7(i) and 7(iii) above, the origin of the property oscillations can be presumed to not come from natural convection flows in the room air nor from any quality associated with the air molecules. This means that their origin is at some other level of reality. Experiments 7(ii) and A7(iv) confirm that behavior at this "other" level of reality is very anomalous compared to expectations from our normal level of reality.

From experiment 8(i), one would deduce that (a) some unique quality is quantitatively partitioned between the room space and each piece of the experimental equipment and (b) the degree of partitioning into the equipment is a necessary condition needed for stable room property oscillation behavior. This appears to be a type of "circuit" oscillation property wherein the numerical value of the equipment component to the circuit is an essential part of the oscillatory behavior for that circuit. This proposal appears to be quite consistent with experimental observation 7(iii) which heretofore we have labeled the "phantom" phenomenon.[7] It is also most likely that experiments 8(ii) and 8(iii) are related to this same partitioning process of some "phantom" substance taking place in the room.

A brief summary of these experimental findings are collected in Table 1.2 for later use in Chapter 3.

Table 1.2
Summary of Key Experimental Findings from "Conscious Acts of Creation"

1.   Human consciousness in the form of a specific intention, can be imprinted into a simple, low tech, electronic device from a deep meditative state by highly inner self managed humans. Such a device, now called an IIED (intention imprinted electrical device), can act as an effective surrogate to robustly influence a unique target experiment in physical reality.

2.   The four unique target experiments studied involved (a) an inorganic material (water) with property changes 100 times larger than measurement accuracy, (b) an organic, in vitro material with property changes of ~20% at $p < 0.001$ and (c) a living, in vivo material with property changes of ~20% at $p < 0.001$, both of the latter having a built-in control.

3.   A unique intelligence was present in an IIED after imprinting so that the measured material property changes were (a) always in the direction of the IIED's intention imprint and (b) always specific to the particular IIED utilized.

4.   An unshielded IIED in the electrically "off" state and physically separated from a UED in the electrically "off" state by ~100 meters, still has a communication channel available to it for transferring the imprint statement to the UED within a week. Thus, the carrier for such information exchange is <u>not</u> conventional electromagnetism.

5.   This new field, although not EM, can be dissipated through EM leakage pathways. Thus, wrapping an IIED in aluminum foil and storing it in an electrically-grounded Faraday cage, prolongs its lifetime of effective use (~3 months before reimprinting is required).

6.   Placing a specific IIED in a room and turning it on "conditions" the room to a state wherein Item 2 above, naturally manifests. Without the presence of this "conditioned" state in the room housing the target experiment equipment, these material property changes do not occur.

7.   One characteristic of a "conditioned" space is that a DC magnetic field polarity effect on the pH of water occurs. Such an effect is thought to require the accessing of magnetic monopoles, a property usually associated with a higher EM gauge symmetry state than our normal, everyday reality. Such a higher EM gauge symmetry state is also a higher thermodynamic free energy per unit volume state.

8.   Another characteristic of a "conditioned" space is the spontaneous appearance of material property oscillations of very large amplitude (air and water temperature, pH, electrical conductivity of water, etc.) that are (a) global throughout the room (b) all exhibit the same Fourier spectral components and (c) all are in the frequency range $\sim 10^{-2}$ to 10^{-3} hertz.

9.   A third important characteristic of a "conditioned" space is that it is sensitive to the presence of an active IIED at separation distances of at least ~ 150 feet. Oscillations generated in the locale of the IIED spontaneously appear (at high correlation coefficient) in a "conditioned" space but not in an unconditioned space.

10.   If the degree of "conditioning" in a space is low and the IIED is removed from the space, the "conditioning" decays slowly with a time constant of ~ 1 month. If the degree of "conditioning" in a space is sufficiently high, the IIED can be completely removed from the space and stored properly and the level of "conditioning" in the room does not appear to change (at least for 1-2 years).

11.   The cause of the air temperature oscillations in a "conditioned" space near an apparent source was shown not to depend upon movements of the air molecules in the space but rather thought to depend on changes at the vacuum level of physical reality.

12.   Removal of the apparent air temperature oscillation source revealed that this vacuum level "phantom" source had a very slow relaxation time (~ 1-2 months) back to zero amplitude.

13.   While in the phantom temperature oscillation source mode of reality, abrupt changes in the orientation of a large natural quartz crystal placed in the initial source region showed abrupt changes in overall oscillation wave shape, wave amplitude and wave frequency. Thus, a quartz crystal appears to be a type of "tuner" for this vacuum source behavior.

14.   In a "conditioned" space, spontaneous and abrupt shifts in computer monitoring behavior of a random number generator (RNG) occurred from time to time for no known reason

15.   Experimenter effect, specific materials effects and specific device effects appeared, on the short term, to alter the "tuning" of the oscillations in a conditioned space.

Figure 1.15

The Payson laboratory (~1000 square feet) was completed by early 2001. We knew from the Minnesota research that a successful prerequisite for any successful research in the IIED area is to first "condition" the laboratory space to a higher internal symmetry state in nature. Special space conditioning IIEDs were created via our standard meditation procedure and six simultaneous IIEDs were placed in various corners of the laboratory. Four pH-monitoring stations, P_1, P_2, P_3 and P_4 are also shown.

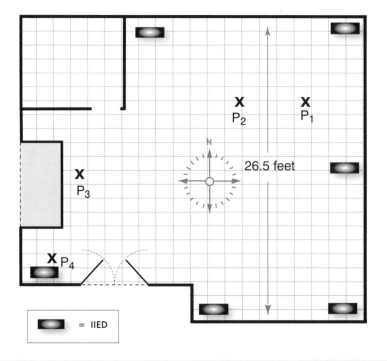

INTENTION for the lab: *"to activate the indwelling consciousness of the Payson laboratory in order to 'condition' it to a higher electromagnetic gauge symmetry state. The special characteristic of this state is to be specifically such that any psychoenergetic experiment subsequently conducted in this space would be significantly benefited".*

The next steps

Since the general scientific method requires that others be able to reproduce some of our Minnesota experimental results anywhere on the planet provided that they closely follow our protocol, we took this on as our next step which we divided into two parts. The first part involved building a new laboratory in Payson, Arizona to continue our IIED research in order to show that *we* could do it again at a new location. The second part involved showing that *others* could do it in their own laboratories at locations very distant from either the Minnesota or Payson sites.

The Payson laboratory (~1000 square feet) was completed by early 2001. We knew from the Minnesota research that a successful prerequisite for any successful research in the IIED area is to first "condition" the laboratory space to a higher internal symmetry state in nature. To accomplish this in the Payson lab, special space conditioning IIEDs were created via our standard meditation procedure (see Appendix 1-C for details). Three differences relative to the Minnesota work occurred; (1) only two of the original meditators rather than the four (the other two were unavailable) were utilized, (2) six simultaneous IIEDs, placed in various corners of the laboratory and turned on (see Figure 1.15), rather than just one, were utilized and (3) a completely new type of intention statement was utilized. The intention imprint statement for these six IIEDs (imprinted simultaneously) was "to activate the indwelling consciousness of the Payson laboratory in order to 'condition' it to a higher electromagnetic gauge symmetry state. The special characteristic of *this* state is to be specifically such that *any* psychoenergetic experiment subsequently conducted in this space would be significantly benefited".

My wife Jean, and I were the two sitters who meditated for the creation of the Payson lab's six IIEDs. Later, for an initial pH-increasing IIED at both the Payson lab and the two initial remote sites, the four meditators were Greg, Walter, Jean and myself. Still later, the original missing pair once again became available so that all the subsequent reimprintings plus the special IIED imprinting for the remote sites utilized six meditators. In all the device imprinting or reimprinting sessions, we have always felt that the unseen universe did the "heavy lifting" while our task was primarily to stay open, present and pure with a clear and silent interior state. We have always felt that, without this unseen assistance, we could not have accomplished such robust and profound experimental results. For this reason, for the remote site experiments, we provided all the IIEDs. We were not certain that the unseen would cooperate as well for all the remote site owners if they had to separately perform the imprinting step in addition to conducting the experiments.

The main purpose of this book is to describe the remote sites experiment along with the main experimental findings at all of the remote sites plus the Payson site plus at the control sites, one for each IIED site. All of this will be provided in Chapter 2. In Chapter 3, all of the key experimental findings will be gathered together and, from this array of data, a general theoretical model will be proposed that can account qualitatively for all of the data. Although this theoretical model has a full quantitative side to it, this book is not the proper place for its description. Chapter 4 will deal with thermodynamic potentials in both unconditioned and "conditioned" spaces and how we go about experimentally tapping faster than light processes in nature so as to build a detector of higher EM gauge symmetry states. Chapter 5 deals with an expanded range of remarkable material property oscillations, plus how they are thought to arise in a "conditioned" space. Chapter 6 qualitatively applies these new concepts to explain all psychoenergetic phenomena while Chapter 7 provides a philosophical perspective on what all this means to today's and future humanity as well as future science and technology.

For whom is this book written

This book is designed for the general public, and particularly for professionals with an interest in how human consciousness might influence processes and phenomena in physical reality. Thus, it is of interest to all those concerned with education about our species and our world; students, parents and teachers. It was written for all those with an interest in science and in the expansion of its frontiers. It was written for all those involved in health care, whether medical doctors, psychiatrists, psychologists, nurses, technicians or practitioners. It was written for technologists, inventors and business people who want to broaden the scope of their opportunities by enhancing the capabilities of their equipment, their processes and their staff. It was also written for all metaphysicians who wish to understand how human consciousness can produce what heretofore would have been called miracles. Finally, it is written for philosophers, so that they can come to understand that the real challenge for their deliberations is to fashion a collective worldview that integrates the following reaction equation into their models of nature

Mass $\rightleftarrows$ **Energy** $\rightleftarrows$ **Consciousness.**

Einstein quantified the relationship between mass and energy. Now, it is time to do the same for the relationship between energy and consciousness. This latter process will change us greatly!

References

1.   S. Ostrander and L. Schroeder, *Psychic Discoveries Behind the Iron Curtain.* (Prentice-Hall, Inc., Englewood Cliffs, N.J., 1970).

2.   W.A. Tiller, (a) *The Science of Crystallization: Microscopic Interfacial Phenomena* and (b) *The Science of Crystallization: Macroscopic Phenomena and Defect Generation* (Cambridge University Press, New York, NY, 1991).

3.   W.A. Tiller, *Science and Human Transformation: Subtle Energies, Intentionality and Consciousness* (Pavior Publishing, Walnut Creek, CA, 1997).

4.   E.E. Green, P.A. Parks, P.M. Guyer, S.L. Fahrion and L. Coyne, "Anomalous Electrostatic Pheonomena in Exceptional Subjects", Subtle Energies and Energy Medicine $\underline{2}$ (1993) 69.

5.   W.A. Tiller, E.E. Green, P.A. Parks and S. Anderson, "Towards Explaining Anomalously Large Body Voltage Surges on Exceptional Subjects, Part I: The Electrostatic Approximation", J. Scientific Exploration $\underline{9}$, (1995) 331.

6.   T. Nørretrander (J. Sydenham, Translator), *The User's Illusion: Cutting Consciousness Down to Size* (Penguin Books, New York, NY, 1999).

7.   W.A. Tiller, W.E. Dibble, Jr., M.J. Kohane, *Conscious Acts of Creation: The Emergence of a New Physics* (Pavior Publishing, Walnut Creek, CA, 2001).

Appendix 1-A
Tiller Psychoenergetic Papers Written Prior to 1992

1.   Radionics, Radiesthesia and Physics; Proceedings of the Academy of Parapsychology and Medicine Symposium on "The Varieties of Healing Experience," Los Altos, CA (October 1971) pp. 55-78.

2.   A General Technical Report on the Association for Research and Enlightenment's Fact Finding Trip to the Soviet Union; A.R.E. Journal 7 (2), 68-80 (March 1972).

3.   A Technical Report on Some Psychoenergetic Devices; A.R.E. Journal 7 (2), 81-94 (March 1972).

4.   Energy Fields and the Human Body, Part I; Proceedings of the Association for Research and Enlightenment's Symposium on "Mind-Body Relationships in the Disease Process," Phoenix, AZ, January 1972.

5.   Energy Fields and the Human Body, Part II; Ibid.

6.   Some Energy Field Observations of Man and Nature; Proceedings of the "First Western Hemisphere Conference on Kirlian Photography, Acupuncture and the Human Aura," New York, May 1972. In *Galaxies of Life*, Eds: S. Krippner and D. Rubin (Gordon & Breach, New York, 1973). Also in *Kirlian Aura: Photographing the Galaxies of Life* (Doubleday, 1974).

7.   Some Physical Network Characteristics of Acupuncture Points and Meridians; Proceedings of the Academy of Parapsychology and Medicine's Symposium on "Acupuncture," Stanford University, June 1972.

8.   Consciousness, Radiation and the developing Sensory System; Proceedings of the Association of Parapsychology and Medicine's Symposium on "Dimensions of Healing," Stanford University, September 1972.

9.   On Corona Discharge Photography; Journal of Applied Physics 44, 3102 (1973). [co-author – D.G. Boyers]

10. The Light Source in High Voltage Photography; Proceedings of the "Second Western Hemisphere Conference on Kirlian Photography, Acupuncture and the Human Aura," New York, February 1973.

11. Some Psychoenergetic Experiments in Russia; Proceedings of the Golden West College Conference on "Science and Psi," May 1972.

12. Devices for Monitoring Nonphysical Energies in *Psychic Exploration*, Eds: E.D. Mitchell and John White (Putnam Press, 1974).

13. Disease as a Biofeedback Mechanism for the Transformation of Man; Proceedings of the Association of Research and Enlightenment's Medical Symposium, Phoenix, AZ, January 1973.

14. Unveiling the Mysteries of Kirlian Photography; Proceedings of the Association of Research and Enlightenment's Medical Symposium on "New Horizons in Healing," Phoenix, AZ, January 1974.

15. The Color in Kirlian Photographs - - Fact or Artifact?; Functional Photography 11. No. 3, 20 (May 1976). [co-author – D.G. Boyers]

16. A Scientist Bridges Two Worlds; Interview of Prof. W.A. Tiller by Science of Mind Magazine (Jan. & Feb. 1974).

17.   Energy Fields and the Human Body in *Frontiers of Consciousness*, Ed: John White (Julian Press, Inc., 1974).

18.   Psychoenergetic Field Studies Using a Biomechanical Transducer, Part I; Proceedings of the Association for Research and Enlightenment's Medical Symposium on New Horizons in Healing, Phoenix, AZ, January 1974. [co-author – Wayne Cook]

19.   Are Psychoenergetic Pictures Possible?; New Scientist <u>62</u>, 160 (1974).

20.   Towards a Kirlian Device for Monitoring Physiological State, Part I: Device Considerations. Unpublished. [co-authors – D.G. Boyers and H.S. Dakin]

21.   Three Relationships of Man; Commencement Address given by Prof. W.A. Tiller at the California Institute of Asian Studies, San Francisco, August 1974.

22.   Three Relationships of Man; Proceedings of the Association for Research and Enlightenment's Medical Symposium, Phoenix, AZ, January 1975. Multidisciplinary Research, 4, part 1, 143 (April 1976).

23.   The Positive and Negative Space-Time Frames as Conjugate Systems; Proceedings of the Association for Research and Enlightenment's Medical Symposium, Phoenix, AZ, January 1975. In *Future Science*, Eds. Stanley Krippner and John White (Doubleday-Anchor, 1976), p 257.

24.   Kirlian Photography, Its Scientific Foundations and Future Potential. REVIEW ARTICLE, 149 pp. Unpublished.

25.   Some Ideas on Healing in the World of Appearances; in *The Truth About Paranormal Healing*, ed: G. Meek (Quest Books, 1977).

26.   New Fields - - New Laws; in *Future Science*, eds: Stanley Krippner and John White (Doubleday-Anchor, 1976), p 28.

27.   Kirlian Photography as an Electro-Therapeutics Research Tool; The Int. J. of Acupuncture and Electro-Therapeutics Research 2, 33 (1976).

28.   Present Scientific Understanding of the Kirlian Discharge Process; J. of the Osteopathic Physician (February 1976). Also, in J. of Psychoenergetic Systems 3, 21 (1979).

29.   Field Effects, Acupuncture Points and Meridians; Psychoenergetic Systems 1, 217 (1977).

30.   Commentary on the Phantom Leaf Effect; Psychoenergetic Systems 1, 232 (1977).

31.   Rationale for Energy Concepts in Medicine; in *Wholistic Healing: New Frontiers in the Treatment of the Whole Person*, eds: H.A. Otto and J.W. Knight (Nelson-Hall, Chicago, 1978).

32.   Future Medical Therapeutics Based Upon Controlled Energy Fields; Proceedings of the Association for Research and Enlightenment's Medical Symposium, Phoenix, AZ, January 1976.

33.   Towards a Future Medicine Based on Controlled Energy Fields, Phoenix 1, no. 1, 5 (1977).

34.   Towards a Medicine of Subtle Energies, in Holistic Dimensions in Healing (A Resource Guide), ed: L. Kaslof (Doubleday-Dolphin Press, 1977).

35.   Dielectric Response in Human Skin. Unpublished. [co-author – L.E. Nagel]

36. A Lattice Model of Space and Its Relationship to Multidimensional Physics; Proceedings of the Association for Research and Enlightenment's Medical Symposium, Phoenix, AZ, January 1977.

37. Creating a New Functional Model of Body Healing Energies; J. of Holistic Health IV, 102 (1979).

38. The Simulator and the Being; Phoenix, 1, no. 2, 28 (1977).

39. The Scientific Foundations of Kirlian Photography as a Medical Diagnostic Tool; Proceedings of Electro/78, Boston, May 1978.

40. A Multidimensional View; Re-Vision 1, no. 3/4, 98 (Summer/Fall 1978).

41. A Rationale for the Potentizing Process in Homeopathic Remedies; J. of Homeopathic Practice II(1), 53 (1979).

42. A Rationale for the Homeopathic 'Law of Similars'; J. of Homeopathic Practice II(1), 48 (1979).

43. Index of Refraction Measurements for a Superluminal Radiation; Proceedings of the Association of Research and Enlightenment's Medical Symposium, Phoenix, AZ, January 1977. [co-author – J.B. Carlton]

44. Towards the Discrimination of Subtle Energies; in *Science and Spiritual Evolution*, ed: H. Motoyama (Autumn Press, Inc., 1978).

45. Two Space-Time Mirror-Like Universes: Some Consequences for Humanity; Phoenix 2, no. 1 (1978).

46.   Positive and Negative Space/Time Energies; Proceedings of the Association for Research and Enlightenment's Medical Symposium, Phoenix, AZ, January 1977. [co-author – J.B. Carlton]

47.   A Lattice Model of Space; Phoenix 2, no. 2, 27 (1978).

48.   On the Explanation of Electrodermal Diagnostic and Treatment Instruments, Part I: The Electrical Behavior of Human Skin; J. of Holistic Medicine 4(2), Fall/Winter 1982.

49.   Homeopathy: A Laboratory for Etheric Science?, J. of Holistic Medicine 5, no. 1 (1983).

50.   Towards a Scientific Rationale of Homeopathy; J. of Holistic Medicine 6(2), 130-147 (Fall 1984).

51.   Forward to *The Science of Homeopathy*, by G. Vithoulkas (Grove Press, Inc., New York, 1980).

52.   Forward contribution to *Parapsychology and Contemporary Science*, by A. Dubrov and V. Pushkin (Consultants Bureau, Plenum Press, New York, 1982).

53.   Preface to *Stalking the Wild Pendulum*, by I. Bentov (E.P. Dutton, New York, 1977).

54.   What Do Electrodermal Diagnostic Acupuncture Instruments Really Measure; Am. J. Acupuncture 15, no. 1, 14 (1987).

55.   On the Evolution of Electrodermal Diagnostic Instruments; J. Advancement in Medicine 1, no. l, 41 (1988).

56.   Preface to *Vibrational Medicine: New Choices for Healing Ourselves*, by R. Gerber (Bear & Co., Santa Fe NM, 1988).

57. Towards the Development of a Mathematical Model for Acupuncture Meridians (with M.J. Friedman and S. Birch), Intl. J. of Acupuncture & Electro-Therapeutics Res. 14, 217 (1989).

58. On the Evolution and Future Development of Electrodermal Diagnostic Instruments, in *Energy Fields in Medicine*, Eds. M.A. Morton and C. Dlouhy (Fetzer Foundation, Kalamazoo, MI 1989).

59. A Dynamic Systems Approach to Modeling Meridians and Ki, in *Energy Fields in Medicine*, Eds. M.A. Morton and C. Dlougy (Fetzer Foundation, Kalamazoo, MI 1989), (with M.J. Friedman and S. Birch).

60. A Gas Discharge Device for Investigating Focused Human Attention, J. of Scientific Exploration 4 (2), 255 (1990).

61. Mathematical Modeling as a Tool for Basic Research in Acupuncture; submitted to Alternative Therapies, January 1977 (with M.J. Friedman and S. Birch).

Appendix 1-B
Tiller Psychoenergetic Papers Written (1992-2001)

62. What are Subtle Energies? J. Scientific Exploration 7, (1993) 293.

63. Subtle Energies in Energy Medicine, in Frontier Perspectives, 4, 2 (1995) 17.

64. New Electrophysiological Correlates Associated with Intentional Heart Focus, Subtle Energies 4, (1995) 251 (with R. McCraty and M. Atkinson).

65.   Towards Explaining Anomalously Large Body Voltage Surges on Exceptional Subjects, Part I: The Electrostatic Approximation, J. Scientific Exploration 9, (1995) 331 (with E.E. Green, P.A. Parks and S. Anderson).

66.   The Effects of Emotions on Short-Term Power Spectrum Analysis of Heart Rate Variability, Am. J. Cardiology 76, 14 (1995) 1089 (with R. McCraty, M. Atkinson, G. Rein and A.D. Watkins).

67.   Cardiac Coherence: A New, Noninvasive Measure of Autonomic Nervous System Order, Alternative Therapies 2, 1 (1996) 52 (with R. McCraty and M. Anderson).

68.   Electrophysiological Correlates of Positive Emotions: Three Patterns of Sympathovagal Balance in Normal Subjects, to be published in Int. J. Psychophysiology 1997 (with R. McCraty, M. Atkinson and A.D. Watkins).

69.   Dialogue Commentary on "But is it Energy? Reflections on Consciousness, Healing and the New Paradigm" and "Healing, Energy and Consciousness: Into the Future or a Retreat to the Past?" by Larry Dossey in Subtle Energies 5 (1994) 253.

70.   Towards Understanding Living Bio-Magnetophotoelectrochemical Systems, Proceedings of the 15th Int. Symp. *On Man and His Environment in Health and Disease* (Dallas, TX, Feb. 20-23, 1997).

71.   Some Physical Domain Correlates of Subtle Energy Actions, Proceedings of the 15th Int. Symp. On *Man and His Environment in Health and Disease* (Dallas, TX, Feb. 20-23, 1997).

72.   *Science and Human Transformation* (Pavior Publishing, Walnut Creek, CA, 1997).

73. Towards a Predictive Model of Subtle Domain Connections to the Physical Domain Aspect of Reality: The Origins of Wave-Particle Duality, Electric-Magnetic Monopoles and the Mirror Principle. J. Sci. Expl. 13 (1999) 41.

74. Electronic Device-Mediated pH changes In Water, J. Sci. Expl. 13 (1999) 155 (with W.E. Dibble, Jr.).

75. Towards Objectifying Intention Via an Electronic Device, Subtle Energies & Energy Medicine 8 (1999) 103 (with W.E. Dibble, Jr. and M.J. Kohane).

76. Subtle Energies, Science and Medicine, May/June (1999) 28.

77. Energy, Fitness and Electromagnetic Fields in *Drosophila Melanogaster*, J. Sci. Expl. 14 (2000) 21 (with M.J. Kohane).

78. Development of pH and Temperature Oscillations in Water Containing $ZnCO_3$ Crystallites Using Intention Imprinted Electronic Devices, Subtle En. & En. Med. 8 (2000) 75 (with W.E. Dibble, Jr.).

79. Can an Aspect of Consciousness Be Imprinted Into an Electronic Device?, Integrative Physiological and Behavioral Science, 35 (2000) 140 (with M.J. Kohane and W.E. Dibble, Jr.).

80. Exploring Robust Interactions Between Human Intention and Inanimate/Animate Systems, submitted to the Proceedings of "Towards a Science of Consciousness - - Fundamental Approaches Conference at United Nations University, Tokyo, Japan, May 25-28, 1999 (with W.E. Dibble, Jr. and M.J. Kohane).

81. Augmented Electromagnetic Waves and Qi Energy, Coherence 1 (2000) 13 (in English) and Journal of Auriculomedicine/Auriculotherapie (2001) (in press, in German).

82. Homeopathy and Allopathy as Dual Expressions of Nature, Part I: Initial Speculations, Subtle En. & En. Med., 9 (2001) 151.

83. Anomalous Environmental Influences on In Vitro Human Enzyme Studies, Part I: Some Faraday Cage and Multiple Vessel Studies, Subtle En. & En. Med. 11 (1) (2000) 75 (with M.J. Kohane).

84. Anomalous Environmental Influences on In Vitro Human Enzyme Studies, Part II: Some Electronic Device Effects, Subtle En. & En. Med. 11 (2) (2000) 99 (with M.J. Kohane).

85. On Enhancing NAD Activity in Living Systems, Subtle En. & En. Med., (in press, 2001) (with M.J. Kohane).

86. Biological Processes, Quantum Mechanics and Electromagnetic Fields: The Possibility of Device-Encapsulated Human Intention in Medical Therapies, Medical Hypotheses 56 (6) (2001) 598-607 (with M.J. Kohane).

87. "The Real World of Modern Science, Medicine and QiGong" Bulletin of Science, Technology and Society, 22 (5) (2002) 352.

88. A Double-Blind EEG-Response Test for a Supposed Electromagnetic Field-Neutralizing Device, Part I: Via the Clinician Expertise Procedure, Subtle En. & En. Med. 9 (2000) 231 (with C.N. Shealy).

89. The Electricity of Touch: Detection and Measurement of Cardiac Energy, in *Brain and Values: Is a Biological Science of Values Possible*, ed., Karl H. Pribram (Lawrence Erlbaum Associates, New Jersey, 1998) pp. 359-380, (with R. McCraty, M. Atkinson and D. Tomasino).

90. New Experimental Evidence Revealing an Unexpected Dimension to Materials Science and Engineering, Mat. Res. Innov. 5 (2001) 21-34 (With W.E. Dibble, Jr.).

91. Exploring Robust Interactions Between Human Intention and Inanimate/Animate Systems, Part I: Experimental, Frontier Perspectives, <u>9</u>, (2) (2000) 6 (with W.E. Dibble, Jr., and M.J. Kohane).

92. Ibid. Part II: Theoretical, Frontier Perspective <u>10</u> (1), (2001) 9 (with W.E. Dibble, Jr., and M.J. Kohane).

93. *Conscious Acts of Creation: The Emergence of a New Physics*, (Pavior Publishing, Walnut Creek, CA, 2001) (with W.E. Dibble, Jr., and M.J. Kohane).

94. Exploring Robust Interactions Between Human Intention and Inanimate/Animate Systems, Subtle En. & En. Med., <u>11</u>, (3) (2000) 265 (with W.E. Dibble, Jr., and M.J. Kohane).

Appendix 1-C
Details of the Payson Laboratory Space Conditioning Process

The UED details plus circuit diagram and the general imprinting procedure can be found in Appendix 1-A of Reference 7 for this chapter. This was the first, and only time to date, that Jean and I had attempted to imprint a device on our own and we had some hesitation about it, however, we placed our trust in the unseen and proceeded in the usual way.

We first meditated together for about fifteen minutes, one of us on each side of the table top on which six UEDs were stacked, connected to their power transformers that were, in turn, all plugged into a wall outlet and all UEDs were turned on so that all their LEDs shown green. This was to strengthen our connection to each other and to the unseen. When we felt our usual sense of attunement to this process we allowed a portion of our attention to rest lovingly on the assembled hardware before us. Then, I read the imprint intention statement for these six devices *"Our intention for these devices and their* *associated power transformers is to activate the indwelling consciousness of the Payson laboratory in order to "condition" it to a significantly higher electromagnetic gauge symmetry state. The special characteristic of this state is to be specifically such that **any** psychoenergetic experiment subsequently conducted in this space would be significantly benefitted".* We held this intention statement in our hearts for the next ~15 minutes before abruptly releasing it via the statement *"so be it. Thy will be done".*

This was followed by our standard secondary imprint statement to seal the prime directive imprint for these IIEDs against any unnecessary energy/information leakage during either device use or storage. To be absolutely sure we had done the best we could do, we repeated the entire process a second time and then I carried the IIEDs to the new laboratory, plugged them in at the locations indicated in Figure 1.15, switched them all on and allowed the "conditioning" gestation period to proceed.

Chapter 2

Mostly The Remote Sites Experiment

...an experimental measurement consists of two parts, one which is the result found for our normal world outer symmetry state and the second which is associated with the raising of the local inner symmetry state as the local space is being "conditioned"

The sites and experimental protocols

Since the general scientific method requires that others be able to reproduce our experimental results anywhere on the planet provided they closely follow our protocol, we sought for and found research funding (from the Samueli Institute for Information Biology) to "condition" several external sites following the Minnesota procedure utilizing a single pH-increasing IIED. Thus, it was one of the water-pH target experiments that we chose for the replication tests - primarily because it was one of the simplest and cheapest to perform. We, in Payson, provided all the $\Delta pH = +1.0$ unit IIEDs to the sites (via FedEx). We also provided unimprinted devices for each control site located within ~2 to 20 miles of an IIED site.

Purified water was used at all sites (HPLC grade); for the Payson lab it was manufactured on the premises; for the remote sites it was delivered to them directly from Fisher Scientific. Likewise, all the laboratory equipment needed for the continuous monitoring of pH, T_W (water temperature) and T_A (air temperature) was delivered to the various sites directly from the manufacturer. At regular intervals, computer diskettes containing the gathered data were sent from the remote sites, via regular postal service, to the Payson site for analysis. Everything reasonable was done to maximize digital information *isolation* between sites.

Figure 2.1 provides a map of the relative site locations (plus their historical dates) as well as their label designations, P, S, K, M, etc. Although the water pH experiments started at Stanford University in early 1997, they were moved to the Minnesota facilities in September of that year and continued there until we left those facilities in 2000. Six identical space "conditioning" IIEDs were turned on in the Payson laboratory (see Figure 1.15) on

Figure 2.1

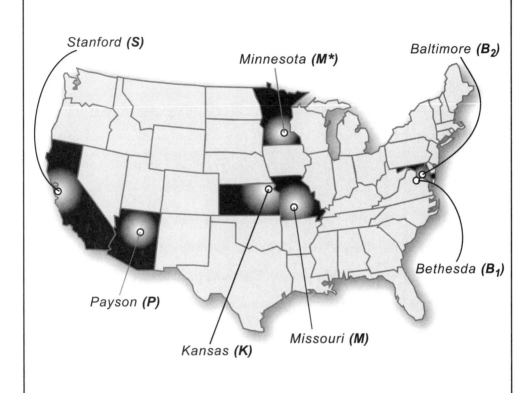

1. P = Payson master site (06/00-present)

2. S = Stanford site (01/97-09/97)

3. M* = Minnesota site (09/97-03/00)

4. K = Kansas site (12/01-06/04)

5. M = Missouri site (12/01-11/04)

6. B_1 = Bethesda site (4/02-03/04)

7. B_2 = Baltimore site (4/02-03/04)

March 15, 2001 and removed to storage three months later. A pH-increasing IIED was turned on in the Payson lab on July 25, 2001 and its main control site was rented on Main Street, Payson, ~November 1, 2001. The Kansas (K) and Missouri (M) IIED sites both began operation in early December of that year. Because of information entanglement signatures that appeared in the data between an IIED-site and its own control-site (to be shown later), we decided to initially utilize the Bethesda-site (B_1) and the Baltimore-site (B_2) as *control-sites* for the total experiment.

Figure 2.2 is a schematic illustration of the primary experimental set-up at each laboratory (either an IIED-site or a control-site). In addition, in most cases, an independent system continuously measured T_A (air temperature). The measurement procedure involved placing the glass pH-electrode and temperature probe in a 250 ml polypropylene bottle filled with purified water (after proper calibration of the pH-electrode using pH-buffers). The water container was then packed or covered closely with lint-free paper (being careful not to disturb the operations of the probes). Computer monitoring of the probe outputs commenced immediately using a sampling interval of either one or three minutes. Initially, data collection by an experimenter was performed either daily or bi-weekly. However, this data gathering was shifted to a two-week basis to minimize experimenter effect associated with the data gathering. This allowed fresh water to be inserted into the measurement vessel on a two-week cycle, recalibration of the pH-electrode at the same time, no intermediate human visits and two-week data diskettes to be mailed to the Payson laboratory for analysis. This new protocol continued through the rest of the site-conditioning phase, at which point the IIEDs were removed, wrapped in aluminum foil and stored in Faraday cages. The fine details of these experiments have been published elsewhere.[1] Measurements continued for a subsequent six weeks in order to see if any significant change occurred in the "state of conditioning" signatures. For ease in cataloging all of this site data, Table 2.1 defines the site designation label for each site. For the Payson laboratory, the actual positions of these experimental stations are also shown in Table 2.1.

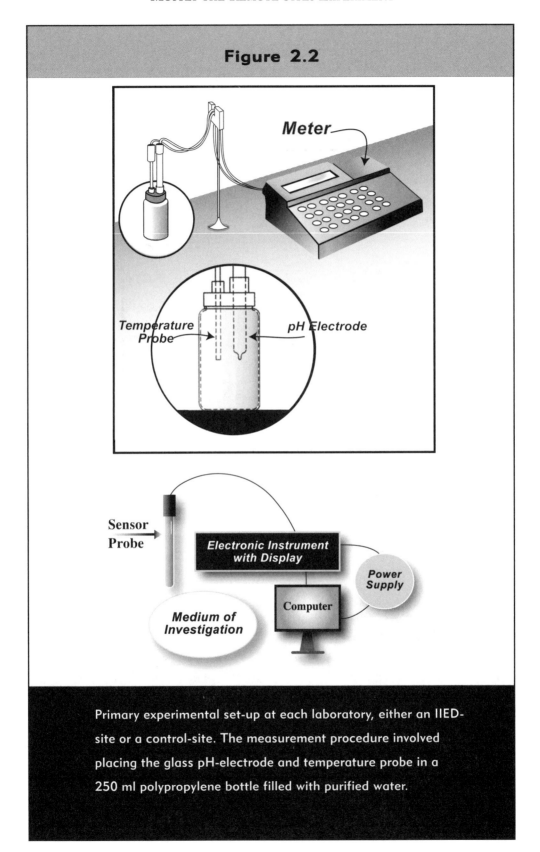

Figure 2.2

Meter

Temperature Probe   **pH Electrode**

Sensor Probe

Electronic Instrument with Display

Power Supply

Computer

Medium of Investigation

Primary experimental set-up at each laboratory, either an IIED-site or a control-site. The measurement procedure involved placing the glass pH-electrode and temperature probe in a 250 ml polypropylene bottle filled with purified water.

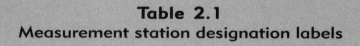

Table 2.1
Measurement station designation labels

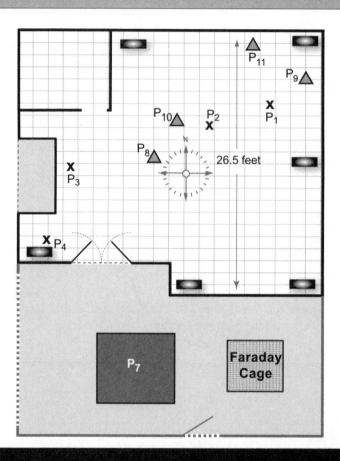

P_1	Payson Lab, ASTM-1 water
P_2	Payson Lab, ASTM-1 water + 0.4% Silica Gel
P_3	Payson Lab, ASTM-1 water
P_4	Payson Lab, ASTM-1 water
P_5	Payson Main Street Control Site, ASTM-1 water
P_6	Payson Upper Garage Site, ASTM-1 water
P_7	Payson Garage, mu-metal Box, ASTM-1 water
P_8	Payson Lab, ASTM-1 water
P_9	Payson Lab, ASTM-1 water
P_{10}	Payson Lab, ASTM-1 water
P_{11}	Payson Lab, ASTM-1 water
K_1	Kansas IIED Site
K_2	Kansas Initial Control Site
K_3	Kansas Final Control Site (K_C)
M_1	Missouri IIED Site
M_2	Missouri Initial Control Site
M_3	Missouri Final Control Site (M_C)
B_1	Bethesda
B_2	Baltimore

First phase experimental results

1.   For the three months prior to installing a pH-increasing IIED at location P_3 in the Payson laboratory on July 25, 2001 (see Table 2.1), a wide variety of pH measurements from the P_1 monitoring station showed very normal behavior. This means that, after a short buffering period, all of the pH plots showed an initial decay which asymptotically approached the temperature and CO_2-determined theoretical value, pH_{th}.[1] This is illustrated schematically in Figure 2.3 for the period prior to July 25, 2001. However, less than a month after installing this pH-increasing IIED, we found that all the pH-curves from the P_1 monitoring station exhibited pH increases well above the theoretical equilibrium value (see Figure 2.3 for the period post to July 25, 2001). The ΔpH-value above the theoretical value steadily increased with time (achieving ΔpH~1.0 pH units increase) in the period 08/15/01 to 03/27/02 after which this IIED was removed to storage. After this IIED was removed, a new type of pH-behavior appeared that is schematically illustrated by Figure 2.4.[2] Here, we noted that the ΔpH value decayed slowly back to zero with time, overshot zero to large negative values and then very slowly oscillated to eventually approach zero in an asymptotic fashion over many months.

2.   One of the most important findings of this study was that, at the remote K and M sites, as well as at the Payson lab sites, when fresh water was placed in the pH-monitoring vessel on a two-week cycle and continuously monitored, the pH quickly dropped to the theoretical equilibrium value (for our normal internal symmetry state) and then began to rise in an approximately exponential fashion with ΔpH increasing with time as illustrated schematically in Figure 2.5. The equation that defines such behavior is

$$pH(t) = pH_{th} + \Delta pH(t)\,[1 - \exp\,(-\beta t)] \qquad (2.1)$$

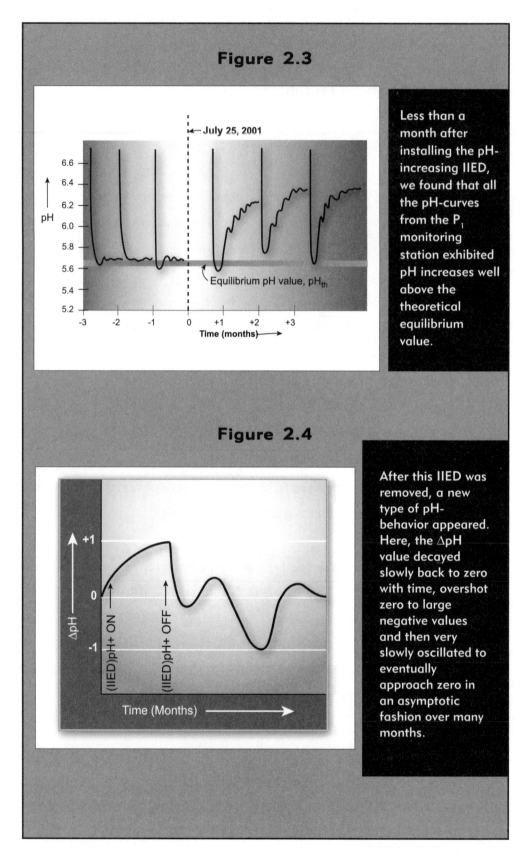

Figure 2.3

Less than a month after installing the pH-increasing IIED, we found that all the pH-curves from the P_1 monitoring station exhibited pH increases well above the theoretical equilibrium value.

Figure 2.4

After this IIED was removed, a new type of pH-behavior appeared. Here, the ΔpH value decayed slowly back to zero with time, overshot zero to large negative values and then very slowly oscillated to eventually approach zero in an asymptotic fashion over many months.

Figure 2.5

One of the most important findings was that, when fresh water was placed in the pH-monitoring vessel on a two-week cycle and continuously monitored, the pH quickly dropped to the theoretical equilibrium value and then began to rise in an approximately exponential fashion with ΔpH increasing with time.

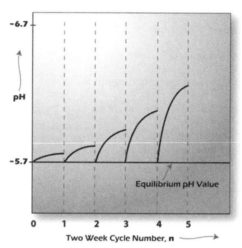

Table 2.2

Time Period	ΔpH	β
M_1: 1/2 to 1/23	0.43	0.017
M_1: 2/19 to 3/5	0.305	0.015
M_1: 3/6 to 3/15	0.19	0.012
M_1: 3/19 to 3/25	.036	0.019
M_2: 1/2 to 2/1	.064	0.0026
M_3: 2/1 to 2/15	.07	0.0039
M_3: 2/15 to 3/1	0.86	0.0127
M_3: 3/6 to 3/10	0.375	0.024
M_3: 3/10 to 3/25	0.525	0.0036
M_3: 3/25 to 4/8	0.72	0.0053
M_3: 4/8 to 4/23	1.37	0.0045
M_3: 4/30 to 5/14	1.6	0.0035
K_1: 2/3 to 3/4	0.6	0.0021
K_2: 1/18 to 1/27	0.3	0.032
P_1: 3/9 to 3/14	0.69	0.015
P_1: 3/14 to 3/29	0.55	0.003
P_1: 10/3 to 11/12	0.97	0.0017
P_1: 4/12 to 4/19	1.1	0.026
P_4: 10/7 to 11/12	0.55	0.003
North P_5: 2/6 to 2/27	0.8	0.00456
North P_5: 2/27 to 3/26	0.57	0.0043
South P_5: 12/21 to 1/2	0.705	0.00445
South P_5: 3/8 to 4/22	0.65	0.0014
P_3: 12/30 to 3/3	0.5	0.0012
P_6: 4/30 to 5/10	0.9	0.011
B_1 4/22 - 5/7	0.55	0.005
Payson Average	**0.74**	**0.0062**
Remote Average	**0.6411**	**0.0112**

In this equation, t is time, pH_{th} is the theoretically predicted value for an *unconditioned* space (our world's normal inner symmetry state), exp represents the exponential function (which is unity at time t = 0 and zero at very long times) and the parameter β determines how rapidly the exponential function decays. At small values of β t, the square bracketed term just becomes β t so the pH(t) behavior is linear with time at small times. For the various sites listed in Table 2.1, the values of both ΔpH and β, for various time periods, are given in Table 2.2 and Figures 2.6.

The Figure 2.5 plot behavior, noted for the Payson laboratory, was also found to occur at the K and M sites. Thus ΔpH increases strongly with time at all sites while the parameter β also increases weakly with time and has a very site-specific value. We thus conclude from this data that all of the IIED-sites, both local and remote, are becoming "conditioned" to a higher inner symmetry state in complete accord with the intention statement for these IIEDs.

3. Perhaps the most remarkable finding of this study was that, at all of the control sites where no IIED was ever present, *the time-dependent behavior of the measured pH was almost identical to that found for the IIED sites.* This exponential time-dependence of the pH for two control sites is shown in Figures 2.6.[1] Both sets of data have excellent fits to exponential functions although the Payson control site is "noisier" than that for the Missouri control site. This is unheard of anomalous pH-behavior for supposed control sites (initially fixed at our world's normal inner symmetry state). Thus, one must conclude that *some unique information entanglement process* exists between these IIED-sites and their control-sites some 2 to 20 miles distant. Later in this chapter we will provide experimental data which shows that the inner symmetry state of the control-site space rises as the IIED-site becomes conditioned.

4. In the earlier Minnesota studies,[3] we encountered an "experimenter" effect wherein close presence of the experimenter influences the magnitude of the measurement.

Figure 2.6 a

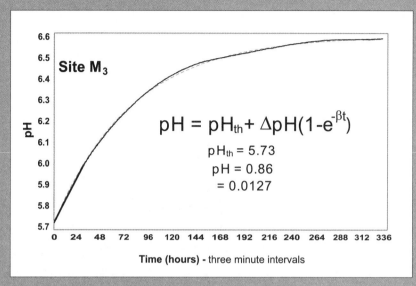

Site M$_3$

$$pH = pH_{th} + \Delta pH(1-e^{-\beta t})$$

$pH_{th} = 5.73$
$pH = 0.86$
$= 0.0127$

Time (hours) - three minute intervals

Figure 2.6 b

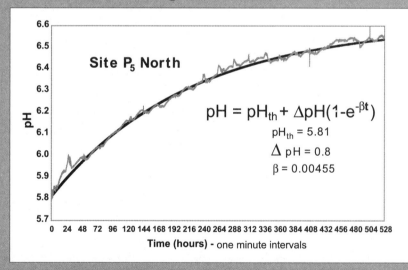

Site P$_5$ North

$$pH = pH_{th} + \Delta pH(1-e^{-\beta t})$$

$pH_{th} = 5.81$
$\Delta pH = 0.8$
$\beta = 0.00455$

Time (hours) - one minute intervals

Perhaps the most remarkable finding of this study is that, at all of the control sites where no IIED was ever present, the time-dependent behavior of the measured pH was almost identical to that found for the IIED sites. One can conclude that some unique information entanglement process exists between the IIED-sites and their control-sites some 2 to 20 miles distant.

Such an effect is common in all psychological research studies and can produce data swings either in the positive or the negative direction. An illustration of such an experimenter effect in this remote site study can be readily seen in Figures 2.7. In Figure 2.7a, at sites P_1 and P_4, the highly correlated drops in pH occurred *every time* the raw data was accessed to make these plots. Figure 2.7b shows a strong negative correlation between the diurnal T_W variations (T_W = water temperature) and the measured pH at site P_4. However, this strong inverse correlation occurs only when people enter the space. One notes that, over the weekend when no human entered the lab, no pH drops occurred (even when diurnal T_W oscillations were present). Similar types of data disturbances were observed for the Kansas and Missouri sites.

5. Using a pH-sensitive paper, litmus paper, as a test vehicle for this water at both the beginning and end of a two week cycle yielded only the value pH_{th}, the temperature-dependent theoretical value for an unconditioned space, with no time-dependent change in pH as found when a pH-electrode was used as our testing vehicle. Via the pH-electrode measurement procedure, repetitive two-week cycles yielded essentially the same type of time-dependent behavior so one can be assured that there is nothing wrong with the electronic systems involved in the measurement/recording chain. Additionally, use of a totally different spectrophotometric pH-measurement technique led to almost identical time-dependent pH-behavior as found by the pH-electrode technique. Thus, although all three techniques measure the hydrogen ion, H^+, concentration in the water, only the two that involve electronic circuitry yield an exponential variation of pH with time during any single two-week cycle.[1]

This is a very interesting result because it suggests that an experimental measurement consists of two parts, one which is the result found for our normal world inner symmetry state and the second which is associated with the raising of the local inner symmetry state as the local space is being "conditioned". This latter part, the consciousness-influenced part, appears to be particularly associated with electronic and digital systems - almost as if we have developed a type of hybrid digital consciousness via this IIED technology.

Figure 2.7a

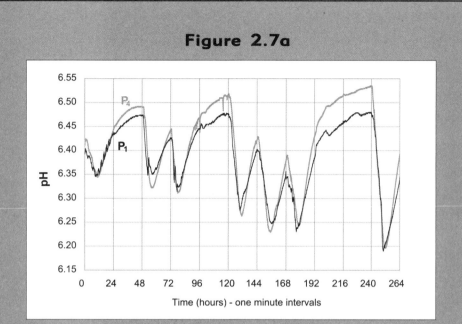

Time (hours) - one minute intervals

Figure 2.7b

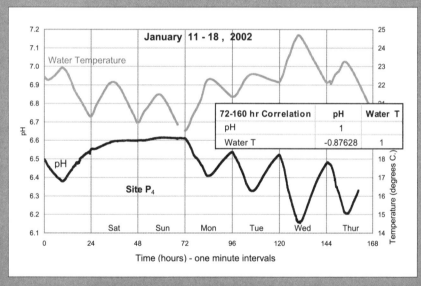

Time (hours) - one minute intervals

In the earlier Minnesota studies, we encountered an "experimenter" effect wherein close presence of the experimenter influences the magnitude of the measurement. The Payson laboratory shows highly correlated drops in pH *every time* the raw data is accessed and the strong inverse correlation occurs only when people enter the space.

6.   Subsidiary experiments were carried out using a commercial de-ionized water from a local market. Although it was less pure than the high purity water of our typical experiments, we experimentally observed only an odd initial transient behavior of ~1 day duration before the typical time-dependent exponential pH-behavior appeared.[1] Additionally, placing our purified water vessel in a mu-metal, double-walled cylinder which was, in turn, placed within a large, mu-metal box (~5 foot cube), designated site P_7 in Table 2.1, also led to the typical exponential time-dependent pH-behavior. Thus, mu-metal, which is known to shield against penetration by normal magnetic flux lines, was not an effective screening material for whatever energies were involved in the "conditioning" process.

Second phase experimental results

Because of the profound information entanglement process occurring between IIED-sites and their control-sites, and perhaps between all sites in the overall experimental system, we decided to introduce the Bethesda (B_1) and Baltimore (B_2) sites to the system first as "control" sites for the rest of the system to experimentally test whether or not the information entanglement process could bridge an ~2000 mile separation distance. Thus, the same two-week cycle procedure of pH-measurement and electrode recalibration as at the K and M sites was instituted at the B_1 and B_2 sites, *but no IIEDs were present*. After many months of this type of baseline pH and temperature gathering (and we had made a satisfactory information entanglement test), unique IIEDs for individual target experiments favored by the site-host were installed at all four sites (with installation date and reimprinting dates noted on many of the subsequent figures).

In late 2002, we invented a new technique allowing us to experimentally measure a quantitative change in the inner symmetry state relative to a totally unconditioned space.[4] From this procedure, which will be partially discussed in Chapter 4, we were able to make plots of a new thermodynamic potential in nature, which we have labeled the magnetoelectrochemical potential energy for the hydrogen ion, Ψ'_{H+}, as a function of time for all sites. For these long-time studies, we now have two experimental measures of change with time, $\Delta pH(t)$, from the exponential time-dependence of pH during 72 hour,

Figure 2.8

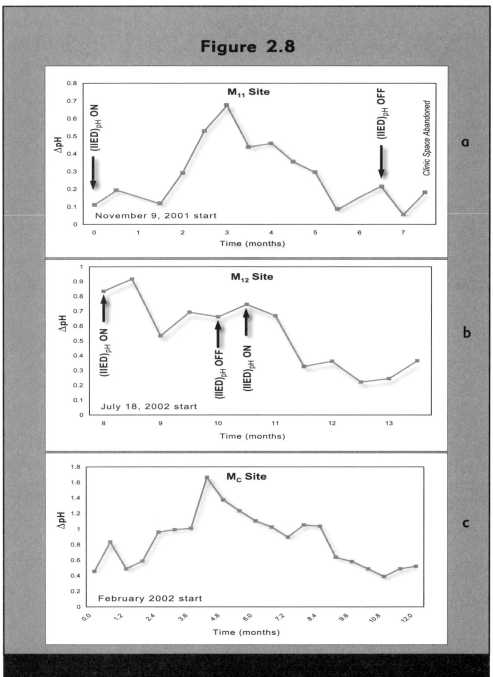

MISSOURI: ΔpH reaches a maximum value at ~3 months for the IIED site, M_{11}, and then begins to decline back to baseline, even though $IIED_{pH}$ is still present. When the equipment was transferred from the M_{11}-site to the M_{12}-site with a newly imprinted IIED, ΔpH was higher than the last data point from the M_{11}-site and the data at the M_C-site begins to rise substantially somewhat after the M_{11} data begins to fall.

1 week or 2 week cycle data, and Ψ'_{H+} (t) which is calculated directly from the pH, T_W and electrode calibration data. This Ψ'_{H+} data will be presented below.

ΔpH(t) Data: For the Missouri IIED-site, the medical clinic that housed the experiments was sold 8 months after the experiments began (reported on in the first phase) and a new IIED site was initiated in the home of one of the nurses. Thus, as identifiers, M_{11} will be used for the first 8 months as the IIED-site designation while M_{12} will be used as the designator for the following period. The Missouri control site will still be labeled M_3 or M_C. In all cases, only data for a 1 week cycle will be presented.

1. Missouri sites: Figure 2.8 provides the combined data for M_{11}, M_{12} and $M_C = M_3$ (the control-site). Here, we note (a) that ΔpH reaches a maximum value at ~3 months for the IIED site, M_{11} and then begins to decline in a somewhat oscillatory fashion back to baseline, even though $IIED_{pH}$ is still present and turned on (suggesting that reimprinting of this device should have occurred at ~3 months), (b) that, when the equipment was transferred from the M_{11}-site to the M_{12}-site with a newly imprinted IIED, ΔpH was immediately and substantially higher than the last data point from the M_{11}-site and (c) that remarkably, the data at the M_C-site begins to rise substantially (to ΔpH ~1.7 pH units) somewhat after the M_{11} data begins to fall (indicating that this site has special properties not characteristic of the other sites).

2. Kansas sites: Figure 2.9 provides the combined K_1 and $K_C = K_2$ (the control-site) data. Here, one notes that the K_1 data oscillates with a period of ~2 months, has a 10-month average value of ~0.6 pH units and sustained these high values for ~3-4 months after the $IIED_{pH}$ had been turned off and placed in storage. For the control-site (the third one to be tried) which was in a house ~0.5 miles from the IIED site, the long-term variations between positive and negative values of ΔpH seem strange. The gaps in the data reflect incomplete data gathering (usually related to insufficient attention to the experimental protocol by the site attendant so the equipment malfunctions).

Figure 2.9

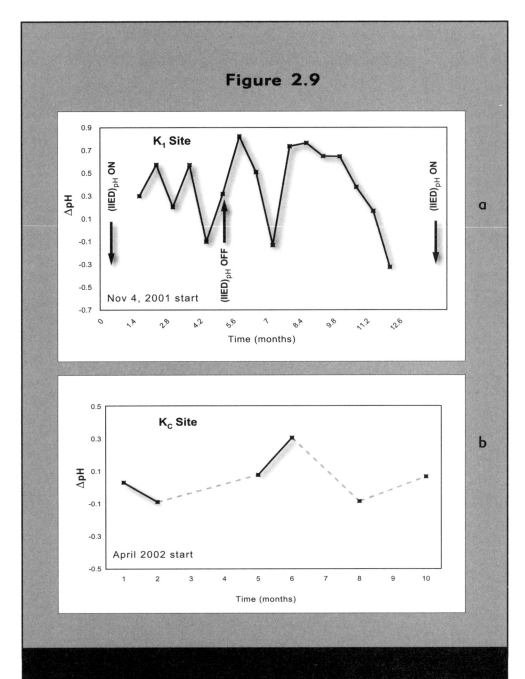

KANSAS: the K_1 data oscillates with a period of ~2 months, has a 10-month average value of ~0.6 pH units and sustained these high values for ~3-4 months after the $IIED_{pH}$ had been turned off. For the control-site (the third one to be tried) which was in a house ~0.5 miles from the IIED site, the long-term variations between positive and negative values of ΔpH seems strange.

3. **Bethesda (B_1) and Baltimore (B_2) sites:** Figures 2.10a and 2.10b provide the one week cycle ΔpH data for the B_2 and B_1 sites, respectively. From Figure 2.10a, one notes that ΔpH achieved and maintained 0.6 pH units for ~7 months and, after a strong dip to negative values, slowly recovered to the same range. Over the same time-frame, Figure 2.10b exhibits a much more fluctuating behavior with a somewhat lower average ΔpH-value over the same time period. The most important point to note here is that neither site had any type of IIED present and turned on for the first ~5 months of these data streams. This *strongly supports the existence of information entanglement from IIED-sites ~1500-2500 miles away.* An additional piece of information to support this hypotheses comes from the exponential time-dependent pH-behavior of the pH-data from these sites.

4. **Payson (P) site:** Figure 2.11 provides 72 hour cycle, ΔpH data from the P_1 and P_4-site monitoring stations in the laboratory. From this, it is interesting to note the type of space polarization response (shift to negative and oscillating ΔpH-values) associated with turning off this IIED. The final interesting point is the abrupt upward shift of the data when the pH-monitoring electrode at each site was changed to new Ultra Ross electrodes..

Ψ_{H+} (t) Data: This new thermodynamic energy contribution arises from the proposed existence of experimentally accessible magnetic monopoles in a "conditioned" space environment. The details of how we evaluate Ψ_{H+} (t) from the gathered data will be discussed in Chapter 4. All we need to realize here is that, although IIED-conditioning of a space raises the thermodynamic free energy per unit volume of that space, the contribution from the H^+ ion in the water (to the overall free energy state) can have both positive or negative values depending on the sign of the monopole involved for a fixed magnetic potential. An unconditioned space would have $\Psi_{H+} = \eta_{H+}$, the electrochemical potential for H^+ and $\Delta\Psi_{H+} = \Psi_{H+} - \eta_{H+} = 0$. Thus, departures of $\Delta\Psi_{H+}$ from zero are of first order significance while the sign of the energy change is of second order significance. The units to be used in the subsequent plots of $\Delta\Psi_{H+}$ is millielectron volts (meV) and it should be noted that the average thermal energy of an atom or molecule at room

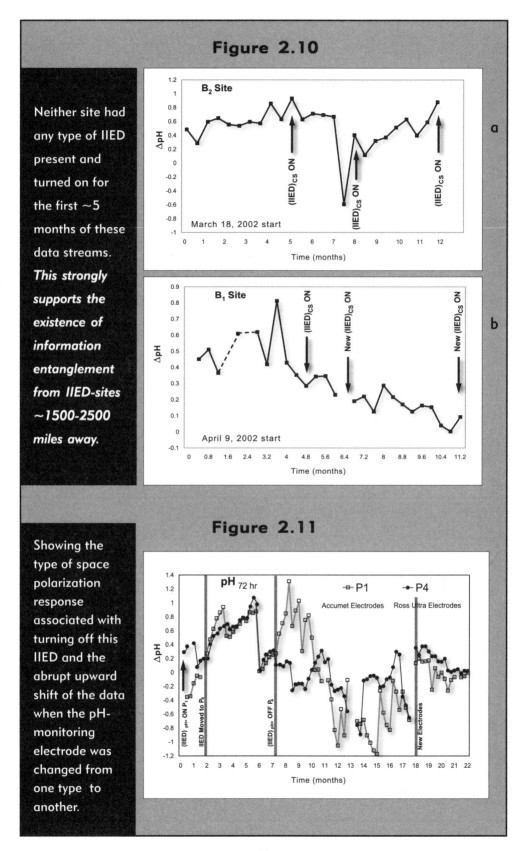

Figure 2.10

Neither site had any type of IIED present and turned on for the first ~5 months of these data streams. *This strongly supports the existence of information entanglement from IIED-sites ~1500-2500 miles away.*

Figure 2.11

Showing the type of space polarization response associated with turning off this IIED and the abrupt upward shift of the data when the pH-monitoring electrode was changed from one type to another.

temperature is kT~25meV. We only discovered this new procedure ~10 months after the pH-measurements began so the starting time-line for the $\Delta\Psi_{H+}$-plots is shifted by ~10 months from the starting time-line for the ΔpH-plots.

Figures 2.12 provide $\Delta\Psi_{H+}$ (t)-plots for the M_{12}, M_C, K_1, K_C, B_2, B_1 and P-sites, respectively.[5] Figure 2.12a shows that $\Delta\Psi_{H+}$ for M_{12} shifts from negative to positive values after the laptop computer, collecting data at the site, malfunctioned and was sent to the Payson lab where the computer was reconfigured and new software installed before returning it to the site. For the M_C site, even though no IIED had ever been located at this site, Figure 2.12a shows that a substantial increase in $\Delta\Psi_{H+}$ (~0.5kT) was manifested at that site. Figure 2.12b shows that the K_1 site started with a low value in June, had a large dip in October but returned to the upward trend and reached a value of $\Delta\Psi_{H+}$ ~ kT at the beginning of 2003. Interestingly, Figure 2.12b for the K_C site shows $\Delta\Psi_{H+}$ exhibiting a net negative slope, albeit with significant oscillatory behavior to bottom out with $\Delta\Psi_{H+}$ ~-kT at the end of 2002 before increasing back to ~0 at the beginning of 2003. Figure 2.12c for the B_2 site exhibits a remarkably linear increase of $\Delta\Psi_{H+}$ with time with a steep positive slope while for the B_1 site, ~50 miles away, it is also net linear with small undulations and a shallow positive slope. Exchanging pH-electrodes between these two sites substantially changes the $\Delta\Psi_{H+}$ plots for these two sites that have never directly experienced a pH-increasing IIED (this electrode exchange caused the B_1-site values to abruptly increase and the B_2-site values to abruptly decrease indicating, once again, that all parts of the equipment are energetically modified by the overall process). Figure 2.12d for the P site with four pH-monitoring stations, but no activated IIEDs present during the entire time period (a pH-increasing device was operated in the lab only between July 2001 and March 2002), shows $\Delta\Psi_{H+}$ at all stations to have ~ zero slopes but with P_1, P_3 and P_4 exhibiting negative values of ~-0.5 kT while P_2 manifests a negative value of ~-1.5kT. The negative values of $\Delta\Psi_{H+}$ appear to be related to the type of electrode used, with the negative values being associated with the Accumet and UltraRoss electrodes and positive values with the regular Ross electrodes.

These plots of $\Delta\Psi_{H+}$ (t) confirm that significant alterations have occurred in the inner symmetry state for all control sites of the experimental system. Since the Bethesda

Figure 2.12, a & b

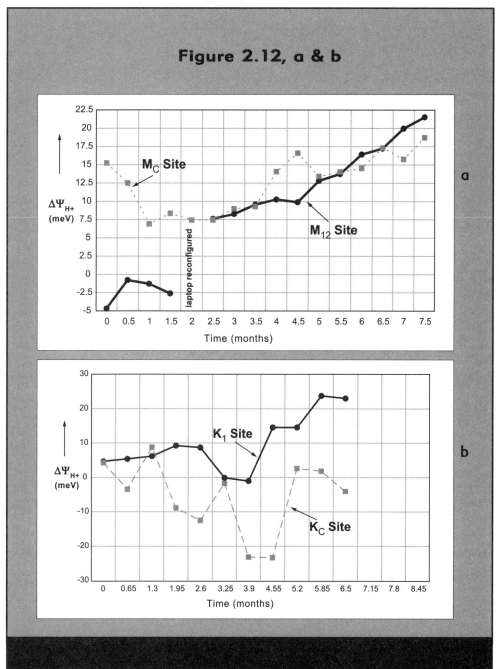

These plots confirm that significant alterations have occurred in the inner symmetry state for all control sites of the experimental system. Since the Bethesda and Baltimore sites initially served as control sites for the M, K and P-IIED sites, *very strong support now exists for the long-range information entanglement,* between various sites of the same overall experimental system.

Figure 2.12, c & d

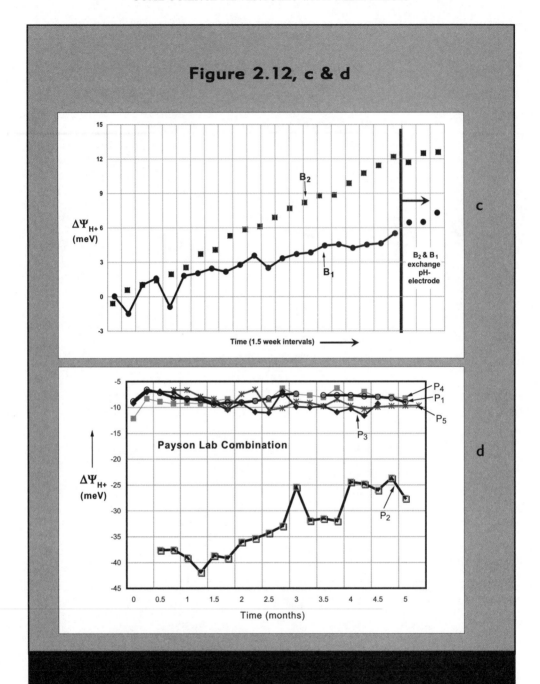

When the pH-electrodes were exchanged between the Baltimore and Bethesda sites , (1) an abrupt change of $\Delta\Psi_{H+}(t)$ values occurred in the direction expected indicative of the different levels of electrode potentization existing at the two sites prior to the exchange and (2) the new slopes of the $\Delta\Psi_{H+}(t)$-plots for the two electrodes were consistent with the extrapolations of the earlier data for the original electrode site.

and Baltimore sites initially served as control sites for the M, K and P-IIED sites, *very strong support now exists for the long-range information entanglement*, between various sites of the same overall experimental system, postulate.

It is also quite interesting to note that, when the pH-electrodes were exchanged between the Baltimore and Bethesda sites , (1) an abrupt change of $\Delta\Psi_{H+}(t)$ values occurred in the direction expected indicative of the different levels of electrode potentization existing at the two sites prior to the exchange and (2) the new slopes of the $\Delta\Psi_{H+}(t)$-plots for the two electrodes were consistent with the extrapolations of the earlier data for the original electrode site. Unfortunately, at these sites, the basic pH and electrode voltage measurements from which $\Delta\Psi_{H+}$ is calculated were shortly thereafter discontinued by the individual investigators so we could not continue to track the state of laboratory "conditioning" (inner symmetry state) with time.

Expanding the experimental sites

In early 2003, a small group of young technical men from the U.K. contacted us about trying to reproduce some of our IIED research data. About three months later a different group from Italy contacted us with the same interest. We suggested that the increasing pH-IIED experiment be done by each of them separately. They would purchase and assemble the necessary equipment, run one-week cycle change, base-line experiments without an IIED for ~3 months and we would then provide an IIED for the continuing phase of experiments by each group. The U.K. group started continuous experiments by mid-March, 2003 in the home of one of the group near London; the Italian group started their experiments by ~mid-September, 2003 in a rented basement in Milan.

For the U.K. group, the background experiments continued until July when a *pH-decreasing* IIED by 1 full pH-unit was installed. Both the 72 hour $\Delta pH(t)$ results and the $\Delta\Psi_{H+}(t)$ results are shown in Figure 2.13a. The interesting and exciting thing for us was that, within only three weeks, very strong information entanglement over a distance from the Payson lab of ~5,000 miles was manifesting. Later (not shown on this figure), the installation of the decreasing pH-IIED drove the ΔpH-values from ~+1 back to ~+0.1. The $\Delta\Psi_{H+}$-values had a steep initial positive slope until a major experimenter effect

Figure 2.13

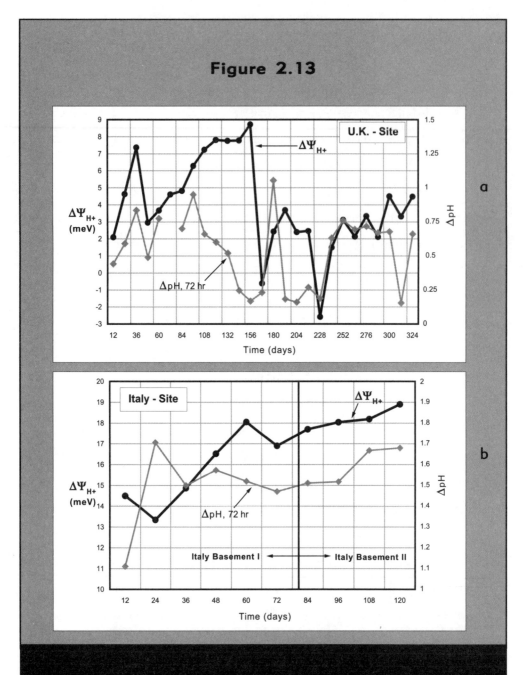

EUROPEAN SITES: The very short time that was required to reach $\Delta pH \sim 1$ and $\Delta \Psi_{H+} \sim 0.3kT$ via the information entanglement process is truly remarkable! Either this process is occurring via a mechanism that functions in a manner ~inversely proportional to distance or our world is becoming "conditioned" so it requires less time for the entanglement result to manifest. Only future experiments can clarify such an issue.

occurred at the 3-week mark (strong irritation from the group leader at lost data by the site-host group member).

Figure 2.13b provides both 72 hr. ΔpH-data and $\Delta\Psi_{H+}$ for the Italian group. No IIED has been introduced into this basement pH-monitoring station. This data is remarkable in that, for the very first measurement (in 1-week), ΔpH was +1.1 pH units and rose to a value of +1.7 pH units at the end of the second week of measurement. Consistently, the $\Delta\Psi_{H+}$-values are quite large. Figure 2.14 is given to show that, at both sites, exponential, time-dependent pH-behavior was observed.[6]

Although these young investigators were very enthusiastic to perform this experiment, the very short time that was required to reach ΔpH~1 and $\Delta\Psi_{H+}$~0.3kT via the information entanglement process is truly remarkable! Either this process is occurring via a mechanism that functions in a manner ~inversely proportional to distance or our world is becoming "conditioned" so it requires less time for the entanglement result to manifest. Only future experiments can clarify such an issue.

Finally, it is interesting to note that, for those remote measurement sites that were below ground level (M_C and Italy), the ΔpH-values achieved levels of ~1.7 while those at ground level (P,M and K-IIED sites) achieved ΔpH ~1.0 (the intention target) and those at ~3 stories above ground level (B_1 and B_2) achieved only ΔpH ~0.8. Figure 2.15 illustrates an aspect of this finding.[6]

What important experimental findings were generated via this "remote sites" experiment

1.   In response to the presence of a pH-increasing IIED at the remote sites (Missouri and Kansas), the pH increased at both IIED sites, largely in an exponential fashion with time, exhibiting a significant ΔpH-value above the theoretically-calculated value for the inner symmetry state of the normal environment. The ΔpH-value increased with the length of IIED conditioning-time towards 1.0 pH units, the actual intention imprint in the IIED.

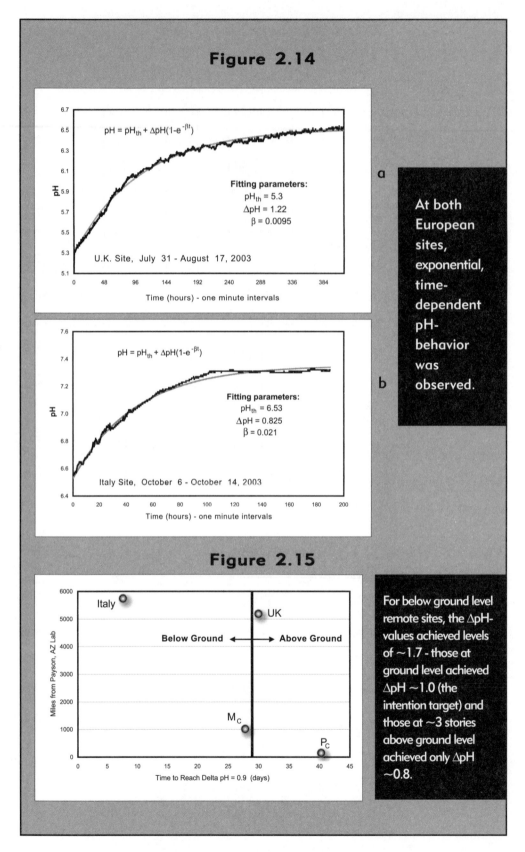

Figure 2.14

pH = pH$_{th}$ + ΔpH(1-e$^{-\beta t}$)

Fitting parameters:
pH$_{th}$ = 5.3
ΔpH = 1.22
β = 0.0095

U.K. Site, July 31 - August 17, 2003

a

At both European sites, exponential, time-dependent pH-behavior was observed.

pH = pH$_{th}$ + ΔpH(1-e$^{-\beta t}$)

Fitting parameters:
pH$_{th}$ = 6.53
ΔpH = 0.825
β = 0.021

Italy Site, October 6 - October 14, 2003

b

Figure 2.15

Italy
UK
Below Ground ← → Above Ground
M$_C$
P$_C$

Miles from Payson, AZ Lab

Time to Reach Delta pH = 0.9 (days)

For below ground level remote sites, the ΔpH-values achieved levels of ~1.7 - those at ground level achieved ΔpH ~1.0 (the intention target) and those at ~3 stories above ground level achieved only ΔpH ~0.8.

2. Including the European data, all control sites, 2.0 - 6000 miles away from the IIED-sites, also exhibited this type of pH(t) behavior although the ΔpH-value was generally ~10% - 20% less than that found for the IIED-sites. However, two control sites that were both below ground level exhibited a ΔpH > 1.0 pH units value. This information entanglement effect between IIED-sites and non-IIED-sites of the total experimental system is real and profound.

3. pH-measurement, using two different types of digital electronic techniques, revealed this anomalous pH behavior in a pH-increasing IIED-conditioned space; however, a purely chemical test, using litmus paper, exhibited only the temperature and CO_2-determined, theoretical value of the pH for an unconditioned space.

4. The pH(t) behavior exhibited strong perturbations associated with an experimenter entering the room to access the computer-stored raw data.

5. Magnetic screening, via mu-metal shielding, does not shield a pH-measuring vessel from this seemingly anomalous pH-behavior in an IIED-conditioned space environment.

6. There is some evidence that ~3 months is the optimum intention imprint lifetime before device reimprinting is needed. However, a beneficial human experimenter effect can extend this period.

7. A new experimental/theoretical technique was invented[4] to display a new thermodynamic potential energy for the hydrated proton, $\Delta\Psi_{H+}$, associated with unique magnetic qualities in an IIED-conditioned space. This new potential is zero for our normal world inner symmetry state but is departed from zero (plus or minus) in an IIED-conditioned space. Plots of $\Delta\Psi_{H+}$ at all sites are a measure of the space's inner symmetry state.

8. pH-measuring electrodes, when exchanged between two laboratory sites, B_1 and B_2, in this overall experiment, showed (1) an immediate change in $\Delta\Psi_{H+}$ at the exchange with $\delta(\Delta\Psi_{H+}) < o$ for B_2 and $\delta(\Delta\Psi_{H+}) > o$ for B_1 since $\Delta\Psi_{H+}$ $(B_2) > \Delta\Psi_{H+}$ (B_1) and (2) the data suggest that, at least the short-term slope of $\Delta\Psi_{H+}$ follows that of the original electrode site rather than that of the new site. This indicates that the experimental equipment is also "conditioned" by the inner symmetry-raising process.

9. These experimental results confirm the earlier Minnesota findings that the inner symmetry state of an experimental space depends upon at least the following four factors, (1) the intention imprint charge level remaining in the IIED, (2) some fundamental nature of the space itself, (3) all the ramifications of the experimenter effect including an experimenter's inner symmetry state and (4) the level of inner state potentization of the equipment relative to that of the experimental space.

10. $\Delta\Psi_{H+}$ values of both positive and negative sign were detected and these generally correlated with the type of pH-electrode used in the particular experiment.

Table 2.3 provides a summary of the key experimental findings from the remote sites experiment.

Is a "conditioned" space a sensitive detector of subtle energies?

Some time ago, one of us[8] defined subtle energies as all those unique kinds of energies functioning in humans and nature that are different than those already accepted as being associated with the four fundamental forces (gravity, electromagnetism, the weak nuclear force and the strong nuclear force) by conventional science. During the remote sites experiment, already described in this chapter, the Payson laboratory was exhibiting phenomena that caused us to postulate that "equipment in a highly conditioned space should be sensitive detectors of one or more types of subtle energy perturbations occurring in the general environment". This was part of our general working hypothesis partially explored earlier,[3] that random number generator (RNG) devices[9] could reveal temporal departures of the completely amorphous local physical vacuum from its normal U(1) EM gauge symmetry condition. For this study, we utilized the services of a world-class expert in advanced kineseological techniques in our Payson laboratory while simultaneously monitoring simple physical chemistry signatures at stations P_1, P_2, P_3 and P_4.[10]

Kinesiology is a type of biofeedback utilizing subconscious muscle response to detect "stressors" within the body. Kinesiology uses manual monitoring of specific muscles, which may either "lock" and hold strong or "unlock" and give, to determine imbalances of stressors not only within the muscles themselves but also within interfacing subconscious

Table 2.3
Summary of key experimental findings from the "Remote Sites Experiment"

1.   The original Minnesota water pH results have been substantially replicated by others.

2.   At all remote IIED-sites, the digitally recorded pH for purified water in equilibrium with air increased exponentially with time with the ΔpH increasing cycle by cycle of water change until it reached $\sim$1.0 pH units.

3.   At all control sites, non-IIED sites, the same type of pH-behavior was observed via an information entanglement process except that (1) for below-ground sites, ΔpH achieved $\sim$1.7 pH units and (2) for well above-ground sites, ΔpH achieved only $\sim$0.8 pH units.

4.   This information entanglement process between IIED and non-IIED, control sites of the overall experimental system occurred over distances from $\sim$2 miles to $\sim$6000 miles. The carrier wave for this information transfer could not have been electromagnetic.

5.   A litmus paper pH-detector only responded to the purely chemical level of the H^+ content present in the water while digital pH-detectors responded to both this level plus an information level associated with the H^+ content.

6.   All sites, both IIED and non-IIED, exhibited substantial values of $\Delta\Psi_{H+}$ after a short time, indicating a raised thermodynamic free energy per unit volume for all sites.

7.   The time required to reach ΔpH $\sim$1.0 pH units appears to be less for below-ground control sites than for above-ground control sites and also appears to be relatively independent of distance.

8.   Strong experimenter and equipment potentization effects were noted.

9.   The optimum reimprinting time for an IIED presently appears to be $\sim$3 months.

10.   Mu-metal screening does not shield water from this new information entanglement field.

Figure 2.16

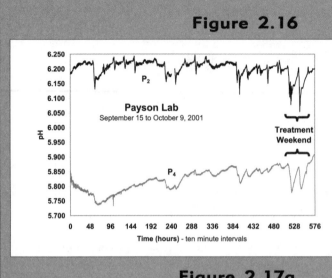

The kind of variation in pH that was observed during the 21 day period immediately preceding the weekend during which kinesiological treatments were performed.

Figure 2.17a

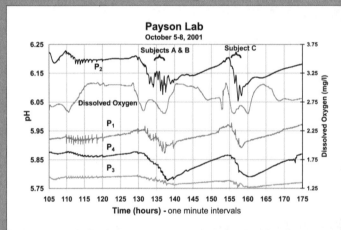

pH and dissolved oxygen levels measured at various locations near and during the time of the treatments.

Figure 2.17b

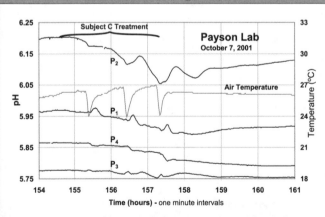

The first major pH drop occurred just *before* actual physical treatments began. Such precursor changes are not unusual in our "conditioned" laboratory space.

body systems. These systems include not only the generally recognized autonomic and proprioceptive feedback of the nervous system but also the subconscious emotional and mental processes underlying our feelings and thought.[11-13] More importantly, from the point of view of our experiments, the subconscious muscle system also interfaces with key subtle energy systems of the body, (1) the acupuncture meridian system of Chinese medicine and (2) the chakra-nadi system of the Yogis.

Initially, Kinesiology was applied only to muscle imbalance and feedback of subconscious nerve reflexes but, early on, a fairly consistent experimental relationship was observed in applied Kinesiology (AK) between specific organ or gland dysfunction and weakness in specific muscles.[14, 15] These findings led to the development of the muscle-organ/gland-Chinese meridian matrix, in which imbalances within organs or glands and their associated meridians were linked to specific muscle imbalances.[16, 17] Thus, when a muscle is monitored manually, it can respond to disturbances or imbalances within the Qi flows of the Chinese meridians or the pranic flows within the chakra-nadi system by suddenly "giving" under pressure when linked to a meridian or chakra via touching the acupoint or nadi point while simultaneously monitoring the muscle. This permits detection of energetic stresses affecting the body's function.

The Chinese meridian Qi flows and the chakra-nadi pranic flows directly affect the physiological function of the organs, glands and nervous system, and are important for the maintenance of homeostasis. Detection of imbalances and stressors affecting these systems thus allows us a means for locating effective acupressure corrections to eliminate these imbalances and so normalize physiological function.

Three human subjects with severe, chronic physiologic imbalances were selected as the subjects for this study. As mentioned above, continuous pH-monitoring at stations P_1 to P_4 plus oxygen solubility- and temperature-monitoring were the simultaneous data streams that we accessed as indicators of change occurring during the healing treatment of these imbalances via use of kinesiological techniques. The subjects were located ~3-5 meters away from these devices and no electrical wire or physical contact occurred between the subjects and these devices. Figure 2.16 illustrates the kind of variation in pH that was observed during the 21 day period immediately preceding the weekend during which kinesiological treatments were performed in our Payson workspace.

In Figure 2.16, background fluctuations that occurred prior to the treatment weekend were generally regular and diurnal but often occurred for unknown reasons. Figure 2.17a illustrates the pH and dissolved oxygen levels measured at various locations near and during the time of the treatments. The levels of dissolved oxygen in water were measured at a location close to P_1 in the laboratory. In all of this, it is interesting to note that the first major pH drop occurred just *before* actual physical treatments began. Such precursor changes are not unusual in our "conditioned" laboratory space and are thought to represent changes in the lab's inner symmetry state associated with focused discussion prior to actually starting the experimental treatments. In Figure 2.17a, note how all the pH-monitors show change in concert with each other during the weekend treatment period even though they are well-separated from each other (see Table 2.1). The smaller fluctuations seen in Figure 2.17a are generally due to changes in the air temperature, one of the observed characteristics of a "conditioned" space. The detail illustrated in Figure 2.17b shows the pH-changes that occurred with Subject C during the following day treatment period. This detail reveals how the change in air temperature cycles correlate with detailed pH-changes during this period. It should be emphasized here that simultaneous measurements of water temperature *did not* show fluctuations that can account for these pH-excursions occurring in concert with the *air* temperature changes. Note the completely different type of pH response at the various monitoring stations to these air temperature fluctuations. Such results are not consistent with standard physical chemistry expectations but are quite common occurrences in this "conditioned" laboratory space.

In order to explore what happened in the laboratory during this weekend event, we wanted to compare the weekend event period of Figure 2.18a with (a) the pre-event period background data and the post-event period background data for the P_2-monitoring station (water plus silica gel vessel). We decided that the Fourier spectra of the pH(t) data from this station might reveal the most clues and Figure 2.18b provides such data. Although the event weekend period constituted only two days and thus does not yield a great deal of clear structure, it provides a good central plot from which to compare the amplitudes of the fundamental and first five harmonics for the 28.44 days prior to and the 28.44 days post to the event weekend. From this, we note that major differences in the amplitudes of

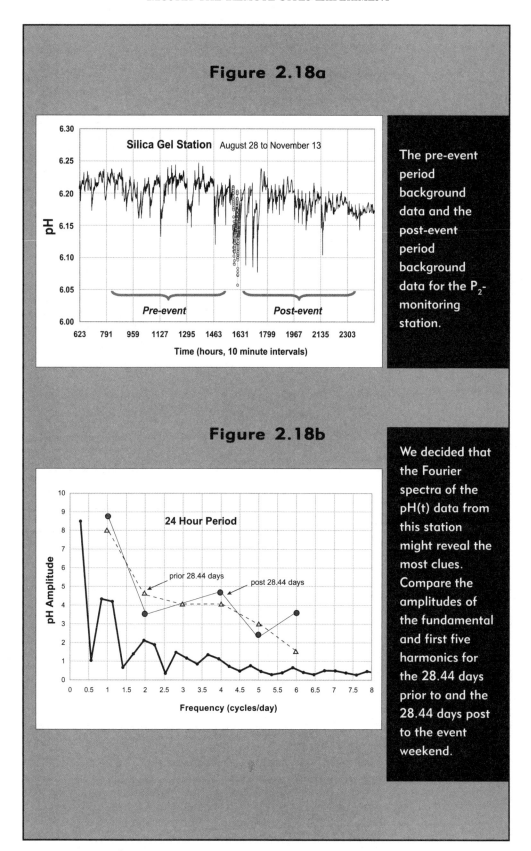

Figure 2.18a

Silica Gel Station August 28 to November 13

pH

Pre-event *Post-event*

Time (hours, 10 minute intervals)

The pre-event period background data and the post-event period background data for the P_2-monitoring station.

Figure 2.18b

24 Hour Period

pH Amplitude

prior 28.44 days post 28.44 days

Frequency (cycles/day)

We decided that the Fourier spectra of the pH(t) data from this station might reveal the most clues. Compare the amplitudes of the fundamental and first five harmonics for the 28.44 days prior to and the 28.44 days post to the event weekend.

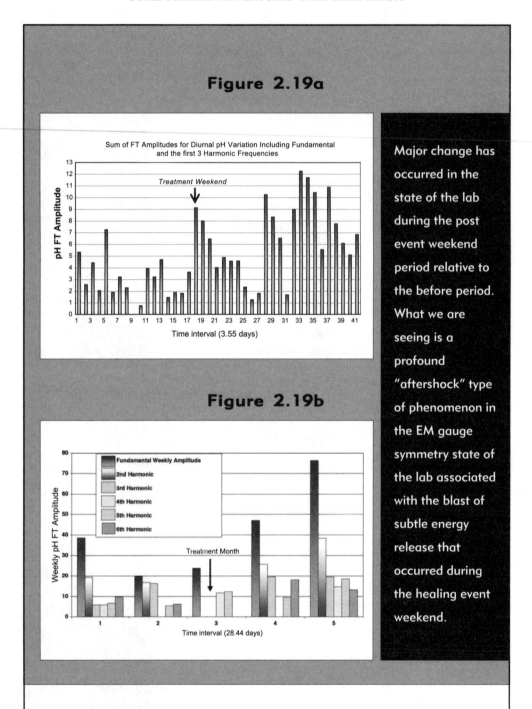

Figure 2.19a

Sum of FT Amplitudes for Diurnal pH Variation Including Fundamental and the first 3 Harmonic Frequencies

Treatment Weekend

pH FT Amplitude

Time interval (3.55 days)

Figure 2.19b

Fundamental Weekly Amplitude
2nd Harmonic
3rd Harmonic
4th Harmonic
5th Harmonic
6th Harmonic

Weekly pH FT Amplitude

Treatment Month

Time interval (28.44 days)

Major change has occurred in the state of the lab during the post event weekend period relative to the before period. What we are seeing is a profound "aftershock" type of phenomenon in the EM gauge symmetry state of the lab associated with the blast of subtle energy release that occurred during the healing event weekend.

"is there some system or mechanism in human subjects that allows them to broadcast such release signatures that are clearly registering themselves simultaneously at these various experimental stations?"

these six key frequency components have occurred relative to the initial baseline period. Figures 2.19 strengthen this picture of change that occurred in the laboratory during a ~150 day period surrounding the event weekend. Figure 2.19a shows the sum of the fundamental diurnal cycle and its first three harmonics. While Figure 2.19b shows its weekly analogue. From this, one readily sees that major change has occurred in the state of the laboratory during the post event weekend period relative to the before period, with the weekly cycle becoming steadily stronger. What we are seeing is a profound "aftershock" type of phenomenon in the EM gauge symmetry state of the laboratory associated with the blast of subtle energy release that occurred during the healing event weekend. Looked at in this way, one might rightfully ask, "is there some system or mechanism in human subjects that allows them to broadcast such release signatures that are clearly registering themselves simultaneously at these various experimental stations?"

To probe this question, we followed up on a fairly common practice in advanced Kinesiology. There, a practitioner can slide a small DC magnet, with a central hole, onto the tip of his/her finger and, bringing this finger/magnet into the biofield of a particular muscle group of a client, can either strengthen or weaken this muscle group *depending upon which magnetic pole points towards the muscle group*. The South-pole facing the group strengthens the muscle group while the North-pole facing the group weakens the muscle's response. This is very similar to the phenomenon we saw in Figure 1.11 and that we utilized to prove that a "conditioned" laboratory space had been transformed to a higher EM gauge symmetry level than that of our normal cognitive domain (The U(1) level). From all this, we can conclude that the human acupuncture meridian/chakra system *must* be at a higher EM gauge symmetry level while the rest of the body functions at the lower EM gauge symmetry level.

One consequence of this very important conclusion is that the thermodynamic free energy per unit volume of the acupuncture meridian/chakra system is at a higher magnitude than that expected in our normal cognitive world. This is illustrated in Figure 2.20 which qualitatively shows the free energy difference, ΔQ, above the U(1) level for the supposed states X, Y, SU(2), Z, etc. This means that, provided some connection or conduit can be made between one of these levels (let us say the SU(2) level) and the U(1) level,

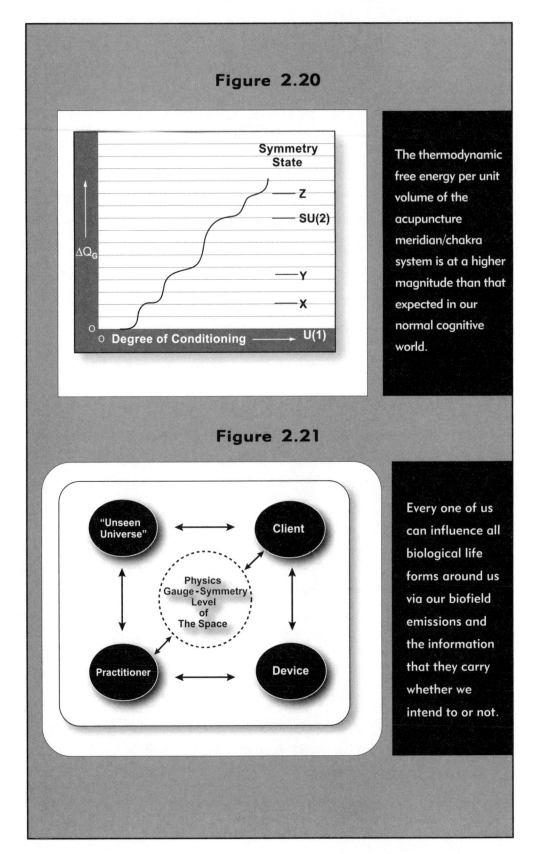

Figure 2.20

The thermodynamic free energy per unit volume of the acupuncture meridian/chakra system is at a higher magnitude than that expected in our normal cognitive world.

Figure 2.21

Every one of us can influence all biological life forms around us via our biofield emissions and the information that they carry whether we intend to or not.

useful work can be done by the higher level on the lower level. Thus, if a single organ or system of the human body was elevated to one of these higher symmetry states at birth, and the rest of the body was not, seemingly all functions of the lower state body could be driven by this energy source to exhibit what we call life; that is, the heart would pump the blood, nerve synapses would switch on and off, electric currents would flow, the brain would be activated to direct various body processes, etc. [3,4]

This differential system can be labeled a "Qi/Prana pump" and, as long as the flow rate of this unique "fluid" in the higher symmetry aspect of the body (the inner layer of our personality self) is sufficient to nourish all of the terrain of the normal, U(1) state aspect of the physical body (the outer layer of our personality self), physical health is satisfactorily manifested. However, if some stagnation or blockage occurs in one or more branches of the Qi/Prana flow field, then pathology can begin to develop in this outer layer of the personality self. In the theoretical model to be developed in the next chapter, a higher dimensional substance called "deltrons" from the emotion domain of the soul self acts as a *necessary* coupler between the energy fields of the substances making up the inner layer of the personality self and the energy fields of the substances making up the outer layer of the personality self. Human intention and consciousness appear to act directly on this coupler substance and thus have an indirect influence on all physical aspects of the human body.[3,18]

Adepts, masters, avatars and general folks: Just as physical exercise in the local gyms, golf courses, track and field, stadium games, etc., leads to both large muscle and small muscle development in the outer layer of the personality self, inner self-management exercises like meditation, Qigong, Tai-chi, remote viewing, local and non-local healing, etc., lead to the development of key structural features of the inner layer of the personality self. For both layers, the details of this extensive development are called necessary infrastructures for potential high human performance. The robustness of these necessary infrastructures allows the sufficiency requirement for this potential to manifest accordingly. Thus, the sustained application of intention and practice, over time, leads to superlative Qi/prana pump development turning normal folks into adepts. At this stage, their inner symmetry state is probably also raised á la Figure 2.20 from X to Y, or from SU(2) to Z, for example. Increased application of sustained intention and practice, over time, converts an adept to a master, also with concommitant raising of his or her inner symmetry state. Thus, these various inner symmetry states can be thought of as the rungs of a very special ladder that we utilize to climb from the level of a normal human to the level of an avatar. In all this, it is important to remember that *we are the product of the process and we are built by the process.*

The experimental summary findings of Tables 1.1, 1.2, 2.3 and 2.4 (see later) indicate to us that there is a profound connectivity between any one part of nature and another. Every one of us can influence all biological life forms around us via our biofield emissions and the information that they carry whether we consciously intend to or not. In this regard, it is useful to have a mental picture of how we operate in life with respect to one another and how energy/consciousness emissions can occur to and from us and from and to our surround all the time. Figure 2.21 provides a simple picture of this general interactive relationship, whether we be a minister, a healer, a medical doctor, an acupuncturist, a teacher, a performer, a spouse, a parent, etc. Usually, all five components of this figure are intimately involved in the interaction even though the practitioner, using some device, may only acknowledge that he/she and the client are involved in the process. Sometimes it is the Qi/Prana pump of the practitioner alone that raises the EM gauge symmetry state of the room to a level where higher dimensional forces can unblock the client's stagnant irrigation levels within the inner layer of the personality self. Sometimes it is simply the practitioner's love, compassion, devotion to service and intent that can elicit the "unseen" assistance of the universe to co-raise the EM gauge symmetry level of the intervening space and thus allow their intention to be more empowered. Finally, sometimes it is a musical performer augmenting their instrument sounds with their own subtle domain modulation, from their Qi/Prana pump, that increases the overall effectiveness of a healing process for someone in the audience.

An important point that we all need to recognize is that (1) material properties are all EM gauge symmetry state specific so that, if we change the EM gauge symmetry state of the space we are in, one must expect changes in the properties of the surrounding materials, (2) all humans (and probably all vertebrates and bio-organisms that contain a rudimentary acupuncture meridian/chakra system) have their own Qi/Prana pump that, via focused intention, can at least metastably raise the local EM gauge symmetry of their surrounding space and (3) this can produce healings of great variety. We also need to realize that, when an obstructed infrastructure circuit, at some level of the human biobodysuit, is restored to harmonious balance, a pulse of released energy/consciousness manifests and this complex signal can be detected by *deltron-enhanced* physical-type instruments that have been thus "raised" in functionality by being "soaked" in this higher EM gauge symmetry space.

For this "conditioned space" experimental data, Table 2.4 provides a summary of the key findings.

Table 2.4

1.   For humans, and perhaps all vertebrates, bioelectromagnetism is quite different than Maxwellian electromagnetism because the human acupuncture meridian system is observed to be at an EM gauge symmetry level where magnetic monopole charge is experimentally accessible.

2.   A laboratory space and equipment, raised to an EM gauge symmetry state wherein magnetic monopole currents are experimentally accessible, is found to be a very sensitive detector of subtle energy emissions by humans (subtle energies are defined as all those beyond the energy aspects of the accepted four fundamental forces).

3.   Large bursts of subtle energy emissions during healing steps in humans located in a "conditioned" laboratory act analogously to earthquakes with reverberating aftershocks for a long time. Thus, the detailed character of the laboratory's energy signature is significantly altered for a long time (greater than three months).

References

1.   W.A. Tiller, W.E. Dibble, Jr., R. Nunley and C.N. Shealy, "Toward General Experimentation and Discovery in Conditioned Laboratory Spaces: Part I, Experimental pH Change Findings at Some Remote Sites", The Journal of Alternative and Complementary Medicine (JACM) 10 (1) (2004) 145-157.

2.   Ibid, "Part II, pH Change Experience at Four Remote Sites, One Year Later", JACM 10 (2) (2004) 301-306.

3.   W.A. Tiller, W.E. Dibble, Jr. and M.J. Kohane, *Conscious Acts of Creation: The Emergence of a New Physics* (Pavior Publishing, Walnut Creek, CA, 2001).

4.   W.A. Tiller and W.E. Dibble, Jr., "Apparatus and Methods of Changing a Thermodynamic Potential of a Limited Physical Space Characterized by a Series of Symmetry States" U.S. Patent Pending.

5.   W.A. Tiller and W.E. Dibble, Jr. "Towards General Experimentation and Discovery in 'Conditioned' Laboratory Spaces: Part V, Data on Ten Different Sites Using a New Type of Detector", to be submitted to JACM ~December, 2005.

6.   W.A. Tiller, W.E. Dibble, Jr., G. Orlando, A. Migli, G. Raiteri and J. Oca, "Towards General Experimentation and Discovery in 'Conditioned' Laboratory Spaces: Part IV, Macroscopic Information Entanglement Between Sites ~6,000 Miles Apart", submitted to JACM, April 2004.

7.   W.A. Tiller and W.E. Dibble, Jr., "A New Category of Medical Intervention Device that Utilizes a Higher Electromagnetic Gauge Symmetry Space Than Our Normal U(1) Level Space", U.S. Patent Pending.

8.   W.A. Tiller, "What Are Subtle Energies?", J. Scientific Exploration, 7 (1993) 293.

9.   D.I. Radin, *The Conscious Unvierse* (Harper Edge, San Francisco, CA, 1997).

10.   W.A. Tiller, W.E. Dibble, Jr., and C.T. Krebs, "Instrumental Response to Advanced Kinesiology Treatments in a 'Conditioned' Space", Subtle Energies and Energy Medicine 13 (2), (2004), pp 91-108.

11.   C. T. Krebs, Chapter 2, In *A Revolutionary Way of Thinking* (Hill of Content, Melbourne, Australia, 1998).

12.   G. J. Goodheart, Jr., *Applied Kinesiology* (Privately Published, Detroit, MI, 1964).

13.   D. S. Walther, *Applied Kinesiology, Volume 1* (SDC Systems DC, Pueblo, CO, 1981).

14.   J. Diamond, *Behavioral Kinesiology* (Harper and Row, New York, 1979).

15.   I. P. Rolf, *Rolfing: The Integration of Human Structures* (Dennis-Landeman, Santa Monica, CA, 1977).

16.   Y. Omura, Meridians, Acupuncture Points and Neurotransmitters of the Central Nervous System Localized by Bi-digital O-ring Test In *Energy Fields in Medicine* (The John E. Fetzer Foundation, Kalamozoo, MI, 1989), pp. 395-399.

17.   R. Utt, *Stress, the Nature of the Beast, Volume I* (International Institute of Applied Physiology, Tucson, AZ, 1977).

18.   W. A. Tiller, *Science and Human Transformation: Subtle Energies, Intentionality and Consciousness* (Pavior Publishing, Walnut Creek, CA, 1997).

Chapter 3

General Theoretical Modeling
For a New Paradigm

$v < c$

*Nature is always richer in untapped possibilities
than we think it is.*

z

x

Θ_A Θ_B

$v > c$

**Wave Group
Aspect**

y

**Particle
Aspect**

k_y

The unstated assumption of science

Our present paradigm of science is quantum mechanics (QM) and just over a century ago it was classical mechanics (CM). The transition acceptance from one to the other occurred between ~1895 and 1925. In both cases, science held the unstated assumption that no human qualities of consciousness, intention, emotion, mind or spirit can significantly influence a carefully designed target experiment in physical reality. Thus, for both paradigms, there is no place in their formal mathematical structure where any of these human qualities might enter. However, the collection of experimental data presented in Chapters 1 and 2 show us that this unstated assumption is very, very wrong!

Others, over the past two centuries have also provided pieces of experimental data that buttress this inescapable conclusion. However, just as in Galileo's time when the priests would not look through the telescope to access the experimental evidence of his thesis, so too today the vast majority of the scientific community around the world have psychologically refused to seriously look at this large array of psychoenergetic experimental data. One can argue interminably about why this is so; however, the bare facts indicate that it is so! In the mindset of today's establishment science, no respectable scientist feels he/she can afford to jeopardize his/her reputation with both his/her peers and with government funding agencies by seriously considering this psychoenergetics stuff.

Another fact that needs to be kept in mind is that, today, the general public of all countries pay for almost all scientific research done in their nation via their taxes. Therefore, in democratic societies, the general public are ultimately responsible for this sustaining of outdated paradigms by their scientific sector. When human consciousness has been shown to significantly influence properties of, and processes in, inorganic, organic and living materials, it is time for the general public to require (demand) that their scientific establishment develop a new reference frame (RF) for viewing nature that has the capability of quantitatively connecting both the seeming outer world aspects of nature and our seeming inner world aspects of nature. And it must be formulated in such a way that the inner can quantitatively affect the outer and vice versa. This is what the experimental data requires.

Truth lies always in the experimental data while uncertainty dwells in the data interpretation and in the theoretical modeling of how nature must be constructed to quantitatively express itself in this way.

As a society and as a species, we periodically need such upgrades and course corrections to our evolutionary path for a variety of reasons. One reason is so that we will have a better picture of what we are, both as individuals and as a species, and of what we are becoming. Another reason is so we can apply the new insights of the new paradigm to enhance old technologies in our society and create new ones. This allows us to be fiscally stable in our world as a nation; to have the kinds of daily jobs that sustain a satisfactory standard of living for our peoples and to have sufficient uncommitted capital to help others in need. We cannot expect to have a stable world unless we continue to create new ideas, new concepts, new technologies, and new types of businesses so that we can happily move former employment opportunities offshore to developing nations so that their standard of living can rise and become closer to ours.

Nature is always richer in untapped possibilities than we think it is. We must always keep planting the new "seed corn" of fundamental research so that we might reveal new levels of nature's expression, new levels of "magic" as interpreted by the old paradigm (because the old paradigm cannot explain the new data). However, all of this new data appears lawful and understandable via the conceptual framework of the new paradigm. And it lays the foundation for all the new applications of this knowledge, the new opportunities to test ourselves, to become more than we were and to help others do likewise. All of this is nested within the many challenges of this chapter's task - to qualitatively communicate a picture of a quantitatively viable new paradigm without the aid of detailed mathematical equations!

The "boggle" effect

Before closing this section it is important to make the reader aware of the psychoenergetics boggle effect amongst scientists. In this regard, there appears to be only three categories of scientists. The first group is the very, very large number of today's scientific community who completely subscribe to the unstated assumption presented in the first paragraph of this chapter. For them, their mantra is that the outcome effect size of any psychoenergetic experiment must be unequivocally *zero!* If one begins to describe any of the robust experimental results of Chapter 1 and 2 of this book, before long their eyes "will start to spin" and they will lose their cognitive capabilities. Their *boggle effect quotient* is practically zero! The second group is a much smaller group who *know* that the outcomes effect size is non-zero but very small so that their mantra is "carefully gathered statistics in a double-blind experimental protocol is an absolute necessity for scientifically discriminating a psychoenergetic effect". For them, one can describe some of the small stuff from Chapter 1 and 2 and they are OK; however, begin to describe some of the large effect size results and their "eyes begin to spin just before they tune out and lose their cognitive capabilities". Their boggle effect quotient is non-zero but small! The third group is quite a small group that includes this book's authors and, for them, the outcomes effect sizes can be incredibly large and the boggle effect never does occur. For them, it is just experimental data for which current theory happens to be inadequate to explain!

Why does the present QM paradigm not provide a viable future path?

As mathematically formulated, QM is a very precise theory whose field of operation is four-dimensional spacetime within the classical particle velocity limits of $0 < v < c$, the velocity of EM light, and involving any of the four fundamental forces (1) electromagnetism, (2) gravity, (3) the long-range nuclear force and (4) the short-range nuclear force. This theory has been remarkably successful for particle physics, small atoms and molecules and photons. Unfortunately, the formulation is something of a "black box" where you input the relevant pieces of information, turn a mathematical crank and out pops the answer for these very small bits of stuff. Large bits of stuff are beyond our computational capabilities at present and the black box procedure-generated results provide us with some, but very little, intuitive insight about what is actually going on in nature to produce such results.

All of us have heard some of the many, many statements extolling the weirdness of QM and many revel in such weirdness as if that is what makes QM a great theory. However, professionals amongst this book's readership know that, whatever theoretical model or RF one uses to predict the behavior of nature's many expressions, built-in constraints, assumptions and other limitations associated with the model's detailed mathematical formalism exist for each such model or RF. A different RF choice always yields a different perspective for viewing nature and the goal of a theorist is to find an RF wherein the explanations for all of the experimental data are straightforward, understandable and relatively simple rather than weird.

Julian Schwinger,[1] along with Feinman and Tomanaga, winners of the Nobel Prize for their discovery and mathematical development of quantum electrodynamics (QED), had a Ph.D. student, Paul Werbos, who made[2] the very important point that all forms of QED; Copenhagen, Bohmian, Schwinger or Werbos-types, yield the same kind of predictions and *none* of them can explain something like remote viewing or other psychoenergetic phenomena. He tells us that the world has spent billions of dollars trying to use QED in the military to see things far away and has failed to do so. The point, here, is that our present formulation of QM, great as it is, is totally inadequate to encompass the inclusion of psychoenergetic phenomena into our scientific worldview. Thus, it is time to formulate a larger perspective or RF for viewing nature that both accounts for all of the old data and provides the possibility of quantitatively accounting for this new psychoenergetic data in an internally self-consistent way.

"What are the cornerstones of QM that must be retained in an expanded paradigm?"

The De Broglie particle/pilot wave concept of the 1920's, for which he won a Nobel Prize, proposed that every particle had a pilot wave envelope enclosing it and moving at the particle's velocity (see Figure 3.1). This was eventually to be called "the wave particle duality of QM"; however, it is important for the reader to realize that all the waves humans experience in our normal cognitive reality are merely modulations of particle densities or particle fluxes in space and time. They are not of the seeming continuum-type drawn in all our textbooks or drawn as in the pilot wave of Figure 3.1. The other cornerstone was Planck's experimental (and theoretical) observations that radiation emission and absorption by physical matter was quantized. This means that the energy levels (Δ**E**) in matter and radiation were not continuous but occurred in discrete steps of Δ**E** = **h**ν, where ν is the frequency of the wave aspects and **h** came to be called Planck's constant.

Some time later, scientists used a combination of Planck's QM and Einstein's relativistic considerations on the concept displayed in Figure 3.1. Calling the particle velocity,

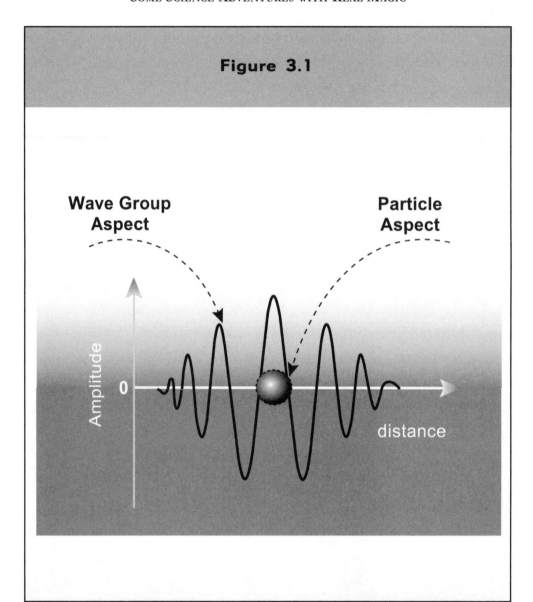

Figure 3.1

The De Broglie particle/pilot wave concept of the 1920's, for which he won a Nobel Prize, proposed that every particle had a pilot wave envelope enclosing it and moving at the particle's velocity. This was eventually to be called "the wave particle duality of QM".

v_p, and the velocity of the wave components that enter and leave the wave group as it moves along with the particle, v_w, they calculated[3] that

$$v_p\, v_w = c^2 \qquad\qquad (3.1a)$$

where c is the velocity of EM light. Since v_p is always smaller than c for particles with mass, from relativity theory, v_w must always be greater than c to satisfy Equation 3.1a. In order to avoid complications with relativity theory, these waves were dubbed "information" waves. As a simple example, if $v_p = 1$ centimeter per second, $v_w = c^2/v_p$ which is $|c|$ times the value of the EM light velocity, a very large number indeed. Since the individual v_w are greater than the pilot wave group velocity, which is the same as v_p, these individual wave components are constantly moving through the group from the rear to the front.[3] When one considers the details of such wave dynamics, one is inescapably led to the fundamental expression for Heisenberg's uncertainty principle,

$$\Delta x\, \Delta p_x > h/2\pi \quad . \qquad\qquad (3.1b)$$

Here, Δx is the uncertainty of the particle's position in the envelope of Figure 3.1 and Δp_x is the uncertainty of its momentum. This uncertainty principle is inherent in the mathematical formalism for waves that led to Equation 3.1a. [3] We may arbitrarily decrease the uncertainty in one of these quantities in Equation 3.1b, but only at the expense of increasing the uncertainty in the other. The reason for this is easy to understand because any physical measurement performed to find the value of one of these quantities will always disturb the particle in such a way as to leave the value of the other uncertain.

A second distillation of experimental insights

The first distillation of experimental insights occurred in Chapters 1 and 2 and resulted in Tables 1.1 and 1.2 plus Tables 2.3 and 2.4. These have been collected in Appendix 3.1 as Tables 1 to 4 so that the reader might have easier access to them while reading the remainder of this chapter. The second distillation comes from these tables and constitutes a list of suggestions that the tables appear to imply. These suggestions are:

1.   Humans emit, via their biofields, a spectrum of energies, some of which are conventional energies like EM. However, some of them we must label as "subtle energies" because they behave differently than the energies associated with the four fundamental

forces. These "subtle energies" are, in part, associated with the human acupuncture meridian system and at least one of them appears to increase its speed on entering dense matter so that it travels at $v > c$.

2.   Table 4 confirms the singular importance of the acupuncture meridian/chakra system in humans, and probably in at least all vertebrates. We see that this is so because this system is at a higher EM gauge symmetry state than our normal U(1) gauge symmetry level. Further, an IIED-conditioned space, because it is at this higher EM gauge state, is sensitive to the subtle energies of this higher level emitted by humans.

3.   Human consciousness, in the form of a specific information pattern, can be made to modulate a subtle energy carrier wave and caused to be stored in a simple electronic device and broadcast into a space to produce "conditioning" of that space. The carrier wave is definitely not electromagnetism.

4.   The treated space is conditioned to a higher EM gauge level than our normal U(1) level and can be tuned to influence specific material properties or processes. This higher gauge symmetry state allows normal digital instruments to access important aspects of magnetic monopoles, and also yields *a higher thermodynamic free energy per unit volume state.*

5.   The physical vacuum is the level of reality at which space-conditioning operates. Changes in basic structural elements at that level produce the DC magnetic field polarity observations, the material property oscillation observations, the information entanglement observations, the $|\Delta\Psi_{H+}| > 0$ observations and the thermodynamic information increase observations.

6.   The inability to shield against this information field penetration connotes the presence of at least one new kind of energy, as does information entanglement between IIED-sites and non-IIED sites separated by ~5,000 to 6,000 miles.

7.   Replication by others assures us that we are dealing with a real, objective energy in nature that can be stored as a specific information pattern in an IIED. The fact that control sites very, very far away can respond in identical ways so quickly, plus the fact that $\Delta pH \sim 1.7$ units for below ground sites suggests, as in Table 1 (5), that we are dealing with a subtle energy here with $v > c$ characteristics.

8.   It appears that any physical measurement contains two key parts, one which appears to be associated with the chemical/electromagnetic nature of an unconditioned space while the other appears to be associated with an information aspect of nature characteristic of a conditioned space and tracked by the new potential energy contribution, $\Delta\Psi_{H+}$.

9.   Everything in a conditioned space appears to be strongly connected with everything else as if subtle energy exchanges are going on all the time between all parts of the system, both local parts and non-local parts. Also, when the level of conditioning is high enough, it does not decline even after the conditioning IIED is removed.

Before we begin to take the key steps involved in creating a preliminary model for the new paradigm, there are three perspectives that it is useful to put before the reader first.

The first perspective relates to medicine. Almost everyone knows that, if we take a glass of water with bacteria in it and then place a small spoonful of silver colloidal particles in it, the bacteria are killed by the silver metal. This would be labeled "chemical medicine" and it holds the implicit assumption that physical contact between the silver and the bacteria is *a necessary condition* leading to the demise of the bacteria. What is not so well known is that placing the colloidal silver particles in a nearby gas discharge tube (like a fluorescent tube) and focusing the emitted light from that tube onto the glass of water, the bacteria will also be killed. Thus, it is *the specific EM information pattern inherent in all silver atoms*, and not physical contact, that is killing the bacteria. A medicine based upon these principles would be called "electromagnetic energy medicine". Most of the science focused on in this book deals with levels of nature beyond conventional electromagnetism but these subtle energies can interact with EM. Thus, these subtle energies could also be utilized to kill the bacteria. A medicine based on these principles would be called "subtle energy medicine" or more probably "information medicine". We can write this triad of bacteria-killing vehicles as

$$\text{Chemistry} \rightleftharpoons \text{Electromagnetism} \rightleftharpoons \text{Subtle Energies} \quad (3.2)$$

and each can become a perfectly viable foundation for a practical form of medicine. It is the material of this book that, among other things, will allow us to fashion a reliable information medicine using subtle energies.

The second perspective that we wish to communicate involves concepts concerning *EM gauge symmetry*. Most people, including scientists, never give this concept much thought although they might know that the macroscopic properties of materials are almost completely determined by their electric and magnetic characteristics. If the topic ever comes up in conversation, it is generally considered to be something from the domain of particle physicists or relativity theorists. However, perhaps they might remember that it somehow enters the concept of the "big bang" theory, a cosmological speculation that the universe began in a state of compression to infinite density and has been expanding since some particular instant of time that marked the origin of our universe in an important way.

They might recall that, a short time after the initiation event and before to after quarks form in this incredibly hot "fireball", the universe evolves to successively lower thermodynamic free energy states during the cooling process via step by step changes in EM gauge symmetry eventually passing through an important state (to us), called the SU(2) EM gauge symmetry state, on its way to another important state (to us), called the U(1) EM gauge symmetry state. Thereafter, the thermodynamic free energy per unit volume of the U(1) state continues to be lowered, via a set of physical material phase transformations, from a plasma state to a predominately gaseous state to a predominantly liquid state to a mixed state of solid, liquid and gas in approximate thermodynamic balance with each other, to our present day U(1) state, cognitive world. From the foregoing, one might deduce that, if one could somehow raise the EM gauge symmetry state associated with a particular environment, such as a laboratory, the properties of materials in that laboratory would change.

As used in this book "EM gauge symmetry" means a characteristic of matter related to the conservation of electric charge. People are generally familiar with "outer" symmetries that are geometrical in appearance, like the hexagonal (6-fold) symmetry of a snowflake or the 4-fold symmetry of a square. The charge symmetry of electric materials is non-geometric in that, for a collection of electric dipoles when the individual charges are suddenly reversed in sign, the energy of the system as a whole remains unchanged (it is invariant to this electric charge reversal) so the forces also remain unchanged. The same type of behavior occurs for magnetic dipoles and electromagnetic fields in general.

Our present-day unconditioned, conventional physical reality is in the U(1) EM gauge symmetry state where material properties depend largely upon the detailed behaviors of electric monopoles (single **+** or **-** charges with overall electric charge neutrality), electric dipoles (**+** and **-** charges separated by a small distance) and magnetic dipoles (north and south-pole magnetic charges separated by a small distance). Because of this, Maxwell's equations define electromagnetic behavior. The governing algebra we use is called Abelian algebra (**XY - YX = o**, where **X** and **Y** are fields, vectors defined by only a single inner symmetry parameter - their phase angle) and is of the kind we all learned in grade school. And the vacuum space between the fundamental particles comprising atoms and molecules in all materials is isotropic.

Another, higher EM gauge symmetry state, is the SU(2) state. Materials in this state exhibit different behavior than in the U(1) state because, now, magnetic monopoles (single north-pole and south-pole charges) coexist with electric monopoles so magnetic currents inducing electric fields are experimentally accessible along with the normal electric currents inducing magnetic fields. Thus, the electro-magnetic equations are non-Maxwellian and the algebra one must use to describe them is non-Albelian (**XY - YX** is not equal to zero because, now, *two* inner symmetry parameters must be used to define these fields). It is also very likely that the vacuum level of space is both partially ordered and non-isotropic for this SU(2) state.

Finally, the third perspective is to say something about the latent energy content expected to reside in the physical vacuum. A number of famous theoretical physicists have calculated that, for relativity theory and QM to be internally self-consistent, the vacuum must contain ~10^{94} grams per cubic centimeter of mass energy (E = mc^2 type of energy), which is a very large number. To put this number in perspective, let us consider a simple comparison. For the approximation that the universe is flat in a curvature sense (and astronomers say that this is OK) then, if we compare the latent vacuum energy contained within the volume of a single hydrogen atom to the total mass energy contained in all the planets, stars, asteroids, dust, etc., within the volume of our detectable universe (a sphere of radius ~15 billion light years), we find that the former is much, much larger than the latter. From this, we can conclude that the vacuum level of physical reality must be a very important aspect of any new paradigm.

In our current lay-public literature, there is a great deal of interest in, discussion of and confusion about, zero point energy so it is perhaps useful to place its magnitude in a hierarchy of energies.

Present day QM shows us that, at the absolute zero of temperature (T=0), atoms and molecules still have modes of vibration so that energy can be exchanged back and forth between these ground state modes via EM photons and phonons (sound vibrations).

By *definition*, this energetic state has been labeled the *zero point energy (zpe) state*. In addition, a wide spectrum of EM radiations traversing the universe in all directions can interact with such zpe atoms and molecules causing them to move back and forth between the zpe state and higher energy states. Thus, for our purpose here, one sees that the zpe consists mostly of a large collection of EM photons because we are dealing with a large number of atoms.

Suppose we consider the simplest possible case, the formation of a single hydrogen atom in space at T=0 (to look at the zpe on a per atom basis). This is thought to occur via the following sequence of events: (1) the spontaneous appearance of an electron plus an anti-electron from the vacuum due to the annihilation of a high energy gamma-ray (at an energy exchange of 1.02 million electron volts), (2) the spontaneous appearance of a proton plus an anti-proton from the vacuum due to the annihilation of another high energy gamma-ray (at an energy exchange of 1.88 billion electron volts), (3) the electron and proton wander around in space until they come into close proximity of each other and (4) the electron and proton interact and combine to form a hydrogen atom at T=0 (with an energy release of 13.6 electron volts). This formation energy for the hydrogen atom from the vacuum is thus 941.0199864 *million electron volts*. If we were to somehow raise the temperature of this hydrogen atom to room temperature, its energy level would be raised by only about 0.04 electron volts. Thus, we see that the thermal energies of atoms and molecules is small compared to the optical EM photon energies from hydrogen (~1-10 electron volts) which is *comparable to the EM zpe for hydrogen* and which is reasonable to be assumed to be smaller than the particle binding energy of the H-atom (13.6 electron volts). This EM zpe is very small relative to the formation energy of the H-atom (by a factor of ~100 million) which, in turn, is very very small compared to the total vacuum energy stored in the volume of an H-atom.

The postulates, pictures and rationales for a new paradigm model

Our current working hypotheses can now be readily articulated via a series of key postulates:

Postulate 1: A better reference frame than our 4-dimensional spacetime for viewing and understanding the many expressions of nature is a biconformal or duplex RF comprised of two, 4-dimensional, reciprocal subspaces, one of which is spacetime, with all of this imbedded in a higher dimensional framework comprised of the domains of emotion, mind and spirit (see Figure 3.2a).

Figure 3.2

A structural representation of our RF with the duplex space in the center. If one counts the entire duplex space as a 4-space, then the entire multidimensional representation is a 7-space. If instead, we count the duplex space as a unique member of the general 8-space, then our RF is eleven-dimensional.

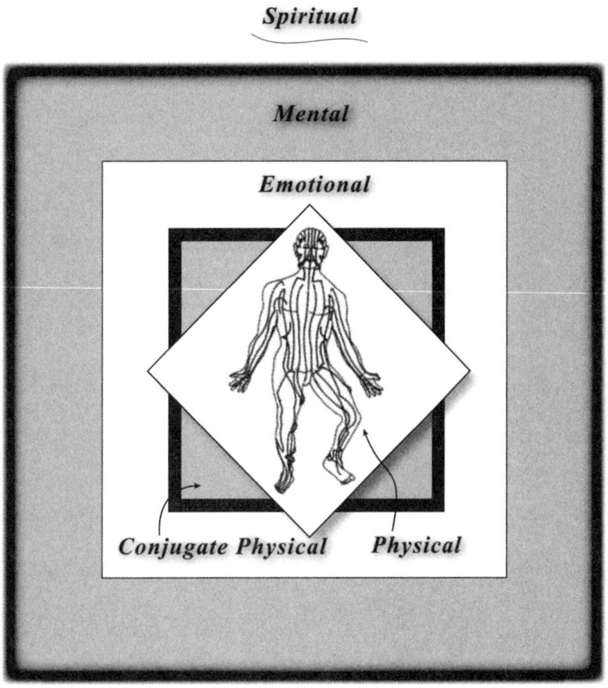

a

An energy level diagram embracing both classical physical substances and "un-seen" vacuum substances.

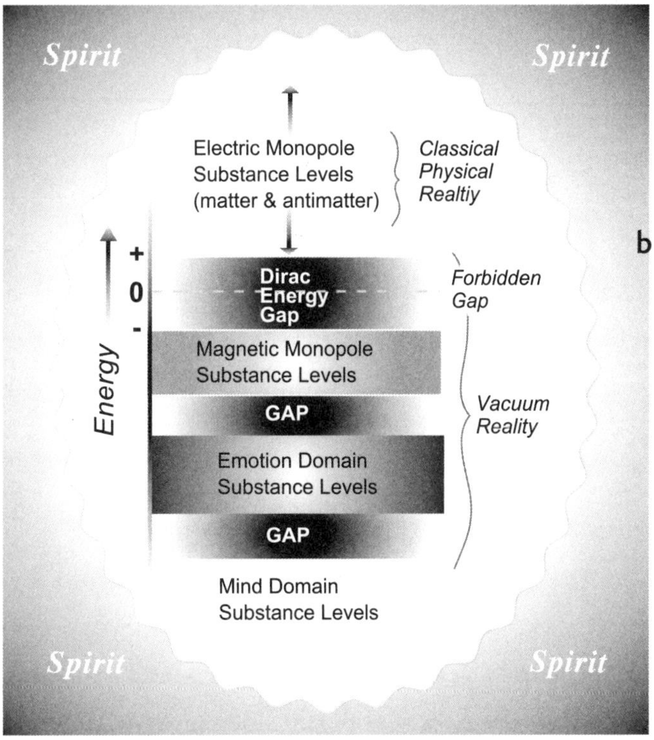

b

Postulate 2: Physical reality expresses itself via two uniquely different kinds of materials (a) relatively coarse, particulate, electric monopole-constructed types of substance, constrained to move at velocities $\mathbf{v} < \mathbf{c}$ and (b) fine, information wave generated patterns from magnetic monopole types of substances traveling at $\mathbf{v} > \mathbf{c}$ in the coarse physical vacuum at a higher EM gauge symmetry level than our standard U(1) gauge (see Figure 3.2b).

Postulate 3: A higher dimensional level substance, labeled deltrons, falling outside the constraints of relativity theory and able to move at velocities $\mathbf{v} \gtrless \mathbf{c}$, acts as a coupling agent between the electric monopole types of substances and the magnetic monopole types of substances to produce both electromagnetic (EM) and magnetoelectric (ME) types of mediator fields exhibiting a special type of "mirror principle" relationship between them (see Figures 3.3 and 3.4).

Postulate 4: Human consciousness, and specifically human intention, can activate this deltron population, and thereby modulate this electric/magnetic monopole substance coupling, so as to alter the specifics of the EM gauge symmetry state of the space wherein an object rests, and thus the experimentally measurable properties of that object (see Figure 3.5).

Postulate 5: A specific intention originates at the level of spirit and manifests first as a unique radiation pattern of consciousness/energy waves at the level of mind (a close-packed hexagonal lattice of transponders). In turn, a conjugate pattern is diffracted to its reciprocal lattice (a hexagonal superlattice of transponders) that is also the reciprocal subspace of the duplex space mentioned in Postulate 1 above (see Figure 3.5).

Focusing, for the moment, on Postulate 1, Figure 3.2a is a schematic structural representation of this duplex space imbedded in a higher dimensional framework. An energy representation of this model is given in Figure 3.2b. One will note the great similarity between Figure 3.2a and aspects of the "whole person" model in Chapter 1 (see Figure 1.3).

Why do we need an RF for viewing nature?

The scientific method does not, and cannot, provide us with *absolute truth* about nature. Rather, what it is capable of doing and tries to do, is to provide us with a set of tools for determining *internal self-consistency* amongst a wide variety of bits of information about nature. In part, it does this by discriminating and highlighting the importance of

Figure 3.3

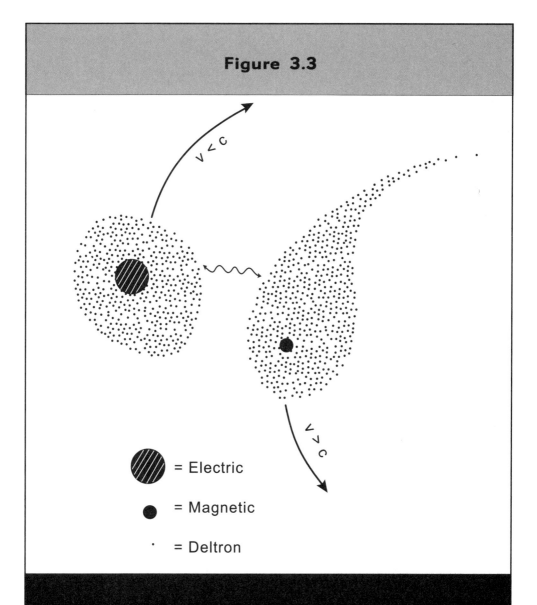

= Electric

= Magnetic

= Deltron

A higher dimensional level substance, labeled deltrons, falling outside the constraints of relativity theory and able to move at velocities $v \gtrless c$, acts as a coupling agent between the electric monopole types of substances and the magnetic monopole types of substances to produce both electromagnetic (EM) and magnetoelectric (ME) types of mediator fields exhibiting a special type of "mirror principle" relationship between them.

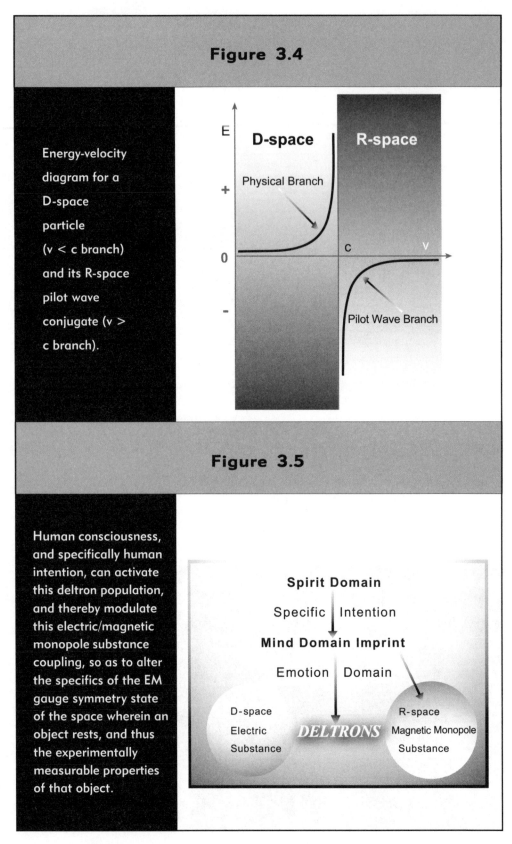

Figure 3.4

Energy-velocity diagram for a D-space particle (v < c branch) and its R-space pilot wave conjugate (v > c branch).

Figure 3.5

Human consciousness, and specifically human intention, can activate this deltron population, and thereby modulate this electric/magnetic monopole substance coupling, so as to alter the specifics of the EM gauge symmetry state of the space wherein an object rests, and thus the experimentally measurable properties of that object.

independent external variables that influence the properties and behavior of the different materials present in nature. It also does this by defining the key parameters in a specific material that respond to specific external variables (that scientists can either fix or intentionally vary in a particular experiment). One of the goals of this "science game" is to discover lawful connections between these different parameters and different variables and express them in the form of equations. In this way, a close simulation of nature's behavior can be generated via requiring simultaneous adherence to a set of these connection equations involving a successively smaller number of independent external variables and material parameters. The smaller is the number of unconstrained variables and parameters, the closer is one to winning the "science game".

Along this path of human scientific progress, we found it to be important to define our reference frame (RF) for viewing nature. Over the past few millennia, we came to realize that two key variables that influenced our observations of nature were distance and time. We also came to realize that things could vary differently with distance in front of us vs. to the sides of us vs. above and below us. Thus, we realized that not only was the distance of the thing from us important but the orientation of the thing relative to us was also important so our two key variables now become space (in three perpendicular directions) and time, with space generally requiring distance along three coordinate directions to be specified. Then Einstein came along a little over a century ago and taught us that nature's quantitative expressions actually depend upon the velocity of our reference frame, via which the variables of space and time were unequivocally coupled, so our RF has, for the past century become *spacetime*, a four-dimensional RF.

In the QM paradigm, spacetime is the RF used but simultaneous particle and wave behavior of all things must be assumed. However, the psychoenergetic experiments of Chapters 1 and 2 have shown us that human consciousness influences the properties of materials and that this occurs via interaction with the "stuff" of the physical vacuum level of total reality. We thus need some new procedure for tracking this "stuff" at the vacuum level of reality and discriminating it from the different types of stuff we have monitored for the past couple of centuries. At the simplest level of description, we now have a book-keeping kind of problem. How do we keep quantitative track of these two very different kinds of "stuff"? The duplex space proposal is one satisfactory way of doing this. Making the two subspaces reciprocals of each other allows us to allocate our particulate type of stuff to one subspace and the physical vacuum level stuff to the other. Since our spacetime coordinates are used to track the particulate stuff, the reciprocal space coordinates as modified by deltrons are used to track the physical vacuum level stuff. By doing this, the particle behavior is in one subspace while the wave behavior is in the other and, although the two interact via the deltrons, there are now several degrees of freedom available to the {particle/deltron/wave} behavior that did not exist with present-day QM. Now the particle can move around within the envelope and now human consciousness can influence this behavior via direct interaction with the deltrons that bind the system together.

What QM's founding fathers should have done

It is our contention that the founding fathers of quantum mechanics (QM) should have realized that there was another important classical mechanics (CM) step to take before their leap into the quantum world. Adoption of the 8-dimensional duplex space at the center of Figure 3.2a as a basis for physical reality would have done a whole variety of useful things for them:

(1) It would have produced a particle and wave simultaneity viewpoint (see Figure 3.6) with the RF for the particles being direct space (D-space or (x,y,z,t)-space or space-time). The RF for the waves, via this duplex space, is labeled reciprocal space (or R-space). The prevailing mathematics, required by the reciprocal nature of these two subspaces, would have revealed to the founding fathers that a particular quality associated with the type of substance (electric, say) in one subspace had an equilibrium conjugate quality manifesting by the type of substance (magnetic, say) in the other subspace with a quantitative connection between them that are called the "Fourier transform pair relationships"[4] They would have deduced that, from this new perspective, every quality manifesting in physical reality consists of two parts, a D-space part and an R-space part with the relative magnitudes of the two parts being determined by the degree of coupling (deltron-related) between the elements of substance functioning in the two subspaces; i.e., between the particle aspect and the wave aspect. Thus, any experimental measurement, Q_M, would have consisted of two parts, one from D-space, Q_D, and one from R-space Q'_R, so that $Q_M = Q_D + Q'_R$. For very weak deltron coupling between D-space and R-space, such as occurs for the U(1) symmetry state, $Q'_R << Q_D$, and very carefully gathered statistical experimental data are needed to discriminate Q'_R from Q_D. However, for fairly strong deltron coupling, Q'_R can be comparable to, or larger than, Q_D so that experimental apparatus can easily discriminate the Q'_R contribution in Q_M without detailed statistical procedures.

(2) It would have shown that every point in one subspace is connected energetically to every other point in that subspace via the interaction with the totality of the other subspace. Once again, the degree of that connectivity increases with the magnitude of deltron activation in the system. This would mean that every object in D-space has some spatial

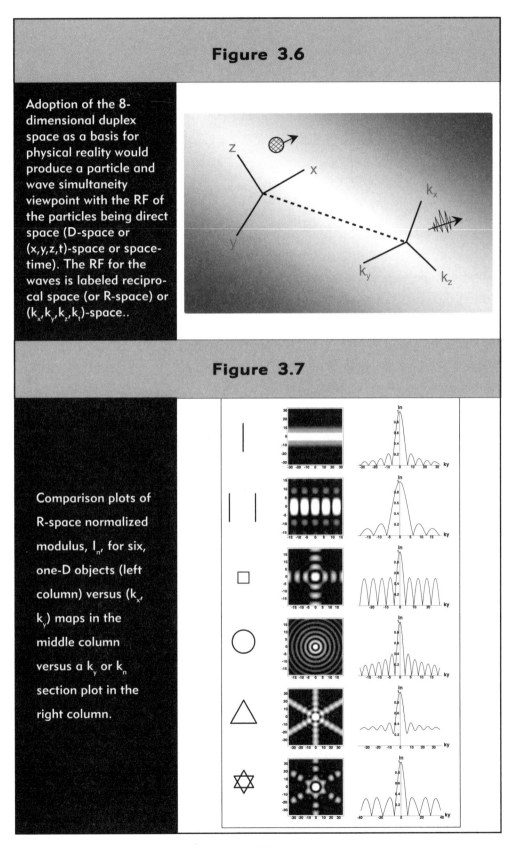

Figure 3.6

Adoption of the 8-dimensional duplex space as a basis for physical reality would produce a particle and wave simultaneity viewpoint with the RF of the particles being direct space (D-space or (x,y,z,t)-space or space-time). The RF for the waves is labeled reciprocal space (or R-space) or (k_x, k_y, k_z, k_t)-space..

Figure 3.7

Comparison plots of R-space normalized modulus, I_n, for six, one-D objects (left column) versus (k_x, k_y) maps in the middle column versus a k_y or k_n section plot in the right column.

extension via the deltron-coupled connection to its conjugate aspect in R-space so that no point-like object can exist. Thus, the very troublesome, proliferating mathematical singularities of present QM would be eliminated. Of course, maybe then the invention of "string theory" would not have occurred because there would have been no critical need for it.

(3) It would also have shown us that, in nature, it is possible to observe both *local* forces from the D-space aspects and *non-local* forces from the R-space aspects. Again, the relative proportions of these two types of force depends upon the degree of deltron coupling mentioned above,

(4) They would have realized that, because most of the material qualities of interest had amplitudes that were vectors, information entanglement would have existed between non-local spaces and objects. This occurs because the amplitude of the R-space contribution involves the vector sum of each part of the experimental system (see Figure 3.8 below for a system of two parts, A and B).

(5) Finally, the founding fathers of QM would have realized that there was an alternative explanation for Young's double-slit experiment, which became a key cornerstone in their present formulation of QM. Working with the duplex space model proposed here, they would have realized that D-space was ideal for particulate behavior while R-space was ideal for wave behavior. From the precise mathematical requirement connecting behaviors in these two subspaces, they would have predicted the equilibrium intensity patterns for R-space waves associated with *any* D-space particulate object. An example of this is illustrated in Figure 3.7 for six simple D-space objects (left column), either thin rod figures or thin slit figures in a solid background mask. Here, the central column provides the R-space (k_z, k_y) map while the right hand column provides a section cut in the k_y - direction (y is along the length of the single slit). These undulations in the k_y - direction diminish in interval as the D-space length, l, of the slit increases. This is just another indicator of the reciprocal character of this RF.

When one uses two slits, as in the second figure of the D-space column, the R-space map in the central column shows that a new periodicity has appeared in the k_x - direction illustrating the information entanglement, in the form of wave interference, that occurs between the two parallel slits. This is a very different interpretation for the classical Young's double slit experiment. It involves the detailed geometry of the mask's R-space structure guiding the D-space particles to produce what appears to be wave interference. Looking at the other D-space figures, one sees that such interference occurs in every case where parallel segments exist in the whole figure. We will return to this topic after a short diversion.

A brief side-road excursion from the main highway.

First leg: In a physics description of nature, we are accustomed to dealing with both extrinsic thermodynamic variables that govern the overall behavior of outer nature and the intrinsic properties of different materials in outer nature. These variables and properties all attempt to characterize a particular quality or qualities *at a given point* in our reference frame (RF) used for viewing nature. These qualities can be thought of as being members of three different classes:

(1) Scalar qualities such as temperature, pressure, concentration or density may vary from point to point but, at any given point, are not also connected with direction around that point. Such non-directional physical qualities are called *scalars* and we note that the value of a scalar is completely specified by giving a single number. We will see below that a scalar is also called *a tensor of zero rank*.

(2) Vector qualities such as mechanical force, electric field, magnetic field, etc., require the use of three numbers at a point in our RF for their complete specification. One of these numbers is *magnitude* and the others are *directions*. Thus, the magnitude of such a quality at a point varies with direction around a point. If we define our spatial RF at a point using the standard $(\mathbf{x},\mathbf{y},\mathbf{z})$ designation, then the three components, $(\mathbf{E_x}, \mathbf{E_y}, \mathbf{E_z})$, are needed to define the electric field vector, $\mathbf{E}$, at a point. A vector is also called *a tensor of first rank*.

(3) Tensor qualities of second rank, such as electric current density, $\mathbf{j}$, is equal to the product of electrical conductivity $\boldsymbol{\sigma}$, and electric field, $\mathbf{E}$, and, in general, both may be vectors (with three perpendicular components). Thus, in such a case, $\mathbf{3x3 = 9}$ numbers at a point are needed to completely specify $\mathbf{j}$. Some other examples of second rank tensors are given in Table 3.1[5] and each has nine components, $\mathbf{T_{kl}}$, where $\mathbf{k = (x,y,z)}$ and $\mathbf{l = (x,y,z)}$, so we have terms like $\mathbf{T_{xx}}$, $\mathbf{T_{xy}}$, $\mathbf{T_{xz}}$, etc.

In science we also have tensor qualities of third rank (piezoelectricity = stress-generated electrical fields, etc.) which require a general matrix of $\mathbf{3x3x3 = 27}$ numbers to completely specify this material property at any particular point in the material. We also have tensor qualities of fourth rank like elasticity of materials which, in general, require the specification of $\mathbf{3x3x3x3 = 81}$ numbers at a point in the material to completely characterize that material property. Of course, various symmetries existing in the particular material under consideration can somewhat reduce the total set of independent numbers needed to completely specify a tensorial material quality of second, third, fourth, etc., rank.

As we will see below on the second leg of this side-road excursion, the rank of these tensorial qualities for materials, fields and spaces lead to important implications for information entanglement between various parts of the same experimental system

Table 3.1[5]		
Some examples of second-rank tensors relating two vectors		
Tensor property	Vector given or applied	Vector resulting or induced
Electrical conductivity	Electric field	Electric current density
Thermal conductivity	(negative) temperature gradient	Heat flow density
Permittivity	Electric field	Dielectric displacement
Dielectric susceptibility	Electric field	Dielectric polarization
Permeability	Magnetic field	Magnetic induction
Magnetic susceptibility	Magnetic field	Intensity of magnetization

Let us suppose that we have two systems, **A** and **B**, and that the field quality of interest for each can be represented by a single frequency, sinusoidal function in time as shown in Figures 3.8a and 3.8b. They both have the same amplitude, α, but they have different frequencies, w_A and w_B, respectively. Let us also suppose that the coupling coefficient of system **B** with system **A** can somehow be varied and let us define this coupling coefficient as γ, which can be varied from zero to one (complete isolation to complete connectedness). Finally, let us suppose that we are cognitively only able to experimentally measure this quality from **A**'s frame of reference. Thus, when $\gamma \sim 0$, we see negligible influence of system **B** on system **A** - it is invisible and therefore *presumed* not to exist even though it does exist elsewhere. However, suppose something causes γ to increase in magnitude, how would this be perceived by us?

To analyze and understand this type of interaction, we represent Figures 3.8a and 3.8b via the circular diagram of Figure 3.9 (called a phasor diagram) for the two vectors, $\underline{Q}_A$ and $\underline{Q}_B$, that rotate counterclockwise at angular frequencies w_A and w_B, respectively. The horizontal component (projection onto the x-axis) for each, as a function of time in

Figure 3.8

Consider the quality, Q, for two systems, A and B, that can interact via a coupling coefficient, γ. These qualities Q_A and Q_B vary sinusoidally with time at frequencies W_A and W_B, respectively. The top two plots are for $\gamma = 0$. The third is for $\gamma = 1$ and the bottom plot is for $\gamma = 0.4$.

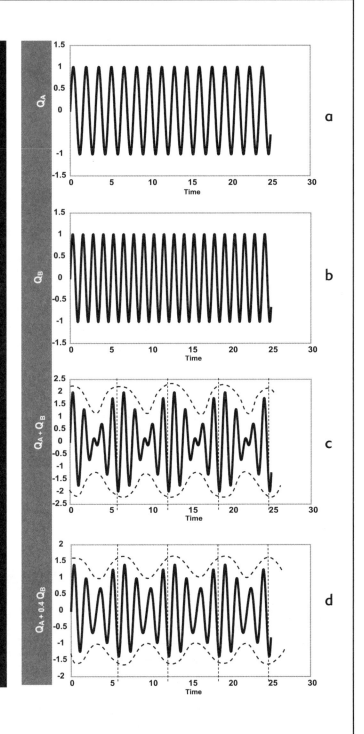

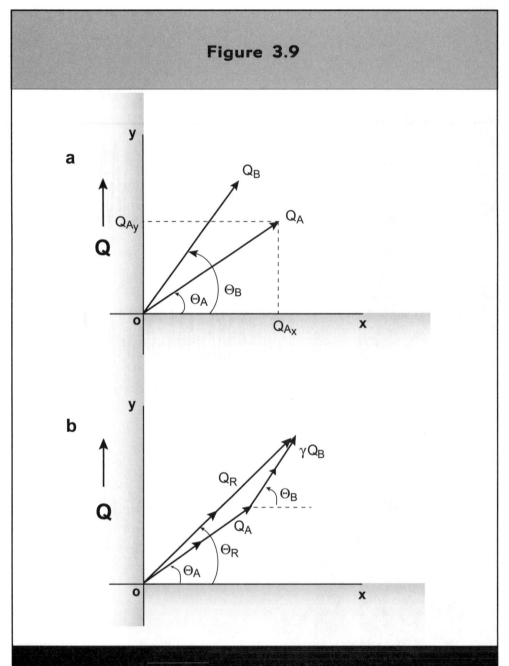

Figure 3.9

Phasor diagrams for rotating vectors.

This is an extremely important and subtle point - in our normal physical reality, called the U(1) EM gauge symmetry state, many of the important qualities of interest are vectors and thus, for a system of multiple parts, there is always an *information entanglement between the parts* unless they are *totally* isolated from each other.

this figure, is exactly that given by Figures 3.8a or 3.8b. We can see that the x-component of $\mathbf{Q_A}$, say goes through its maximum value whenever $\mathbf{\theta_A} = 0$, its zero value whenever $\mathbf{\theta_A} = \mathbf{90°}$ or $\mathbf{270°}$ and its minimum value whenever $\theta_A = \mathbf{180°}$. To make this analysis specific, let us allow the two amplitudes to be equal with $\mathbf{\gamma = 1}$ and $\mathbf{w_B = 1.25\ w_A}$, then Figure 3.8c represents the measured amplitude of the interacting systems with time. These two vibrations of the same amplitude produce the well known beat pattern of Figure 3.8c which is the product of two contributions, (1) a rapid oscillation at the mean frequency $\frac{1}{2}$ $\mathbf{(w_A + w_B) = 1.12\ w_A}$ and (2) a slow modulation of the amplitude with maxima occurring whenever $\frac{1}{2}$ $\mathbf{(w_B - w_A)}$ times $\mathbf{t}$ equals $\mathbf{n}$ times $\mathbf{180}$ degrees, where $\mathbf{n}$ is an integer $\mathbf{(n = 1, 2, 3, \ldots)}$.

If the coupling coefficient, $\mathbf{\gamma}$, is reduced from unity to $\mathbf{0.4}$, the depth of modulation is correspondingly less but the beat frequency is the same. This is illustrated in Figure 3.8d.

It is useful to construct a vector diagram to see how the two vectors are added to construct the resultant. This is illustrated in Figure 3.9b. To obtain this plot, one draws $\mathbf{\underline{Q}_A}$ from the origin, at angle $\mathbf{\theta_A}$, as in Figure 3.9a and then one draws the vector $\mathbf{\gamma\underline{Q}_B}$, at angle, $\mathbf{\theta_B}$, from the end of $\mathbf{\underline{Q}_A}$. The resultant vector, $\mathbf{\underline{Q}_R}$, connects the origin to the end of the $\mathbf{\gamma\underline{Q}_B}$ vector and it ends up having an angle $\mathbf{\theta_R}$ with the x-axis.

Although the magnitude of the resultant vector, $\mathbf{|Q_R|}$ is an important quantity, it is the resultant intensity that is most important and this quantity is given by the square of the magnitude. Using Figure 3.9b and the Pythagorean theorem (for a right angle triangle, the square of the hypotenuse is equal to the sum of the squares of the two sides) we have, via some simple algebra,

$$\mathbf{Q_R}^2 = \mathbf{Q_{R_x}}^2 + \mathbf{Q_{R_Y}}^2 = \mathbf{Q_A}^2 + (\mathbf{\gamma Q_B})^2 + 2\mathbf{\gamma}[\mathbf{Q_{A_x}Q_{B_x}} + \mathbf{Q_{A_Y}Q_{B_Y}}] \quad . (3.3)$$

The sum of the first two term after the second equal sign is exactly what one would have if one didn't have to mathematically treat these qualities as vectors but could treat them as scalar quantities (just as a number). However, because they must be treated mathematically as vectors, we must include the third term on the right which represents an *information entanglement* between the two vectors (between the basic components of the particular field quality for the two interacting systems **A** and **B**).

This is an extremely important and subtle point for the reader to realize - in our normal physical reality, called the U(1) EM gauge symmetry state, many of the important qualities of interest are vectors and thus, for a system of multiple parts, there is always an *information entanglement between the parts* unless they are *totally* isolated from each other **(γ = 0)**. But the meaning of a *system* of parts indicates that they are not totally isolated from each other so **γ** cannot be identically zero. Thus, there must always be *information entanglement* of vectorial qualities between different parts of the same system. This does not happen between scalar qualities.

Walter Harrison, in his textbook on quantum mechanics[6] states that *everything is at the same time a particle and a wave* and that simply figuring out how this seemingly self-contradictory statement can be true leads one to *all* of quantum theory. In the ensuing 300 plus pages of his book, he goes on to quantitatively show how this is true for most of the major phenomena embraced by today's material science and engineering. Here, in this chapter, we have started at a similar place, the De Broglie particle/pilot wave concept, but utilized an RF consisting of duplex reciprocal four-spaces with one four-space housing the particles and the other four-space housing the waves and, because one must always travel at **v < c** and the other at **v > c** in the physical vacuum, it was necessary to invent the deltron coupler medium to allow the particle aspect and the wave aspect to meaningfully interact with each other. In this way, we validate the Harrison postulate and all of the main qualitative features of QM are predicted to occur but via use of a unique duplex RF rather than via the single, spacetime RF. Let us now go forward to see what else this new RF can reveal to us.

To illustrate a useful conceptual picture, take two transparent sheets and, on one, draw a spherical particle of radius **R** moving along a straight line (which we will call the x-axis of D-space) at velocity v_x, which is just the change in distance, **Δx**, that the particle traverses in some very small time increment, **Δt**. On the other sheet, draw a pilot wave intensity envelope like that shown in Figure 3.1 or Figure 3.6. This pilot wave is moving at the vacuum level of reality in the k_x-direction of R-space with the same average velocity as the particle and, here, this is just the change in spatial frequency, Δk_x, that the wave transverses in a very small temporal frequency increment, Δk_t. The vacuum level information waves making up this envelope travel rapidly through this envelope from the rear to the front at the velocity given by Equation 3.1a, $v_w = c^2 / v_x$. The deltron profile within this particle/wave group binds these two very different classes of substance together and provides some latitude for relative particle movement back and forth as it moves along at average velocity v_x. This deltron coupling is actually between the particle and the rapidly moving information waves because (a) otherwise a pilot wave envelope could never have been built and (b) the relevant information waves could never have been selected and correlated with each other in order to construct a $v_p = v_x < c$ envelope profile.

By placing one of these sheets over the other and adjusting their relationship, we reproduce either Figure 3.1 or Figure 3.6. The primary information waves travel at $v_w > c$ and are thus undetectable by present-day instrumentation. However, their collective correlations produce a wave packet that travels at $v_p = v_x < c$ and is thus potentially detectable by our U(1) gauge symmetry instrumentation. Likewise, interference effects between this construct and other D-space objects are detectable by present day instrumentation.

Since it can be shown that the Heisenberg uncertainty relationship (see Equation 3.1b) arises from the frequency spectrum of these presently undetectable information waves, Equation 3.1b is definitely present in this duplex space representation of De Broglie's original concept. One major new feature added by the duplex space plus deltron factors is that the coupling between the particle and its equilibrium pilot wave allows relative adjustments to occur between them. Another is that, since experiments have shown that human intention can modulate the degree of this coupling, human consciousness can now act in a potentially detailed way on the most basic of processes in physical reality. Thus, we must begin to deal with all aspects of the following expansion of Einstein's original reaction equation

$$\text{Mass} \rightleftharpoons \text{Energy} \rightleftharpoons \text{Consciousness.} \qquad (3.4)$$

It is this general procedure that will allow us to expand both our perspectives about nature, our reformulations of QM to include the effects of human consciousness and to find practical ways of moving beyond the limitations imposed by the velocity of EM light.

This will not be an easy task but it now becomes a doable task. It is beyond the scope of this book to proceed down this path here because a great deal of mathematics is involved. However, we can pursue further qualitative understandings and expectations consistent with this new line of thinking.

Before closing this section, it is perhaps useful to say something relevant to "hidden variables" theory and the many arguments, pro and con, about it that still rage through the physics community. The text surrounding Figures 3.8 and 3.9 plus Equation 3.3 can be brought to bear here.

Perhaps the main problem with the past work concerning hidden variables is that everything said to date presumes a single four-dimensional RF (spacetime) for viewing the various behaviors of nature and, further, this RF is constrained to the U(1) EM gauge symmetry level. Our experimental work of Chapters 1 and 2 strongly suggests that a U(1) state physical vacuum is largely uncoupled from, and therefore instrumentally inaccessible from, the conventional atom/molecule level of physical reality so that, at the U(1) level, there should be no easily discriminatable hidden variables via experiment. However, when one uses an aspect of consciousness, as in our experiments with IIEDs, the EM gauge symmetry state of the experimental space is raised to approach the SU(2) level. Now, the natural processes going on in the physical vacuum level of reality become strongly and instrumentally coupled to those going on at the atom/molecule level of physical reality so that the net, observable physics of the space has been changed. Since, to understand the physics of the physical vacuum, one needs an RF other than just spacetime to deal with *its* own internal variables, when meaningfully coupled to our atom/molecule level instrumentation, these new variables of the combined domains are no longer hidden.

As mentioned on page 119, think of two parallel universes, each operating with their own internal variables, and you can only make measurements from one. When they are almost completely uncoupled, ($\gamma \sim 0$), the second universe is almost completely hidden. When they are strongly coupled ($\gamma >> 0$), our instruments now detect effects from the parallel universe (whose variables set is no longer hidden). In addition, even when γ is small, fluctuations in deltron activation are expected to occur in this duplex RF so that fluctuating glimpses of hidden variables might be expected to instrumentally appear.

Something more about D-space/R-space pattern relationships

Let us first consider some experimentally generated Fourier transforms using light diffraction from a set of optical masks through which a specific geometrical arrangement and size of holes has been drilled.[7-9] The Fourier transform arises in *any* wave diffraction process and connects the superposed diffracted wave pattern to the physical geometry of the object causing the waves to diffract. Thus the mask with holes is

Figure 3.10 a & b

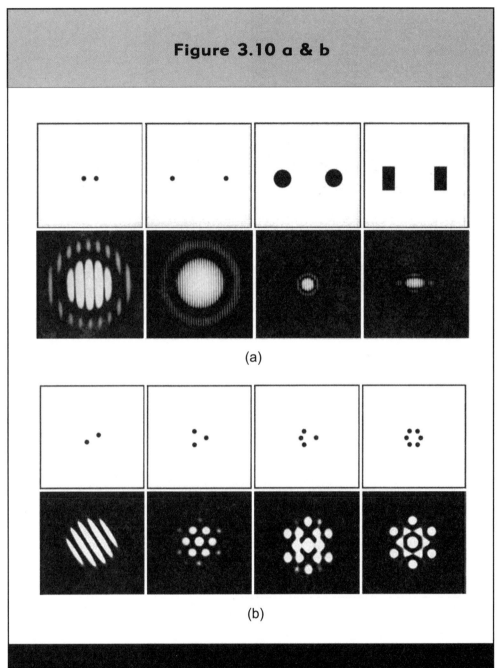

(a)

(b)

The mask with holes is our D-space object and the diffracted wave intensity pattern focused onto a screen is intimately connected to its R-space counterpart. As size goes up in one, it goes down in the other; as separation increases in one, it decreases in the other; as clockwise rotation occurs in one, equal counter-clockwise rotation occurs in the other and shape changes in a particular direction for one leads to changes in the perpendicular direction for the other.

Figure 3.10 c & d

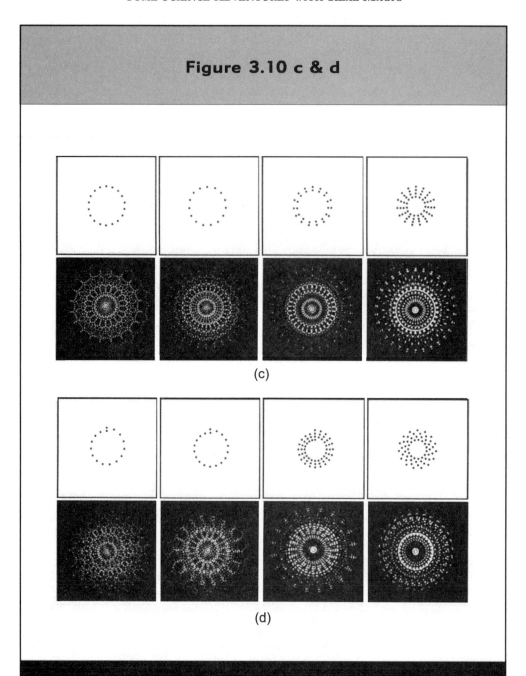

(c)

(d)

These mandala-like diffraction intensity patterns are similar to what many individuals see internally in their mind's eye while in a deep state of meditation.

our D-space object and the diffracted wave intensity pattern focused onto a screen is intimately connected to its R-space counterpart. Since wave diffraction forms the basis for holography, this will further illustrate D-space/R-space pattern relationships using light. The top panel in Figures 3.10a and b show masks with multiple holes of different size, shape and spacing. Immediately below this, the intensity map of the diffracted light at the screen is displayed for each mask. Here, one can see that (1) increasing the spacing between a pair of holes in D-space decreases the periodic spacing of the perpendicularly oriented fringes in the basic ring pattern that is observed from a single hole, (2) increasing the radius of the hole decreases the radius of the segmented ring pattern, (3) rotating the orientation of the holes in one direction, rotates the segmented ring pattern in the opposite direction by exactly the same amount, (4) rectangular holes, elongated in one direction, lead to elliptical ring patterns elongated in the perpendicular direction and (5) increasing the number and symmetry of the holes in the mask increases the complexity of the diffraction pattern. Most of these behaviors between a D-space pattern and its conjugate R-space pattern (the diffraction intensity pattern) illustrate the detailed reciprocal nature of these two spaces. As size goes up in one, it goes down in the other; as separation increases in one, it decreases in the other; as clockwise rotation occurs in one, equal counterclockwise rotation occurs in the other and shape changes in a particular direction for one leads to changes in the perpendicular direction for the other.

The richness of detail in the diffraction patterns can be seen by contrasting Figures 3.10c and d for a set of holes arranged in circular and spiral patterns, respectively. These mandala-like diffraction intensity patterns are similar to what many individuals see internally in their mind's eye while in a deep state of meditation and one wonders what D-space pattern in the brain evoked such responses.

Pribram's Holonomic theory[10] of brain processing appears to be based on a very slight modification of the Fourier transform duality picture between D-space information patterns and spectral domain information patterns (R-space patterns). His experimental data strongly indicates that cortical neurons act like individual receiving antennas in a large array which converts spacetime information into a diffraction pattern whose mathematical representation is very close to the Fourier transform of the incoming spacetime information. This information conversion to the frequency domain appears to be ideal for subsequent brain processing and brain perception. Of course, the brain must also contain a Fourier transform inverter mechanism so that our consciousness perceives the outer reality just as we think we do.

Figure 3.11

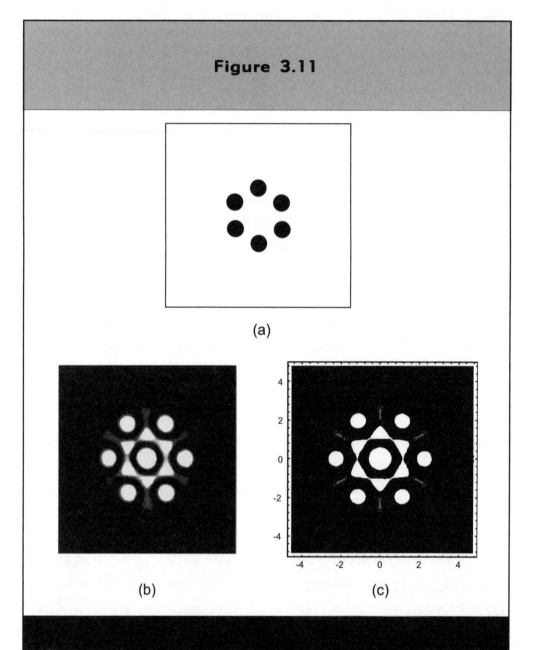

(a)

(b)   (c)

This is a very interesting and profound result, telling us something of how deltrons enter the quantitative picture.

This comparison completely supports the assertion that the theoretical Fourier transform quantitatively reproduces the experimental diffraction result provided we allow the deltron activation function to adjust the R-space frequency coordinate scale to equal the D-space spatial coordinate scale on the projection screen.

Returning to the upper and lower pair at the far right of Figure 3.10b, this is the experimental outcome for a hexagonal array of six holes. To prove to the reader that the Fourier transform truly represents the diffraction pattern, we calculated the R-space intensity, I_n, for the case of such a hexagonal array of holes and, in Figure 3.11, we compare it with the experimental result. This comparison between b (experimental) and c (calculated) completely supports the assertion that the theoretical deltron-empowered Fourier transform quantitatively reproduces the experimental diffraction result provided we allow the deltron activation function to adjust the R-space frequency coordinate scale to equal the D-space spatial coordinate scale on the projection screen. This is a very interesting and profound result, telling us something of how deltrons enter the quantitative picture.

The mirror principle and some projected consequences

Although everyone is familiar with a reflection mirror, this mirror principle is quite different in that it relates to conjugate qualities starting with the particle and wave aspects of substance associated with basic modes of operation in our reciprocal subspaces. Figure 3.4 represents the velocity aspect; electric monopole/magnetic monopole represents the charge aspect; coarse physical and vacuum physical represents the structural aspect. All in all, it appears to be a representation of *unity* in that, if we label a quality as $\tilde{Q}$ in one subspace, its conjugate quality in the other subspace is $1/\tilde{Q}$ so that

$$\tilde{Q} \cdot \frac{1}{\tilde{Q}} = \text{unity} \qquad (3.5a)$$

Even this duplex space has, in D-space, coordinates that extend from zero to infinity and, if we use the same coordinate information for defining the R-space coordinates, they extend from infinity to zero so that

$$0 \cdot \frac{1}{0} = \text{unity} \qquad \text{and} \qquad \infty \cdot \frac{1}{\infty} = \text{unity} \qquad (3.5b)$$

There is a kind of "wholeness" about this duplex space RF, like a loop from zero to infinity in D-space and back from infinity to zero via R-space. A source in one subspace acts like a sink in the other and vice-versa.

Just as Equation 3.1a and Figure 3.4 illustrate the reciprocal velocity aspect, Table 3.2 provides a more complete spectrum of property relationships. Following Einstein, the positive mass quality of D-space substance is thought to create curvature effects in that frame such as to create a gravitational force. Likewise, in the R-space frame, the negative mass substance acting via deltrons should develop levitational force effects in the D-space frame. Astronomers, today, tell us that the outer reaches of the universe are accelerating faster and faster as if a repulsive force were present and growing in magnitude, a feature exactly opposite from standard gravitational theory expectations. Could this be an R-space effect that is finally bleeding through and contributing to our D-space-based observations? In addition, physicists, today, talk about the presence of dark matter and dark energy being observed indirectly by their instruments. Could these also be manifestations of R-space qualities from the perspective of D-space? When one adds consciousness to the mix, as in Equation 3.4, and acting through modulation of deltron activation, many physical laws may exhibit the presence of a new contribution.

There is another conundrum present in today's physics that can be simply addressed by using this duplex space model with duplex monopoles. This is "why is the population of positive energy particles significantly greater than that of anti-particles?". With a single four-space (spacetime) picture, positive energy particles created out of the physical vacuum via using the Dirac concept always leads to equal populations of positive energy particles and anti-particles. However, Figure 2.9 of Reference 8 illustrates a second process path for the creation of positive energy particles in a multidimensional model of the type proposed via Figures 3.2. Consider a quality fluctuation in either the 9th or 10th dimension whose total energy content is zero but the creation is of a positive energy particle in D-space and its conjugate counterpart in R-space with negative energy of the same magnitude. For slight to moderate differences between these two particles, either an EM or an ME photon could be emitted to produce a total energy change of zero in this higher dimensional domain. Combining this concept with the Dirac concept would lead directly to a greater population of positive energy particles than anti-particles because many of the anti-particles from the Dirac reaction would be annihilated by the new R-space entity created by the Tiller reaction.[8]. This proposal has interesting consequences with respect to nuclear reactions and "cold fusion" physics. Of course, present day $U(1)$ gauge state instrumentation would be unable to detect the superluminal ME photons for the R-space counterpart created via the second process path. This particular prediction strongly supports the new conceptual RF of a duplex system of four dimensional subspaces imbedded in several higher dimensional spaces rather than just the single four dimensional RF, spacetime.

Table 3.2

Physical Direct space & Direct time	Conjugate Physical Reciprocal space & Reciprocal time
Electric Monopoles	Magnetic Monopoles
Forms atoms, molecules, etc.	Forms atoms, molecules, etc.
Allopathic medicine	Homeopathic medicine
Positive mass	Negative mass
Velocity < c	Velocity > c
Positive energy states	Negative energy states
E_p increases as velocity increases	E_E increases as velocity increases
Positive entropy, S_p	Negative entropy, S_E
Positive free energy, $G_p=H_p-T_pS_p$	Negative free energy, $G_E=H_E-T_ES_E$
Positive temperature	Negative temperature
Electromagnetism	Magnetoelectrism
Gravitation	Levitation
Body sensory systems delineated	Body sensory systems not delineated
Photons at velocity c	Photons at velocity $c'>>c$ ($\sim 10^{10}c$)
Fastest in vacuum	Slowest in vacuum
Slows down in dense material	Speeds up in dense physical matter
Faraday cage screening	Screening by magnetic cage

Some consequences of a steadily increasing deltron population

From our earlier discussion, there are two levels of physical reality wherein basic processes can operate, (1) the atomic and molecular level of a particular material and (2) the vacuum level of the same material. In the former case, the particles of the electric-type with mass and of the photon-type without mass make up these dynamic atoms, molecules and EM light. These all have positive energy states above the arbitrarily assumed zero level in the middle of the Dirac energy gap of Figure 3.2b. In the latter case, the information waves propagating in the physical vacuum occupy negative energy states below this Dirac energy gap. These information waves propagate at velocities greater than c, the EM light velocity in vacuum, and it is presumed that they can have conformations that can manifest various qualities of magnetic charge. Without the presence of some deltrons, from the emotion domain level of Figure 3.2b, it would never be possible for these information waves to interact with particles of the photon-type or the electric mass-type. Thus, there could never be formation of a pilot wave for either type of positive energy particle without the availability of deltrons.

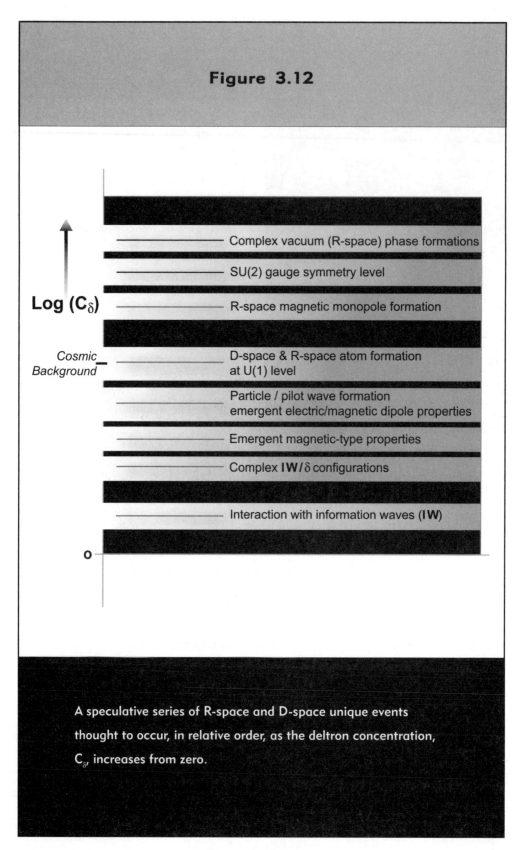

Figure 3.12

Complex vacuum (R-space) phase formations

SU(2) gauge symmetry level

R-space magnetic monopole formation

D-space & R-space atom formation at U(1) level

Particle / pilot wave formation emergent electric/magnetic dipole properties

Emergent magnetic-type properties

Complex IW/δ configurations

Interaction with information waves (IW)

Log (C$_\delta$)

Cosmic Background

0

A speculative series of R-space and D-space unique events thought to occur, in relative order, as the deltron concentration, C$_\delta$, increases from zero.

If the deltron population is identically zero, then the coupling coefficient, γ, between these two levels of physical reality is also zero ($\gamma = 0$) and these two levels of dynamic processes are totally isolated from each other. In fact, any particle moving at the molecular level cannot have a companion pilot wave because there is nothing available to attract and bind even a single information wave momentarily to it. Thus, there would be no diffraction phenomenon present in physical reality and no quantum mechanics.

For modeling purposes, suppose we think of the deltron as being partially wave-like but with associated particle-like domains containing seeming intelligence. They are thought to be attracted preferentially to the information waves and entwine with them with the complexity of this entwined structure increasing as the deltron concentration increases. At some stage, interaction between the information wave/deltron structure and the D-space particles can now occur to produce the particle/deltron/pilot wave construct. It is thought that both the electric charge state and the magnetic dipole state of this {particle/deltron/pilot wave} entity are emergent properties of the specifics of this construction process. It is further thought that particle spin, and thus the magnetic moment of the particle, are misinterpretations of the original experimental data and that it is the detailed structural form of the pilot wave envelope that is the origin of the magnetic moment for the particle. At this point, protons, neutrons and electrons can combine to form D-space atoms and molecules. Likewise, in the vacuum, faster than light atoms and molecules can form.

In order to have stable D-space atoms and molecules, electromagnetism, life, etc., some minimum deltron population density, called the cosmic background level, must exist for the construction of gluons, quarks, photons, protons, neutrons, electrons, atoms, molecules, etc., to spontaneously occur. As the deltron population increases further, the coupling coefficient, γ, increases so that, from the perspective of our D-space measuring instruments, measurements of a particular quality, Q, yields two contributions acting in parallel, one labeled Q_D from the D-space aspect and the other labeled γQ_R from the conjugate R-space aspect (the difference, here, from that given on page 116 is that the former, Q'_R, has the deltron activation internally imbedded inside Q'_R instead of bringing an effective value, γ, outside so that $Q'_R = \gamma Q_R$). This is fully consistent with observation (5) of Table 3 in Appendix 3.1.

The litmus paper detector of pH is only capable of measuring the actual concentration of hydrogen ions in the water while the pH-electrode and the optical information detector, with their associated digital information processing systems, detect, in addition, a type of thermodynamic activity effect for the hydrogen ion that goes beyond a pure concentration contribution. Here, perhaps for the first time, one is measuring a true information contribution from another level of physical reality. From Table 3.2, the mirror principle indicates that R-space contains substance with a well-defined thermodynamics, and, via the coupling coefficient, γ, we now appear to be accessing it to some degree by our digital instrumentation.

From an information thermodynamics perspective, as one considers basic information waves in the vacuum to which we add a certain concentration of deltrons, new and unique combinatorial interactive structures are formed in the vacuum as unique stable phases. In fact, in analogy with D-space (see Figure 3.12), two-component phase equilibria are expected to occur and, utilizing the mirror principle, we might consider the existence of a binary phase diagram for the vacuum domain wherein the thermodynamic driving force for change is not to reduce the thermodynamic free energy, with concomitant increase in entropy production, but the inverse - an *increase* in thermodynamic free energy with concomitant *decrease* in entropy production via the formation of unique information wave-deltron structural phases.

In this vacuum level phase field, one might expect to find a domain of concentration/temperature stability for what is called spinodal decomposition versus simple precipitation in the D-space analogue. In D-space, these two modes of phase change are visually distinguished one from the other via spatial coherence and concentration wave development at some wavelength from an initially homogeneous phase field versus a spatially incoherent precipitation of the new phase. At this point in time, when we know so little about the vacuum level phase transformation details, what is perhaps important to deduce is that there are probably thermodynamically-driven phase transformations yielding (a) growing and decaying oscillations of both the (k_x, k_y, k_z) - type and of the k_t-type in the vacuum as triggered by temperature oscillations and (b) a type of phase formation that is magnetic monopole-like.

Because, when the coupling coefficient is greater than zero, any phase change occurring in the vacuum will change the properties of the vacuum. This will be reflected to the coarse physical level and our measuring instruments will detect oscillatory changes in accord with ambient temperature changes (like observation (8) of Table 2 in Appendix 3.1) and should also detect DC magnetic field polarity effects on D-space property measurements (like observation (7) of Table 2 in Appendix 3.1). Of course, when $\gamma > 0$, D-space material phases will also affect the thermodynamic free energy of R-space (the vacuum level) so one is no longer dealing with a binary R-space phase diagram but a ternary R-space phase diagram, etc. Perhaps the most important thing to realize here with this qualitative description is that, with $\gamma > 0$, the vacuum level thermodynamics provide a measurable input into D-space measured thermodynamics so that D-space phase equilibria can be altered by this new variable. Likewise, with $\gamma > 0$, R-space (vacuum level) phase equilibria can be shifted via coupling with different aspects of D-space. In fact, with $\gamma > 0$, one can expect (a) a time-dependent change in a D-space property measurement depending on the rate of R-space phase transformation, (b) a change in R-space thermodynamics driving *this* vacuum level phase transformation due to the coupled D-space thermodynamics, (c) a subsequent correlated change in D-space property measurements due to this change in the R-space phase transformation kinetics, (d) etc. Thus, a kind of oscillatory back and forth response between the two domains, that are deltron driven to some degree, will occur.

This is an incredibly important area for future research exploration!

Is it magic?

A reasonable definition of magic is "when one has a set of experimental data or personal observations that *cannot* be explained by the prevailing scientific paradigm or worldview of the time". By this definition, the experimental data described in Chapters 1 and 2 are mostly magic. However, the theoretical model, described in this chapter, to explain the data, is completely lawful with respect to an expansion of the prevailing paradigm. Thus, with this work, we have moved beyond many of the limitations of the presently accepted paradigm and are learning some of the limitations implicit in what will eventually be the new paradigm.

In the existing paradigm, four limitations are: (1) $E = mc^2$, (2) $v \leq c$, (3) the vacuum is empty and (4) human consciousness cannot influence physical phenomena. Equation 3.4 expands Einstein's famous equation given above so that materialization and dematerialization of coarse physical substance becomes allowed. Using Equation 3.4 and Table 3.2, levitation of objects and humans also becomes an allowable phenomenon under certain conditions. Certainly observation number (5) of Table 1 in Appendix 3.1 indicates that the EM light barrier can be broken and, with Postulate 3, our instruments can extend their range of detectability to include part of the $v > c$ region. Certainly observations (12) and (13) of Table 2 in Appendix 3.1 and much of the discussion of this chapter indicate that the vacuum is not empty and that we can begin to seriously work with it, once we condition a space to a higher inner symmetry state where $|\Delta\Psi_{H+}| > 0$. From observations (1) and (2) of Table 4 in Appendix 3.1 and Equation 3.4 we learn that, particularly in a conditioned space where $|\Delta\Psi_{H+}| > 0$, human intention can appreciably change material properties and processes.

The foregoing means that, now, humanity can meaningfully move towards the development of a quantitative science and technology that includes directed human consciousness. A new "doorway" has been opened into our understanding of some of nature's mysteries and, eventually, practitioners of science and technology will feel comfortable enough to walk through this doorway and explore the new territory beyond.

In this new potential future for humanity, there is a real limitation with respect to the willingness of individuals to make the sustained effort to become inner self-managed. Our experiments have shown that a strong experimenter effect can occur in any psychoenergetic (consciousness $\rightleftharpoons$ energy) experiment (see observation (15) of Table 2, observation (8) of Table 3 and observation (1) of Table 4 in Appendix 3.1). Thus, there are "pumper-uppers" and "drainer-downers" who, respectively strengthen or weaken the level of conditioning (and thus alter the inner symmetry level) of a space. For this category of new technologies to be effective in the future, a specific higher EM gauge symmetry level (as determined by the $\Delta\Psi_{H+}$-detector) must be maintained in each case. This will require a certain level of inner self-management achievement on the part of the employees so that a relatively fixed level of $|\Delta\Psi_{H+}| > 0$ can be maintained over time. The side-benefit of this human self-discipline is that normal folks will become adepts and, in turn, will become masters and then onward towards becoming planetary avatars. It is the degree of developed internal infrastructure at the inner layer of the personality self and at all layers of the soul self that signal the transition to these higher emergent states of our being. At each stage of development, new physics comes into play, old limitations fall away and a higher set of natural laws form the limits for one's activity.

The unfoldment of nature seems to be very much like the careful peeling of a multilayered onion - one doesn't have much good insight about the details of the next layer of nature until one has almost reached it. However, our human limitations are defined by the layer we are in and they change when our evolution allows us to proceed to the next layer.

In closing this chapter, it is perhaps useful to provide a brief reminder of some of the points covered. These are:

- There are two important levels of physical reality, (1) the conventional atom, molecule and EM photon level where everything travels at velocities less than the velocity of EM light in the physical vacuum (v = c) and (2) the information wave level in the physical vacuum where everything travels at v > c.

- A postulated coupling substance, called deltrons from the domain of emotion (outside of physical reality), exists and has the quality of being able to travel at velocities both above and below c and to interact with substances from both levels of physical reality.

- Deltrons also embody intelligence so that all aspects of human consciousness can interact with deltrons and thus modulate the coupling coefficient, γ, between the two categories of physical substance.

- A reciprocal mirror principle for various qualities operates between these two, deltron-coupled levels of physical reality so that a quality of one level times the quality of the other level form a unity in the proposed duplex RF used to describe nature's behavior.

- The human acupuncture meridian/chakra system is an intention-modulated system in the human body with $\gamma > 0$ so that (1) strong coupling can develop between the two body-levels of physical reality, (2) such intention-directed coupling can enhance human performance and behavior by many orders of magnitude relative to current levels and (3) humans matter; they can dramatically and beneficially evolve themselves to significantly higher states of being.

References

1.   J. Schwinger, *Particles and Sources* (Gordon and Breach, Science Publishers, New York, 1969).

2.   P. Werbos, "What do neural nets and quantum theory tell us about mind and reality?" in *No Matter, Never Mind*, eds. K. Yasue, M. Jiba and T.D. Senta (John Benjamins Publishing Co., Philadelphia, 2001).

3.   R.M. Eisberg, *Fundamentals of Modern Physics* (John Wiley and Sons, Inc., New York, 1961) pp 140-146.

4.   R. Bracewell, *The Fourier Transform and its Applications* (McGraw-Hill Book Co., New York, 1965).

5.   J.F. Nye, *Physical Properties of Crystals* (Oxford University Press, London, 1957).

6.   W.A. Harrison, *Applied Quantum Mechanics* (World Scientific, Singapore, 2000).

7.   G. Harburn, C.A. Taylor and T.R. Welberry, *Atlas of Optical Transforms* (Cornell University Press, Ithaca, New York, 1975).

8.   W.A. Tiller, *Science and Human Transformation* (Pavior Publishing, Walnut Creek, CA, 1997).

9.   W.A. Tiller, W.E. Dibble, Jr., and M.J. Kohane, *Conscious Acts of Creation* (Pavior Publishing, Walnut Creek, CA, 2001).

10.   K. Pribram, *Brain and Perception. Holonomy and Structure in Figural Processing* (Lawrence Erlbaum Associates, Hillsdale, New Jersey, 1991).

Appendix 3 - 1

Assembling the key experimental findings from Chapters 1 and 2

<u>Table 1</u>
Summary of Key Experimental Findings from "Science and Human Transformation"

1.   A highly developed human biofield can alter the properties of materials and the functioning of devices so as to reveal deeper levels of nature not anticipated from our normal every-day observations. The radiations from such levels of nature pass through materials that are optically opaque to EM radiations in the visible range.

2.   Non-EM emissions from the biofields of normal humans, when modulated by their attention and directed intention, can enhance or not enhance electron microavalanches in a simple gas discharge device depending upon the actual focus of the human's intention.

3.   Some humans emit bursts of subtle energy from various body chakras and, via a subtle energy/electrical energy conversion process involving the acupuncture meridian system, large voltage pulses appear both on the body and at sites remote to the body.

4.   When focusing on the heart with loving intent, the human EKG becomes harmonic at the baroreflex frequency, 0.14 hertz, where the heart entrains the brain and simultaneously all the other major electrophysiological systems of the body. In this heart entrainment mode of functioning, body chemical production becomes healthier and focused intent can psychokinetically influence molecular structures both inside and outside of the body.

5.   Most young children perceive both EM and subtle energies. Lens and prism experiments indicate that the latter travel at velocities , $v>c$, the EM light velocity, and speed up on entering denser matter.

6.   Dowsing is a natural human body response mechanism, for those who give it meaning, wherein the unconscious communicates valuable information to the conscious via involuntary small muscle movements or the creation of localized heat patterns.

Table 2
Summary of Key Experimental Findings from "Conscious Acts of Creation"

1.   Human consciousness in the form of a specific intention, can be imprinted into a simple, low tech, electronic device from a deep meditative state by highly inner self managed humans. Such a device, now called an IIED (intention imprinted electrical device), can act as an effective surrogate to robustly influence a unique target experiment in physical reality.

2.   The four unique target experiments studied involved (a) an inorganic material (water) with property changes 100 times larger than measurement accuracy, (b) an organic, in vitro material with property changes of ~20% at p<0.001 and (c) a living, in vivo material with property changes of ~20% at p{0.001, both of the latter having a built in control.

3.   A unique intelligence was present in an IIED after imprinting so that the measured material property changes where (a) always in the direction of the IIED's intention imprint and (b) always specific to the particular IIED utilized.

4.   An unshielded IIED in the electrically "off" state and physically separated from a UED in the electrically "off" state by ~100 meters, still has a communication channel available to it for transferring the imprint statement to the UED within a week. Thus, the carrier for such information exchange is *not* conventional electromagnetism.

5.   This new field, although not EM, can be dissipated through EM leakage pathways. Thus, wrapping an IIED in aluminum foil and storing it in an electrically-grounded Faraday cage, prolongs its lifetime of effective use (~3 months before reimprinting is required).

6.   Placing a specific IIED in a room and turning it on "conditions" the room to a state wherein Item 2 above, naturally manifests. Without the presence of this "conditioned" state in the room housing the target experiment equipment, these material property changes do not occur.

7   One characteristic of a "conditioned" space is that a DC magnetic field polarity effect on the pH of water occurs. Such an effect is thought to require the accessing of magnetic monopoles, a property usually associated with a higher EM gauge symmetry state than our normal, everyday reality. Such a higher EM gauge symmetry state is also a higher thermodynamic free energy per unit volume state.

8.   Another characteristic of a "conditioned" space is the spontaneous appearance of material property oscillations of very large amplitude (air and water temperature, pH, electrical conductivity of water, etc.) that are (a) global throughout the room (b) all exhibit the same Fourier spectral components and (c) all are in the frequency range ~10^{-2} to 10^{-3} hertz.

9.   A third important characteristic of a "conditioned" space is that it is sensitive to the presence of an active IIED at separation distances of at least ~150 feet. Oscillations generated in the locale of the IIED spontaneously appear (at high correlation coefficient) in a "conditioned" space but not in an unconditioned space.

10.   If the degree of "conditioning" in a space is low and the IIED is removed from the space, the "conditioning" decays slowly with a time constant of ~1 month. If the degree of "conditioning" in a space is sufficiently high, the IIED can be completely removed from the space and stored properly and the level of "conditioning" in the room does not appear to change (at least for 1-2 years).

11.   The cause of the air temperature oscillations in a "conditioned" space near an apparent source was shown not to depend upon movements of the air molecules in the space but rather thought to depend on changes at the vacuum level of physical reality.

12.   Removal of the apparent air temperature oscillation source revealed that this vacuum level "phantom" source had a very slow relaxation time (~1-2 months) back to zero amplitude.

13.   While in the phantom temperature oscillation source mode of reality, abrupt changes in the orientation of a large natural quartz crystal placed in the initial source region showed abrupt changes in overall oscillation wave shape, wave amplitude and wave frequency. Thus, a quartz appears to be a type of "tuner" for this vacuum source behavior.

14.   In a "conditioned" space, spontaneous and abrupt shifts in computer monitoring behavior of a random number generator (RNG) occurred from time to time for no known reason

15.   Experimenter effect, specific materials effects and specific device effects appeared, on the short term, to alter the "tuning" of the oscillations in a conditioned space.

Table 3
Summary of key experimental findings from the "Remote Sites Experiment"

1.   The original Minnesota water pH results have been substantially replicated by others.

2.   At all remote IIED-sites, the digitally recorded pH for purified water in equilibrium with air increased exponentially with time with the ΔpH increasing cycle by cycle of water change until it reached 1.0 pH units.

3.   At all control sites, non-IIED sites, the same type of pH-behavior was observed via an information entanglement process except that (1) for below-ground sites, ΔpH achieved ~1.7 pH units and (2) for well above-ground sites, ΔpH achieved ~0.8 pH units.

4.   This information entanglement process between IIED and non-IIED, control sites of the overall experimental system occurred over distances from ~2 miles to ~6000 miles. The carrier wave for this information transfer could not have been electromagnetic.

5.   A litmus paper pH-detector only responded to the purely chemical level of the H^+ content present in the water while digital pH-detectors responded to both this level plus an information level associated with the H^+ content.

6.   All sites, both IIED and non-IIED, exhibited substantial values of Ψ_{H+} after a short time, indicating a raised thermodynamic free energy per unit volume for all sites.

7.   The time required to reach ΔpH ~1.0 pH units appears to be less for below-ground control sites than for above-ground control sites and also appears to be relatively independent of distance.

8.   Strong experimenter and equipment potentization effects were noted.

9.   The optimum reimprinting time for an IIED presently appears to be ~3 months.

10.   Mu-metal screening does not shield water from this new information entanglement field.

Table 4
Two recent key experimental results from the Payson laboratory

1.   For humans, and perhaps all vertebrates, bioelectromagnetism is quite different than Maxwellian electromagnetism because the human acupuncture meridian system is observed to be at an EM gauge symmetry level where magnetic monopole charge is experimentally accessible.

2.   A laboratory space and equipment, raised to an EM gauge symmetry state wherein magnetic monopole currents are experimentally accessible, is found to be a very sensitive detector of subtle energy emissions by humans (subtle energies are defined as all those beyond the energy aspects of the accepted four fundamental forces).

Chapter 4

Detecting a Magnetic Monopole Potential Energy

One of our most difficult to handle experimental problems is the proper interpretation for pH-values measured in "conditioned" spaces that, on the surface, appear to have no link to any normal pH-value.

As mentioned in Chapter 1, during the Minnesota phase of the experimentation, we discovered that a DC magnetic field polarity effect on the pH of water was one of the signature characteristics of an IIED-conditioned space. This behavior should not be present in a normal, U(1) EM gauge symmetry space because, in that state, only magnetic dipole behavior should be exhibited by materials, and reversing the sign of the magnetic field for materials in such a state does not change the thermodynamic potential energy for any atom or molecule, whether they are electrically neutral or electrically charged. From this experimental observation, we deduced that an IIED-conditioned space must be in an elevated EM gauge symmetry (inner symmetry) state wherein magnetic monopoles were now experimentally accessible by our detection equipment. From theoretical considerations, we supposed that an IIED-conditioned space would have an inner symmetry state approaching the SU(2) state where both electric and magnetic monopoles had been predicted to naturally coexist. Certainly, the imprinting process itself was thought to raise the inner symmetry state of a UED (unimprinted electrical device) from the U(1) state to the SU(2) state for the IIED (intention imprinted electrical device).

We have recently discovered a combined experimental/theoretical procedure for gaining a quantitative measure of this energy change associated with increasing the inner symmetry state of a space above the U(1) state.[1] This measure manifests itself as an effective magnetic monopole potential energy that we have labeled "the magnetoelectrochemical potential energy for the proton, $\Psi'_H{}^+$". Time-dependent maps, $\Delta\Psi_H{}^+$ (t), have been generated for all IIED-sites and control sites of the remote-sites, $\Delta pH = +1$ units experiment described in Chapter 2. Several of these plots were presented in Chapter 2. This chapter is devoted to a discussion of the physics underlying this new discovery. Although $\Delta\Psi$ builds on the electrochemical potential, η, and applies to all species, it is here specific to the proton, $\mathbf{H}^+$, because that is what is being measured when one studies pH.

Some readers will have considerable unease with our introduction of experimentally accessible aspects of magnetic monopoles because they will know that both the U.S. and many other governments have spent billions of dollars, via their competent scientists over the past several decades, to detect the presence of magnetic monopoles with their sophisticated apparati. Unfortunately, their experiments have been unsuccessful. This does not mean, as most have assumed, that magnetic monopoles do not exist in nature; rather, it means only that they are not experimentally accessible when their equipment and laboratory space is in the U(1) EM gauge symmetry state! All of the aforementioned scientists, presumably had their laboratories and specialized equipment anchored in the U(1) state so they have only proven *nonaccessibility from the U(1) state*.

Now that we have an IIED-source at the SU(2) state *plus* a detector to measure the degree of elevation of the proton's energy state above the U(1) state, these different categories of experimental tests can, in principle, be run again and show that, although magnetic monopoles are not accessible when $\Psi'_{H^+} = \eta_{H^+}$ (the U(1) state) for the experimental space, they begin to become accessible when $\Psi'_{H^+} \geq \Psi'^{MM}_{H^+} > \eta_{H^+}$ (some minimum value of Ψ'_{H^+}). We would certainly be willing to cooperate with any competent scientist having such specialized equipment who is willing to redo his/her experiments at higher inner symmetry levels.

One key question that we all must ask ourselves is why might magnetic monopoles not be accessible from the U(1) state, yet be accessible from an IIED-conditioned space with $\Psi'_{H^+} > \Psi'^{MM}_{H^+}$. Sophisticated theorists would respond that inner symmetry state *breaking* occurs when one drops below $\Psi'^{MM}_{H^+}$. But that does not tell us what such an event really means in more readily understandable terms. For example, perhaps this means that magnetic monopoles travel only at $\mathbf{v} > \mathbf{c}$ in the physical vacuum as implied from Equation 3.1a. If so, conventional U(1) EM gauge state equipment would not detect their presence because such equipment is limited to signal velocities less than $\mathbf{c}$. However, the same equipment in an IIED-conditioned space has an appreciably higher deltron population present in the equipment so the deltron coupling coefficient, γ, is significantly higher than zero and such superluminal phenomena now can be accessed (see Figure 3.3). We propose here that that is exactly what happens with equipment in an IIED-conditioned space! We assume, throughout this chapter, that such deltron enrichment allows *conventional equipment* to access some measure of superluminal phenomena.

[It was our initial goal to reveal *all* of our procedures involved in the evaluation of the new $\Delta\Psi_{H}+(t)$ detector within the confines of this chapter. However, delays in the U.S. Patent Office[1] indicate that it will be several months more before this patent can be issued. Thus, not wanting to compromise the granting of this patent, we must leave out a couple of crucial steps from our description of this important process. Sorry about that!]

How conventional pH-electrodes function

An overly simplified picture of water

Water is a remarkable substance, and we probably know more about it than we do about any other substance in nature, yet we still only know a very little about it. It is an exceedingly complex material, even in its purified state, and thus has an extensive range of anomalous properties. The published literature on the subject is vast and often confusing, covering a variety of chemical features, spatial size scales and temporal response times. The spatial size scales can be conveniently divided into three categories:

(1) molecular level properties, including small clusters, with the system being treated as an "effective" single phase water that is homogeneous on a size scale of 1 to 10 nanometers (one, ten millionth to one, one millionth of a centimeter). Figures 4.1a, 4.1b and 4.1c illustrate some aspects of these molecular/structural features.[2,3] Although it is common practice in today's science to think of a liquid as a perfectly random arrangement of molecules, for water this is definitely not true as it behaves more like silica (SiO_2) in its microstructural arrangements and this is extremely important for its properties.[4]

(2) Two phase or polyphase water properties associated with either classical critical point phenomena or cooperative internal electromagnetic (EM) mode interaction phenomena;[5] with this size scale of composite nature being treated as another "effective" single phase that is homogeneous over a size range of 100 to 1000 nanometers and

(3) a heterogeneous mix of the foregoing plus foreign bodies, such as $H_{2n}O_n$ water clusters, colloids, long chain molecules, microscopic gas bubbles and electric space charge layers, in the 100 to 10,000 nanometer size scale range. It is these microstructural elements that are sensitive to fluid convective fields as well as electric, magnetic and electromagnetic fields of specific frequencies.[3,6]

Temporal size scale changes for the various water phenomena in categories (1) and (2) above run from one trillionth of a second to one second while, for category (3) they can run from seconds to many days.

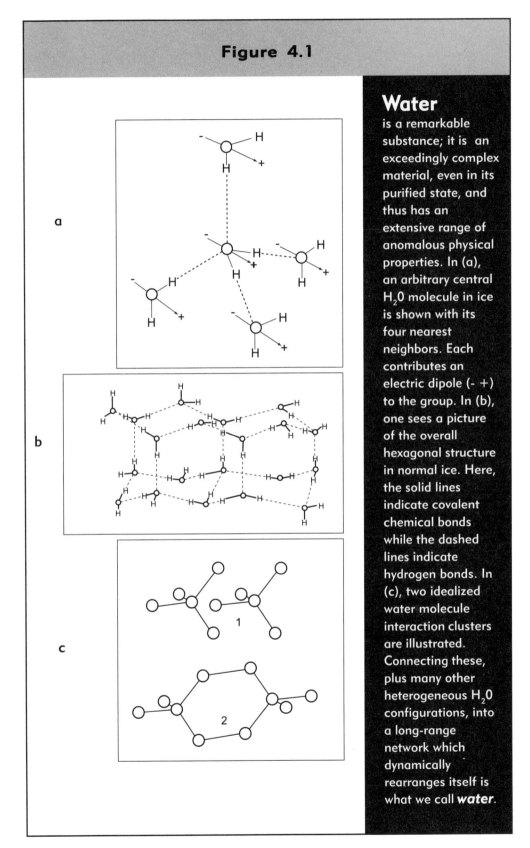

Figure 4.1

Water

is a remarkable substance; it is an exceedingly complex material, even in its purified state, and thus has an extensive range of anomalous physical properties. In (a), an arbitrary central H_2O molecule in ice is shown with its four nearest neighbors. Each contributes an electric dipole (- +) to the group. In (b), one sees a picture of the overall hexagonal structure in normal ice. Here, the solid lines indicate covalent chemical bonds while the dashed lines indicate hydrogen bonds. In (c), two idealized water molecule interaction clusters are illustrated. Connecting these, plus many other heterogeneous H_2O configurations, into a long-range network which dynamically rearranges itself is what we call *water*.

The key atomic and molecular bonding features of water that lead to such a range of macro and micro-heterogeneities is not just the well-known hydrogen bonds of water but, more importantly, the wide range of weak van de Waals bonds between and amongst the various structural units. It is this wide range of very weak bonds that accounts for the remarkable ease with which structural changes occur and this, in turn, explains the dozens of well-known property anomalies. In part, this would also allow for the structural changes caused by electric and magnetic fields, by radiations of all kinds and particularly by subtle energies as discussed in Chapters 1 and 2.

Since this chapter is devoted to considerations involving the proton or hydrogen ion, H^+, which, in turn, relates to the acidity of an aqueous solution, it is important that we understand what $U(1)$ gauge state chemical processes can occur in purified water that is in equilibrium with local air so as to alter the H^+ ion concentration.

Experience tells us that there are three types of generic reactions that can readily occur in bulk water that has been in contact with air so as to alter the H^+ concentration. The first of these is the water molecule *dissociation/ionization reaction* given by

$$H_2O \;\rightleftharpoons\; OH^- + H^+ \qquad (4.1a)$$

This reaction is thermally or photon activated which means that, as temperature is increased or the flux of photons in a specific energy range is increased, more H_2O molecules of the water dissociate and the H^+ concentration increases (but so also does the concentration of the hydroxyl ion, OH^-, increase). In the dark, for purified water at room temperature and not in contact with air, this H^+ concentration is about ten parts per billion. The second important reaction to consider is the dissolution of oxygen (O_2), nitrogen (N_2) and carbon dioxide (CO_2) into water from the air. Of these, it is the ionization reaction of CO_2 that is the important one because this reaction occurs easily to yield

$$H_2O + CO_2 \;\rightleftharpoons\; HCO_3 + H^+ \qquad (4.1b)$$

In this case, the concentration of dissolved CO_2 is usually such that the H^+ concentrations can be factors of ten to a thousand times larger via reaction 4.1b than via reaction (4.1a). The third important type of chemical reaction that occurs in our water/air system arises due to the presence of impurities like calcium, magnesium, etc., in the water. These dissolved impurities ionize in the water and begin to interact with equation 4.1b in the following way

$$Ca^{2+}+HCO_3 \quad \rightleftharpoons \quad CaCO_3+H^+ \qquad (4.1c)$$

to further increase the H^+ ion content of the water. This reaction removes the HCO_3 ion from the water to produce calcium carbonate particles (that eventually settle to the bottom of the vessel as a precipitate) plus a further increase in H^+. The commercial bottled water called Evian is a calcium/magnesium bicarbonate solution that is oversaturated with CO_2 compared to the same water in equilibrium with local air. On opening an Evian bottle, this "excess" CO_2 leaves the water for the air and the H^+ ion content of the water slowly decreases over time (via reaction 4.1b) and the water pH is said to increase. The importance of pH is discussed below.

The definition of pH is given by

$$pH = \log_{10} a_{H^+} \sim - \log_{10} C_{H^+} \qquad (4.2)$$

for dilute aqueous solutions (where C_{H+} is very small). Here, C is concentration, a is thermodynamic activity and $\log_{10}$ means the base 10 logarithm. pH runs from very acidic solutions (pH ~2) to very alkaline solutions (pH ~10) with the neutral solution (pH = 7) in the middle. Using litmus paper as a pH-detector, it is actually measuring C_{H+}.

pH-electrodes actually work on a different principle for the measurement of pH. To understand this principle it is necessary to say a little about the total thermodynamic potential energy, $\mathbf{\Phi}$, for any chemical species, that we will label as the j-species ($j = \mathbf{H^+}$ is the one we are particularly interested in). Written out in word format, $\mathbf{\Phi}$ for the U(1) EM gauge state is given by

$$\Phi_j = \left(\begin{array}{c}\text{standard state}\\\text{contribution}\end{array}\right)_j + \left(\begin{array}{c}\text{chemical}\\\text{contribution}\end{array}\right)_j + \left(\begin{array}{c}\text{electric and}\\\text{magnetic dipole}\\\text{contribution}\end{array}\right)_j + \left(\begin{array}{c}\text{electric}\\\text{monopole charge}\\\text{contribution}\end{array}\right)_j \quad (4.3)$$

Here, the standard state contribution is the value of $\mathbf{\Phi}_j$ at normal temperature and pressure (25°C and 1 atmosphere for example). For our purposes, we have also included any gravitational and other states of strain contributions into the standard state contribution in order to make things simpler and yet be precise. The chemical contribution is qualitatively similar to that given in Equation 4.2 (without the minus sign). The electric and magnetic dipole contributions account for the j-species having an electric or magnetic dipole associated with it and also the presence of an external electric and magnetic field (this term could also have been included in the standard state contribution). The last term on the right is needed when the j-species has an electric charge, $\mathbf{q}$, given by the product of the electric valence, ± 1, ± 2, ± 3 and the electron charge, $\mathbf{e}$. It is given by the product of $\mathbf{q}$ and the electric voltage, $\mathbf{V}$, present at the location of charge $\mathbf{q}$. There is no term present for any magnetic monopole charge because they are not detectable for a U(1) state (where $\mathbf{\Phi}_j = \eta_j$, the electrochemical potential).

One of the governing laws for a system at thermodynamic equilibrium is that $\mathbf{\Phi}_j$ = constant everywhere throughout the system for each of the j - species. Thus, for an electrically charged species like H^+, provided any external electric and magnetic fields are constant throughout the system, a concentration difference between any two points in the system will be exactly balanced by an electric voltage difference between these two points. Thus, if one of the points is located in the solution to be measured and the other is located inside a standard cell maintained at unit activity for protons, the voltage difference between these two points will be equal to -1/$\mathbf{q}$ times the chemical contribution at the measurement point in the solution. Thus, if we electrically measure this voltage difference, we unequivocally measure the pH via the following equation

$$\mathbf{V} - \mathbf{V_o} = \mathbf{A\,pH} .\qquad\qquad(4.4a)$$

Here, $\mathbf{A}$ is a constant equal to -59.16 millivolts (mV) at 25°C for an ideal electrode. Figure 4.2 shows a typical experimental plot between water pH and pH-electrode output, $\mathbf{V}$, in millivolts (mV) and one notes that $\mathbf{V} = 0$ at $\mathbf{pH} = 7$.

In commercial pH-electrodes, a glass membrane is most often used to separate the standard cell from the aqueous solution to be measured. The glass membrane contains small pores that are sufficiently large to allow H^+ ions (protons) to readily migrate through the membrane but not large enough to allow larger ions to pass through. Thus, in operation, some of the H^+ ions on the standard cell side of the glass membrane migrate through the glass in order to equilibrate with the H^+ ions in the bulk liquid to be tested. As illustrated in Figure 4.3a, this leaves an excess of negative ions on the standard cell side and an excess of H^+ on the bulk liquid side. This is just a conceptual picture to illustrate that there is (1) a monatomic layer of tightly bound positive charges on the right side plus (2) a spatially distributed zone of negative and positive charges (excess negative) to screen the bulk liquid from this positive interface charge so that the total of (1) and (2) yield a net positive charge. On the standard cell side of the membrane a similar situation exists but with a net negative charge. The effective thickness of the electrical double layers on the two sides are in the range of one-millionth to one-thousandth of a centimeter with the smaller thickness

Figure 4.2

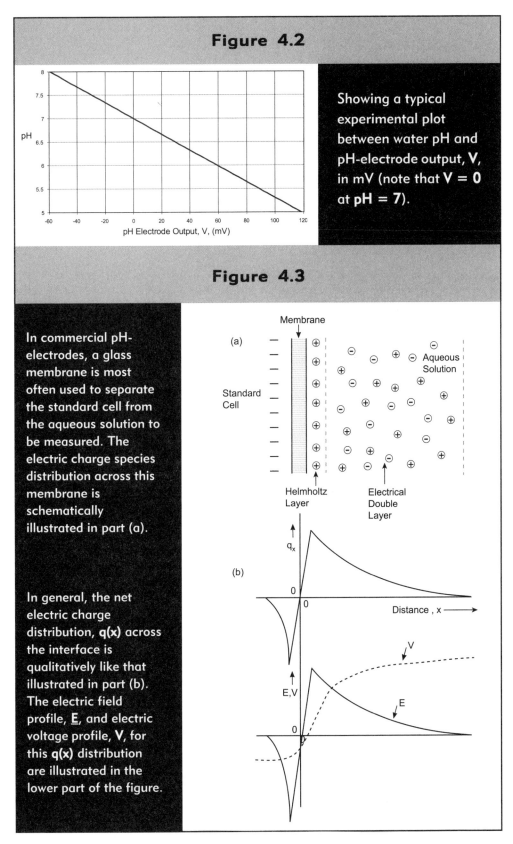

Showing a typical experimental plot between water pH and pH-electrode output, **V**, in mV (note that **V = 0** at **pH = 7**).

Figure 4.3

In commercial pH-electrodes, a glass membrane is most often used to separate the standard cell from the aqueous solution to be measured. The electric charge species distribution across this membrane is schematically illustrated in part (a).

In general, the net electric charge distribution, **q(x)** across the interface is qualitatively like that illustrated in part (b). The electric field profile, **E**, and electric voltage profile, **V**, for this q(x) distribution are illustrated in the lower part of the figure.

usually being on the standard cell side (because the electrolyte concentration is usually much higher in the standard cell).

This picture is only conceptual for the following reasons: (1) the electrically neutral water molecule, itself, has a strong electric dipole moment so, by its alignment perpendicular to the membrane, with its positive end closest to the membrane for the bulk solution side, can also act as a screening agent and (2) counter ions from the other electrolytes in the solution can also enter the electrical double layer and contribute to the space charge electric field distribution. These factors will contribute somewhat to the third term on the right of Equation 4.3 for $j = H^+$.

A more correct picture is that (1) there are two kinds of electrically neutral water. One having the hydrogen nuclear magnetic dipoles opposed to each other in an H_2O molecule (called ortho water) while the other has the two magnetic dipoles aligned (called para water) and, in bulk water at equilibrium, a fixed ratio of ortho to para water exists and (2) for transport of the proton in bulk water, it can be thought of as either an isolated species with its own electric charge and magnetic dipole or as attached to a neutral H_2O molecule to make H_3O^+ so that proton transport occurs as a hopping process from molecule to molecule. In this case, the proton is really treated as H_2OH^+ and it has an electric charge, an electric dipole and a magnetic dipole. This becomes important, even in the simplest case of absolutely pure water, because the laws governing the concentration profile of H^+ from one side of the membrane to the other are:

(1) Constancy of thermodynamic potential, Φ_{H^+}, everywhere via Equation 4.3.

(2) Overall electrical neutrality considering the whole spacecharge layer of Figure 4.3,

(3) Conservation of electrical charge point-to-point throughout the space-charge layer,

(4) Conservation of magnetic charge point-to-point throughout the space-charge layer and

(5) Minimization of the total thermodynamic free energy for all species.

The fourth item is easily satisfied for the U(1) EM gauge symmetry state because only magnetic dipoles exist.

In general, the net electric charge distribution, $q(x)$ across the interface is qualitatively like that illustrated in Figure 4.3b. The electric field profile, $\mathbf{E}(x)$, and electric voltage profile, $\mathbf{V}(x)$, for this $q(x)$ distribution are illustrated in the lower part of the figure. The important point for us to note is that the third term on the right of Equation 4.3 is always negative and is proportional to the product of the electric dipole moment and $\mathbf{E}^2$ (plus the magnetic dipole moment and $\mathbf{H}^2$). The magnitude of the fourth term on the right of Equation 4.3 is proportional to the product of the proton electric charge and the voltage $\mathbf{V}$. Earlier, we said that $\mathbf{A}$ in Equation 4.4a was -59.16 millivolts for an ideal electrode. This will hold true even when aligned electric dipoles are present in the space charge layer.

For the U(1) gauge symmetry state ($\gamma \sim 0$), and Equation 4.4a is the required relationship that one must use to connect the measured pH-electrode voltage to the actual pH of the solution. However, when the deltron coupling-coefficient, γ, is no longer insignificant in our measurement space, we must add an additional contribution to the right side of Equation 4.3 to account for the effective magnetic monopole image, manifesting in D-space due to the deltron-coupling with the actual magnetic monopoles present in R-space (the physical vacuum level of reality). The measurement of this magnetic monopole image by our deltron-saturated equipment is what produces $\Delta\Psi_H{}^+$. When we add this new contribution to Equation 4.3 and demand that thermodynamic equilibrium occur for the H^+ ion , the mathematical solution for the pH-electrode voltage, V, is no longer that of Equation 4.4a but is given by

$$\mathbf{V\text{-}V_0 = A\ pH - \frac{\delta(\Delta\Psi_H{}^+)}{|e|}} \quad . \tag{4.4b}$$

Where $\boldsymbol{\delta}$ means the difference in $\Delta\Psi_H{}^+$ between the measurement point in the solution and the unit activity point in the standard cell where V_0 obtains. Figure 4.4 provides a plot of pH-electrode vs. solution pH values for both the U(1) and the SU(2) gauge symmetry state spaces under the special condition that $\boldsymbol{\delta(\Delta\Psi_H{}^+)}$ is independent of pH. Of course, the greater is the magnitude of $\boldsymbol{\delta\Delta\Psi_H{}^+}$, the larger will be the millivolt offset between the two parallel lines.

Experimental measurement procedures

The experimental determination of the pH-electrode slope, **A** in Equation 4.4a, requires one to periodically calibrate the electrode using at least two pH-buffer solutions (at pH=4 and pH=10, for example). Most of the uncertainly in the ultimate pH measurement arises from the uncertainty in the pH of these buffers (± 0.01 pH units, depending on pH magnitude and manufacturer). When, for example, the device of a particular commercial manufacturer[7] detects the sensing membrane signal, the meter software calculates the pH via Equation 4.4a for an ideal electrode wherein the value of $\mathbf{V_{measured} = 0}$ at $\mathbf{pH = 7.0}$. Thus, for our normal inner symmetry state as a U(1) EM gauge space, we can define a new parameter, **N**, which we label the "Nernst-parameter". For the U(1) state, **N** should equal unity and experience shows us that it does. For higher inner symmetry states than the U(1) level, **N** should be departed from unity. Thus, experimental determination of **N** via careful pH measurement is one procedure for gaining an experimental measure of IIED-conditioning for any specific space.

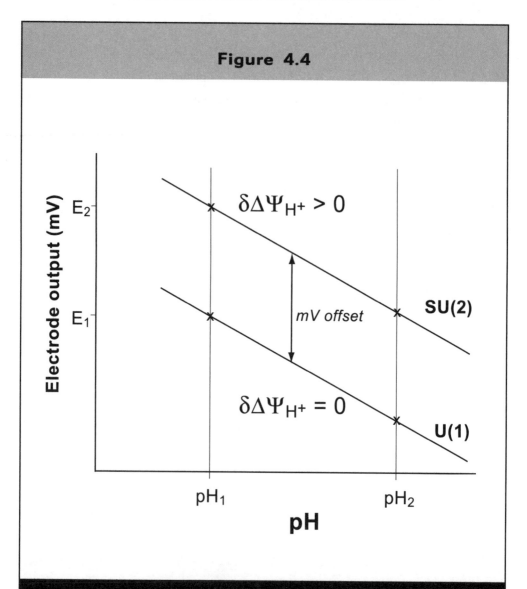

Figure 4.4

The electrode output vs. pH plots for both U(1) and higher EM gauge symmetry states is illustrated for the special case where the slope of $\delta\Delta\Psi_{H^+}$ is independent of pH. The millivolt offset between the two lines increases directly with $\delta\Delta\Psi_{H^+}$.

Each experimental station, either in our Payson laboratory or at a remote site laboratory, consists of a vessel of purified water containing both a pH-electrode and a temperature probe connected to an electronic display instrument and a computer monitor as illustrated in Figure 4.5. This constitutes the essential equipment package for most of the research described in this book. Using ThermOrion® electrodes and their SensorLink®[7] measurement system, values of T_w and pH are continuously monitored; this data, plus a periodic calibration of the electrode slope, **A**, using buffer solutions, allows **N** to be readily calculated and displayed as a function of time.

For an ideal pH-electrode with slope efficiency of 100%, Figure 4.2 shows the calculated relationship between pH and **V** at 25°C. At the Payson laboratory site, P_4, between 11/21 and 12/11 in 2002, Figure 4.6 shows the time-average exponential variation of pH after fresh purified water was introduced into the measurement cell on 11/21. Using this data, **N(t)**-data was calculated and shown on the right hand ordinate of Figure 4.6. The overall linear fit of **N** with time is excellent. From the values of **N(t)** corresponding to this pH(t) data, we see that **N** is appreciably different than unity so the EM gauge symmetry state at the P_4-station is definitely not at the U(1) level. Figure 4.7 shows a strong correlation between **N** and **1/V** at the P_5-station in Payson for a closely similar time-frame.

In Chapter 2, plots of $\mathbf{\Delta\Psi_{H^+}} = \mathbf{\Psi'_{H^+}} - \mathbf{\eta_{H^+}}$ have been provided for a variety of remote IIED-sites and remote non-IIED sites (supposed control sites). It is the anomalous **N(t)** data that leads directly to the $\mathbf{\delta\Delta\Psi_{H^+}}$ (t)-plots. We find that a linear relationship is theoretically predicted to occur between $\mathbf{\delta\Delta\Psi_{H^+}}$ and **N** (see Equation 4.5) and, for example, from the slope of $\mathbf{\delta\Delta\Psi_{H^+}}$ vs. **N**, at $\mathbf{\Delta N = 1.0}$, one can calculate $\mathbf{\delta\Delta\Psi_{H^+}} = \mathbf{\delta\Delta\Psi_{H^+}}^*$ and thereby compare different sites with each other. In Table 4.1, values of $\mathbf{\delta\Delta\Psi_{H^+}}^*$ are compared for 8 measurement stations. The foregoing clearly demonstrates that (1) this category of special device (an IIED) can indeed alter some important environmental condition in an experimental space so that it behaves lawfully (see below) but in an anomalous way compared to *normal* electrochemical behavior, (2) this anomalous behavior is consistent with the theoretical hypothesis that the inner symmetry state of the experimental space has been raised above that of our standard U(1) inner symmetry state and (3) consistent with analytical theory. A quantitative measurement of the thermodynamic magnetoelectrochemical potential energy change, $\mathbf{\delta\Delta\Psi_{H^+}}$, for the aqueous solution-solvated hydrogen ion, H^+, can be readily made.

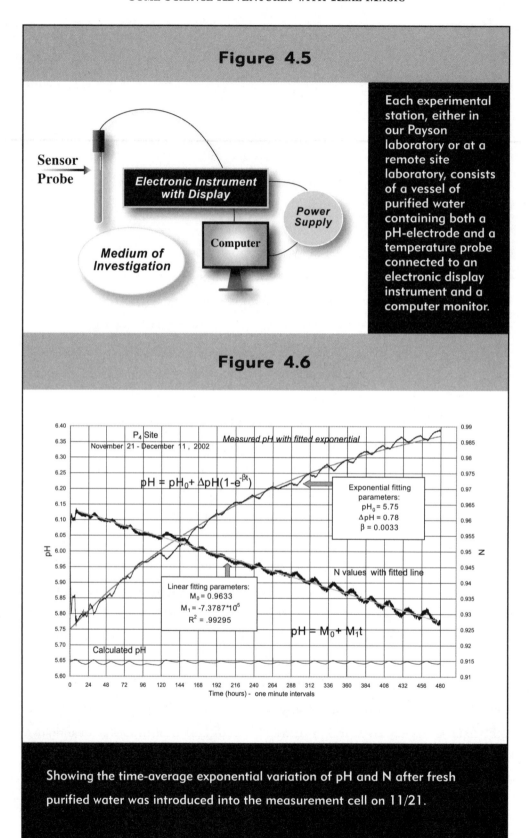

Figure 4.5

Sensor Probe →

Electronic Instrument with Display

Power Supply

Computer

Medium of Investigation

Each experimental station, either in our Payson laboratory or at a remote site laboratory, consists of a vessel of purified water containing both a pH-electrode and a temperature probe connected to an electronic display instrument and a computer monitor.

Figure 4.6

P_4 Site

November 21 - December 11, 2002

Measured pH with fitted exponential

$$pH = pH_0 + \Delta pH(1 - e^{-\beta t})$$

Exponential fitting parameters:
$pH_0 = 5.75$
$\Delta pH = 0.78$
$\beta = 0.0033$

N values with fitted line

Linear fitting parameters:
$M_0 = 0.9633$
$M_1 = -7.3787 \times 10^5$
$R^2 = .99295$

$$pH = M_0 + M_1 t$$

Calculated pH

Time (hours) - one minute intervals

Showing the time-average exponential variation of pH and N after fresh purified water was introduced into the measurement cell on 11/21.

Figure 4.7

Showing a strong correlation between **N** and **1/V** at the P$_5$-station in Payson for a closely similar time-frame to Figure 4.6.

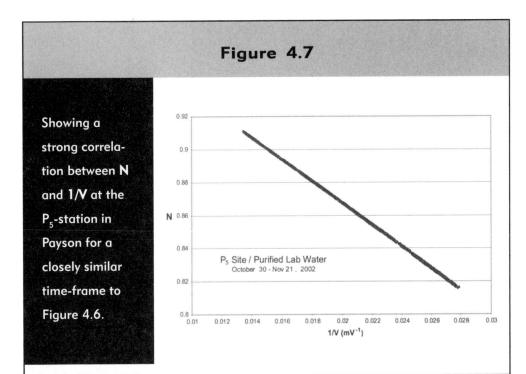

P$_5$ Site / Purified Lab Water
October 30 - Nov 21 , 2002

Table 4.1

Values for $\delta\Delta\Psi_{H+} = \delta\Delta\Psi_{H+}^{*}$ (meV) when $\Delta N = 1$ for all of the various sites operating in our overall experimental system.

Site	$\delta\Delta\Psi_{H+}^{*}$ (meV)	Recent N-values	% departure from 1.00
P$_1$	36.87	.89	-11
P$_2$	65.0	1.14	+14
P$_3$	51.13	.98	-2
P$_4$	54.22	.87	-13
M$_1$	-11.25	1.30	+30
K$_1$	76.0	.98	-2
B$_2$	20.85	1.23	+23
B$_1$	59.84	1.04	+4

pH-electrode functioning when the deltron coupling coefficient, γ, is significant

When γ is no longer insignificant, theory shows us that

$$N\text{-}1 = \frac{B\delta\Delta\Psi_{H^+}}{V_{U(1)}} \tag{4.5}$$

where B is a constant so that, for constant pH-electrode voltage, V, N changes linearly with $\delta\Delta\Psi_{H^+}$ and vice versa. Equation 4.5 also tells us that $\delta\Delta\Psi_{H^+} = 0$ when N = 1 (the U(1) state) as expected by the definition of the Nernst-parameter, N. Experimentally we find that N is not sensitively dependent on either water temperature, T_w, or A (see Equation 4.4a) near the normal inner symmetry state for an unconditioned space.

In the Payson laboratory, we have conducted a series of experiments using buffered solutions of originally purified water with controlled chemical additions. Figure 4.8 shows some of this data. It is interesting to note the following, with the definition, $\delta\Delta\Psi_{H^+} = \gamma_{H^+_i}\Psi_{H^+}$, where $\gamma_{H^+_i}$ is the deltron coupling-coefficient for the H^+ ion as a function of various environmental factors, i, (1) the experimental plots for N vs. $\Delta\Psi_{H^+}$ are all linear as expected theoretically via Equation 4.5, (2) the N vs. $\Delta\Psi_{H^+}$ plots all go through the (N = 1, $\Delta\Psi_{H^+} = 0$) point as expected from Equation 4.5 and (3) $\gamma_{H^+_i}$ changes strongly with electrolyte type and electrolyte concentration. It is as if a partitioning of some unique ingredient (like deltrons) occurs between the solvent (purified water) and some solute species (the electrolyte) in the solution. Values for these partition coefficients, k_1, assuming $k_1 = $ unity for pure water, are provided in Table 4.2.

The slopes, $\Delta(\gamma_{H^+_i}\Delta\Psi_{H^+})/\Delta N = R_{pH}$, obtained from all the plots in Figure 4.8 have been plotted vs. the normal., or U(1) state, pH-values in Figure 4.9 and the best fit linear relationships shown for four different Payson experimental stations. It is interesting to note that the largest scatter band occurs for the pure water case, where the total electrolyte concentration is smallest. The best fit value for the slope is $R_{pH} = 400 - 54.85$ pH [U(1) state]. Figure 4.9 illustrates the very important relationship between the U(1) inner symmetry state pH and the value of R_{pH} determined from experimental data like that shown in Figure 4.8 (and also predicted by theory via Equation 4.5). Since the pH-electrode is calibrated using the pH-buffers that have values defined by the normal inner symmetry

Figure 4.8

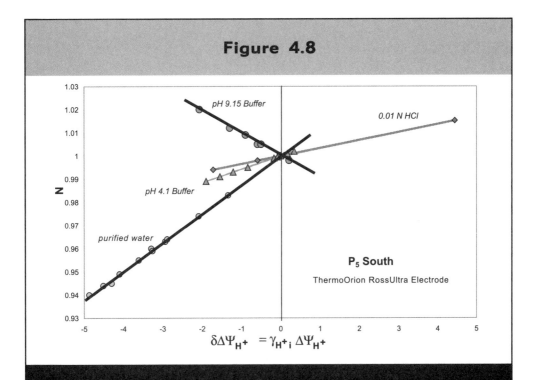

It is comforting to note both the linear relationships between N and $\delta\Delta\Psi_{H^+}$ for these four solutions, and that all of them pass through the point ($\delta\Delta\Psi_{H^+} = 0$, N = 1) as assumed in the theoretical development of Equation 4.5. From this data and Equation 4.5, it is clear that γ_{H^+i} depends on local environmental factors such as electrolyte type and concentration, etc. It is as if a partitioning of some special ingredient (like deltrons) occurs between the solvent (H_2O) and the solute (electrolyte) species in the solution.

Table 4.2

Substance	K_1	pH-Electrode Type
Pure Water	+1.0 (defined as such)	RossUltra®
pH 4.1 Buffer	+0.0492	RossUltra®
pH 9.15 Buffer	-0.816	RossUltra®
0.01 N HCl	+0.291	RossUltra®
0.01 M Borax	-0.746	RossUltra®

state pH, this figure is an important link between "conditioned" space-measured pH-values and "normal U(1) space-measured pH-values".

The importance of the Figure 4.9 finding, with regard to the relative constancy of R_{pH}, cannot be overstated. One of our most difficult to handle experimental problems is the proper interpretation for pH-values measured in "conditioned" spaces that, on the surface, appear to have no link to any normal pH-value. From a purely conventional U(1) gauge perspective, the most likely rationales would be either (1) the equipment is malfunctioning or (2) there is some conventional environmental contaminant modifying the pH of the supposedly pure water. The Figure 4.9 linear relationship and Equation 4.5 provide us with an empirical and theoretical procedure for determining the U(1) inner symmetry state pH, even in a highly "conditioned" space. At the very least, the discovery represented by Figure 4.9 provides one with a means of *correcting any measured pH for the influence of field effects not normally considered.*

From Equation 4.5, we can note that, for a given $\mathbf{N}$, $\delta\Delta\Psi_{H+} = \gamma_{H+_i}\Delta\Psi_{H+}$ will depend sensitively on the value of $\mathbf{V}$. Further, we have empirically found that different commercial brands of electrode can exhibit opposite signs of $\mathbf{V}$. Thus, at the same "conditioned" site, if one changes from one type of pH-electrode to another, the value of $\gamma_{H+_i}\Delta\Psi_{H+}$ can reverse sign. In Figure 4.8, that the sign of $\gamma_{H+_i}\Delta\Psi_{H+}$ can change during the course of measurement using the same electrode is also thought to be a γ_{H+_i}-effect. From Chapter 2, page 77, item 8, where pH-measuring electrodes were exchanged between the two laboratories B_1 and B_2, an immediate change in $\gamma_{H+_i}\Delta\Psi_{H+}$ occurred with $\Delta(\gamma_{H+_i}\Delta\Psi_{H+}) < 0$ for B_2 and $\Delta(\gamma_{H+_i}\Delta\Psi_{H+}) > 0$ for B_1 since $\gamma_{H+_i}\Delta\Psi_{H+}(B_2) > \gamma_{H+_i}\Delta\Psi_{H+}(B_1)$. This could have been due to either a $\Delta\Psi_{H+}$-effect or a γ_{H+_i}-effect for the two locations.

Two other aspects of the γ_{H+_i} - effect

The commercial pH-electrode effect: In Table 2.1 (see Page 60), site-P_7 is a ~5 foot cubic, wood-framed box that is completely covered with mu-metal plate (even the door in the cube). Mu-metal has a very high magnetic permeability which diverts local magnetic flux lines to travel through the mu-metal to significantly lower the magnetic field intensity,

Figure 4.9

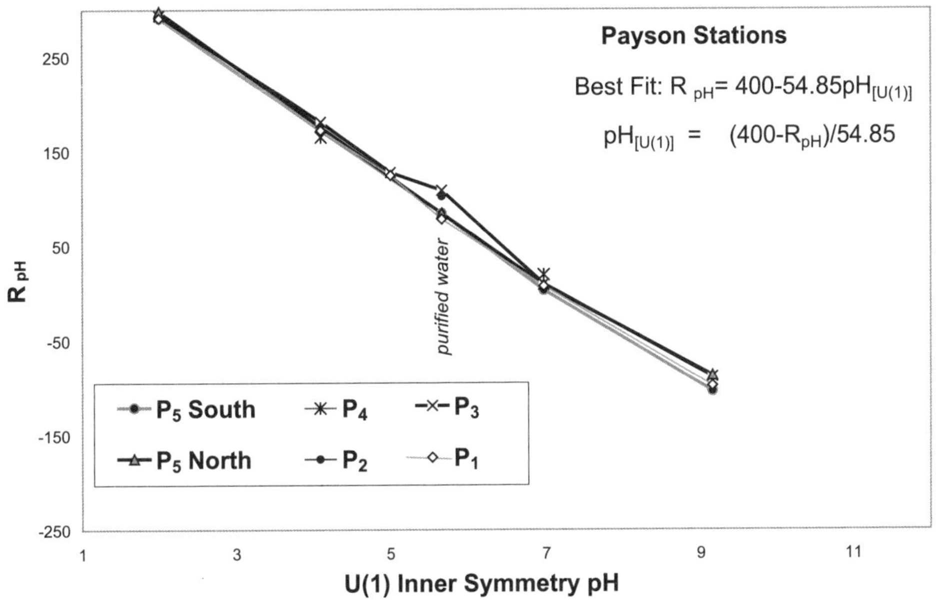

The linear relationship provides us with an empirical procedure for determining the U(1) inner symmetry state pH, even in a highly "conditioned" space. At the very least, the discovery represented by this figure provides one with a means of *correcting any measured pH for the influence of field effects not normally considered.*

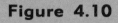

Figure 4.10

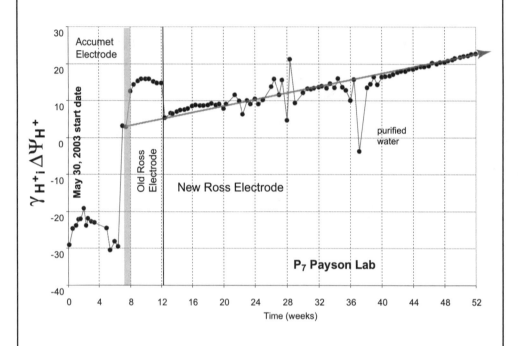

Another major $\gamma_{H^+{}_i}$-effect is clearly associated with the type of pH-electrode being used in the overall measuring equipment package.

H, inside the box. In addition, a double-walled, mu-metal cylinder, of ~1 foot in diameter and 2 feet long with caps on each end, was placed centrally in the cube to further lower H inside this cylinder. The combination of the two mu-metal enclosures reduces the value of H inside the cylinder to almost zero. Such a system almost completely screens out the earth's D.C. magnetic-field and greatly reduces the ambient intensity of A.C. EM-fields.

The container holding the purified lab water plus sensors was placed inside this cylinder with the leads from the pH-electrode and temperature (T_W) probe being connected to an adjacent laptop computer. These connecting leads went through a small hole in the top mu-metal cap on the cylinder. Measurements of pH and T_W of purified water commenced in May, 2003.

The pH-calibration cycle occurred twice weekly yielding two values for N and $\gamma_{H^+i} \Delta\Psi_{H}+$ per week. After a year of data collection wherein the type of pH-electrode used was changed several times; Figure 4.10 shows us what happened to the magnitude of $\gamma_{H^+i} \Delta\Psi_{H}+$ (t). We started with an Accumet® pH-electrode and, at the 6 week point, switched to a new ThermOrion Ross® electrode. This new Ross® electrode was used only for one week (week 7), indicated by the shaded region in Figure 4.10. Note the *abrupt upward shift* in measured $\gamma_{H^+i} \Delta\Psi_{H}+$ when this occurred. Starting at week 8, the pH-electrode was again changed to a Ross® electrode that had previously seen considerable use in the main lab (IIED-conditioned) of Table 2.1. Once again, note the abrupt upward shift in $\gamma_{H^+i} \Delta\Psi_{H}+$. In the middle of week 12, this pH electrode was changed back to the new Ross® electrode that had been previously used during week 7. Note the abrupt *drop* in $\gamma_{H^+i} \Delta\Psi_{H}+$. There were no further pH-electrode changes for the next 40 weeks and the $\gamma_{H^+i} \Delta\Psi_{H}+$ values for this Ross® electrode climbed ~linearly (99% fit) with time to a value of +20 (meV) at the end of the year. It is interesting to note that the backward extrapolation of this linear result, from week 12 to week 7, placed the week 7 data points exactly on this line. The bottom-line conclusion that we draw from the Figure 4.10 data is that the particular pH-electrode used in these experiments has its own deltron-partition coefficient, k_1, with the local state of environment conditioning just as illustrated in Table 4.2 for the aqueous solution used for measurement. This is a very clear γ_{H^+i} effect.

Figure 4.11

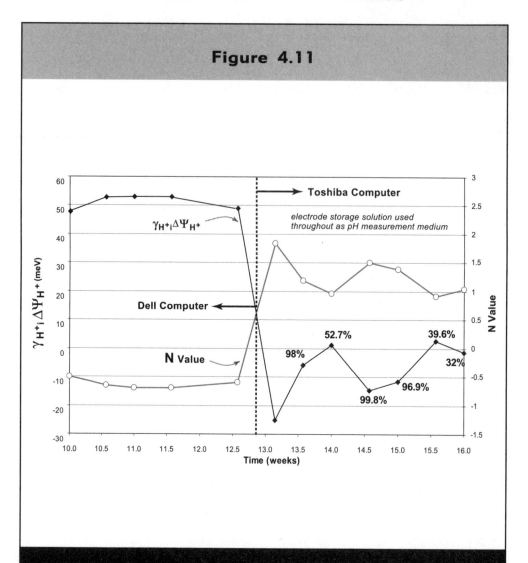

Electronically switching from one type of computer to a different type of computer in the overall measurement system clearly illustrates another γ_{H^+i}–effect.

The commercial computer effect: At our final Missouri control site, M_C, which was an underground measurement station, large departures of $\Delta\Psi_H{}^+$ from zero had been observed over a period of several months. The researcher at this site encountered trouble calibrating her ThermOrion Ross® electrode and she sent it back to the Payson lab for analysis. In late September, 2003, we began using this electrode in the Payson lab at site P_9 in order to observe its behavior. Immediately, we measured purified water values of $\Delta\Psi_H{}^+$ over +40 meV, one of the highest values recorded to date.

Later, this particular electrode was placed in an electrode storage solution at pH ~6.9. We noted that the $\Delta\Psi_H{}^+$ rose to 50 meV (see Figure 4.11 at 10 weeks). In addition, **N < 0** values were measured for the first time.

Next, using this pH-electrode and storage solution we proved the existence of a $\gamma_H{}^+{}_i$ -effect associated with the type of computer used in the measurement circuit. As can be seen in Figure 4.11, for times less than ~12.8 weeks, a Dell® computer was used in the circuit. At the 12.8 week point, an electronic switch was used to remove the Dell® computer from this circuit and replace it with a Toshiba® computer. One should note that the next $\gamma_H{}^+{}_i \Delta\Psi_H{}^+$ -data point had dropped from ~50 meV to ~-25 meV while the N-data point rose from ~-0.5 to ~+1.8. Perhaps even more significant was that, for later times, $\Delta\Psi_H{}^+$ began to approach zero in an oscillatory fashion, (values of ~0 had never been observed in the Payson lab before).

The percentage numbers on the $\delta\Delta\Psi_H{}^+ = \gamma_H{}^+{}_i \Delta\Psi_H{}^+$ plot illustrate the degree of fit for a linear relationship between $1/V$ and N (see Equation 4.5) used in the calculation for $\Delta\Psi_H{}^+$. As $\gamma_H{}^+{}_i \Delta\Psi_H{}^+$ approaches zero, N approaches 1 and the percent fit approaches zero also. This is a typical behavior when a state of zero conditioning is approached. What appears to be happening here is that the introduction of a new computer into the measurement system led to a several week-long erasing of the high state of space conditioning that was initially observed. Subsequently, after the Figure 4.11 data was collected, the pH-electrode being used was placed in a 0.068 molar cupric nitrate solution and, using the same Toshiba laptop computer, we observed an immediate recovery of $\gamma_H{}^+{}_i \Delta\Psi_H{}^+$ to pre-Toshiba levels (over 40 meV). Finally, we returned to using this pH-electrode in a purified water vessel plus the same Toshiba computer as our measurement system and have observed, up to the present time, an oscillating approach of the calculated $\gamma_H +_i \Delta \Psi_H +$ -values to a zero level in a fashion very similar to that illustrated in Figure 4.11. Clearly, this is another $\gamma_H +_i$ -effect associated with the *type of computer* used in the equipment measuring circuit located in an IIED-conditioned space, even though we do not fully understand all of these behavioral changes.

A closing speculation

It is interesting to note that particle theorists have noticed that the relevant energy scale of dark energy is about 1 milli electron volt, approximately the same as the masses associated with the three known types of neutrinos.[9] It has been learned that neutrino oscillations can be described by a time-varying field. Such models also predict the existence of a fourth type of neutrino for which no experimental evidence has yet been found.[9] Two speculations might be made here: (1) since the *magnitude* of $\gamma_{H+_i} \Delta \Psi_H +$ has been experimentally observed by us to be in the range of $0 < |\gamma_{H+_i} \Delta \Psi_H +| < 100$ meV, could this perhaps be associated with the sought-for fourth neutrino? In an unconditioned space (a U(1) gauge space), compared to our "conditioned" spaces, the appreciably lower deltron population, and thus lower γ_{H+_i}, could readily reduce $|\gamma_{H+_i} \Delta \Psi_H +|$ into the 0 to 1 meV range and (2) since neutrinos are very weakly interactive with D-space matter, the mirror principle of Table 3.2 would suggest that γ_{H+_i} for neutrinos, compared to other D-space species, might be substantially large for R-space substances.

References

1.   K. Moriyasu, *An Elementary Primer for Gauge Theory* (World Scientific Publishing Co, Pte. Ltd. Singapore, 1983).

2.   W.A. Tiller, *Science and Human Transformation* (Pavior Publishing, Walnut Creek, CA, 1997).

3.   W.A. Tiller, W.E. Dibble, Jr., and M.J. Kohane, *Conscious Acts of Creation* (Pavior Publishing, Walnut Creek, CA, 2001).

4.   R. Roy, W.A. Tiller, I. Bell, "The Structure of Liquid Water: Novel I n s i g h t s from Materials Research; Relevance to Homeopathy" (2004)

5.   G. Preparata, *QED Coherence in Matter* (World Scientific Publishing Co., Singapore, 1995)

6.   M. Yamashita, C. Duffield and W.A. Tiller, "Direct Current Magnetic Field and Electromagnetic Field Effects on the pH and Oxidation-reduction Potential Equilibration Rates of Water. 1. Purified Water", Langmuir 19 (2003) 6851-6856.

7.   ThermOrion® SensorLink® PCM 500 pH meter. ThermOrion® RossUltra® pH electrode, Model 8102 BNU.

8.   K.L. Cheng, "Explanation of Misleading Nernst Slope by Boltzman Equation", Microchemical Journal, 59 (3) (1998) 457-461(5).

9.   Cowen R, "Dark doings: searching for signs of a force that may be everywhere . . . or nowhere", Science News 165, May 22 (2004) 330-332.

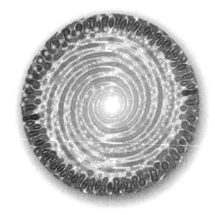

Chapter 5

Property Oscillations and Information Entanglement

T_A

...the greater the level of deltron activation, the higher does the EM gauge symmetry state of the inner layer rise above the U(1) state and the more effective is a human's intention for broadcasting both ME and EM radiations via their biofield to influence the world around them. This is thought to form what has been called Qi by the Asian community and we have labeled the overall flow system as a "Qi/Prana pump".

I n IIED-conditioned spaces, besides vacuum level magnetic monopole appearance leading to experimental measurement of $\Delta\Psi_{H^+}$ as one defining characteristic of such a space, two other unique behaviors are also defining characteristics. These are (1) temporal oscillations in the magnitude of a material property measurement and (2) information entanglement between D-space separated parts of the experimental system.

The last chapter focused on how and why one is able to use D-space technology instruments to have measurement accessibility to superluminal magnetic monopole behavior in R-space. In this chapter, the focus is directed towards the reasons why temporal property oscillations occur and why information entanglement occurs between (1) different instrument stations in the same laboratory, (2) different instrument stations in laboratories thousands of miles apart, (3) different humans involved in an interpersonal communication or activity and (4) an instrument station-human interaction.

Types of temporal oscillations observed to date

We will be discussing oscillations in material properties in conditioned spaces in some detail in this chapter and some may wonder exactly what oscillations are and why they are important. The word oscillation, in the way we are using it, refers to the variation in some quantity we measure in the lab with time. All are familiar with the variation in outside air temperature during the day. At night, the temperature goes down and during the day, as the sun heats the air, the temperature goes up. This up and down variation in temperature during a day we refer to as a diurnal *oscillation in temperature* driven by solar heating. If we have a heating/cooling system in our homes, we are familiar with the temperature changes that occur as the air is heated or cooled. These variations in air temperature with time are *temperature oscillations* driven by the A/C (air conditioning) system.

In our lab, we have an A/C system that may be either off or on for periods of time. When the system is on, the air in the lab is being heated or cooled at some frequency depending on the thermostat setting. The temperature oscillations that we measure in this case at some location in the lab are related to the A/C-controlled on/off cycle. With the A/C system off, we find that temperature oscillations are controlled by the diurnal solar heating cycle. In any case, oscillations in air temperature are driven by some mechanism that can normally be identified with conventional heating/cooling sources.

So temperature oscillations are changes in temperature with time that everyone is familiar with. Other oscillations can occur in other quantities that we measure in the lab. We measure the pH of water, the electrical conductivity of water, the oxygen content of water, the oxidation/reduction potential of water (related usually to the oxygen content). We can also measure the concentration of other chemical components that we add to the water. In addition to measurements on water, we can measure other things over time such as the mass (weight) of some mass standard using a computer-monitored balance, the ambient level of α, β and γ radiation, the electrical output of electronic components such as a coil of wire or a standard cell (battery) or a solar cell.

Some of these quantities should not vary much over time (if at all), so it is important if we observe that some of these measurable quantities vary with time. In other words, if we see significant oscillations in radiation, that we normally do not expect, it is important to note these. Also, some of these measurable quantities have well-defined variations with temperature. For example, the pH of pure water and pH buffers that we measure routinely vary with temperature in known ways. If we see water pH oscillating with temperature in a way that is not consistent with the way pH should theoretically vary with temperature, then that is an important anomaly to note. In other cases, the temperature we measure is flat with time (no change) but we see oscillations in pH (or other measurable quantities). This is also anomalous and is important to note. In some cases, the measurable quantities vary with temperature but in exactly the opposite way that they should - another significant anomaly. Thus, it is important to study oscillations observed in a conditioned space for what they may tell us about the nature of that particular environment as opposed to other more "normal" spaces. What is interesting in conditioned spaces such as our lab is that we often measure oscillations that have no conventional source. Some examples of these are discussed below.

Before discussing our oscillation data, it is perhaps best to illustrate two important characteristics of a periodic oscillation in time. Such an oscillation can exhibit a wide variety of shapes but the wave train repeats itself periodically in time. From theory and experience, we find that any wave shape can be decomposed into a set, or sum, of very simple mathematical waveforms called cosine and sine functions that differ one from the other only in amplitude, A, frequency, w, and phase angle, θ. Figure 5.1a illustrates a pure sine wave with phase angle zero in that the wave height is zero at time = 0. The wave amplitude is the maximum wave height which occurs at time = ½ (π/w). Here, A=1. In figure 5.1b, we have two sine waves of frequency w and amplitude A that are shifted in phase by an amount $\Delta\theta$. The wave labeled 1 is the same as the wave labeled 2 but it has been shifted to the left some amount, Δ(time), so that its wave height at time = 0 is greater than zero. A cosine wave is just a sine wave whose phase angle, θ, is 90 degrees so it is a sine wave shifted to the left until the wave height at time = 0 is A. In Figures 5.1c and 5.1d, waves 1 and 2 are almost completely in phase and completely out of phase, respectively. For each of the two wave cases, superposition has been applied to provide a resultant waveform labeled superposition that yields constructive interference (Figure 5.1c) when the two sine waves are close to being in phase, and destructive interference (Figure 5.1d) when the two sine waves are close to being out of phase. The superposed wave energy is proportional to the square of the superposed wave height and one can readily see the significant change from the ~in-phase state (Figure 5.1c) to the ~out-of-phase state (Figure 5.1d).

In the early Minnesota experiments,[1,2] after IIED-space conditioning, time-varying oscillatory behavior was observed for air temperature, T_A, water temperature, T_W, water pH and water electrical conductivity, σ_W. Examples of such measurements are illustrated in Figure 5.2. These oscillations typically have frequencies in the range ~one-one hundredth to one-one thousandth hertz compared to our U.S. wall voltage outlets at 60 hertz (cycles per second). For the upper example of Figure 5.2, the pH-measuring vessel was located at the center of a small, one foot diameter Faraday cage (FC) while T_A was measured both inside the cage and at 6 inch intervals along a particular radial line outside the cage for a distance of 11 feet, through the door to the room and into an adjacent hall. Figure 5.3a shows that the first 5 frequency components of the $T_A(t)$ waveforms at two locations inside this FC and one outside, are identical. Likewise, the components for $T_W(t)$ and $T_A(t)$

Figure 5.1

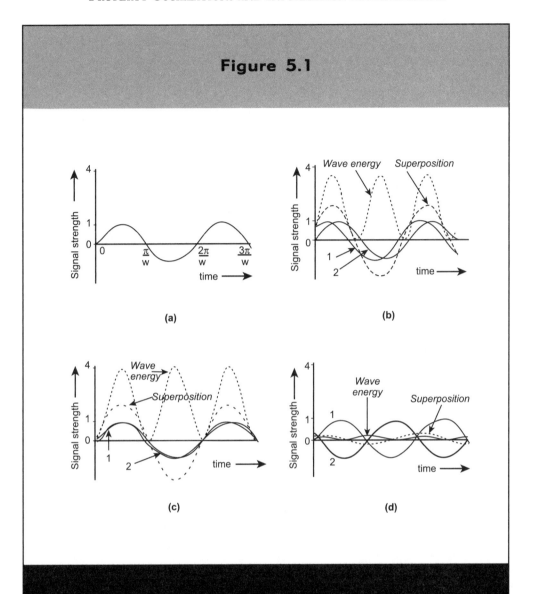

(a)

(b)

(c)

(d)

Illustrating two important characteristics of a periodic oscillation in time. Such an oscillation can exhibit a wide variety of shapes but the wave train repeats itself periodically in time. From theory and experience, we find that any wave shape can be decomposed into a set, or sum, of very simple mathematical waveforms called cosine and sine functions that differ one from the other only in amplitude, A, frequency, w, and phase angle, θ.

Figure 5.2

In the early Minnesota experiments,[1,2] after IIED-space conditioning, time-varying oscillatory behavior was observed for air temperature, T_A, water temperature, T_W, water pH and water electrical conductivity, σ_W

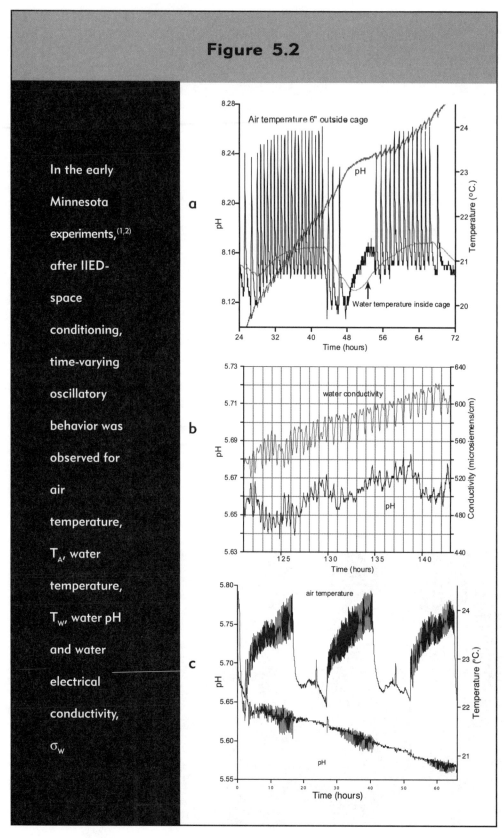

Figure 5.3

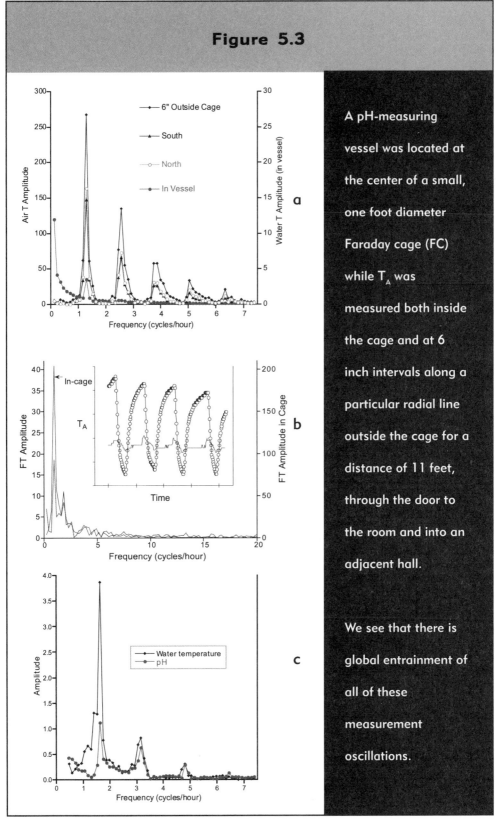

A pH-measuring vessel was located at the center of a small, one foot diameter Faraday cage (FC) while T_A was measured both inside the cage and at 6 inch intervals along a particular radial line outside the cage for a distance of 11 feet, through the door to the room and into an adjacent hall.

We see that there is global entrainment of all of these measurement oscillations.

are also identical. Figure 5.3b shows that 10 feet away from this cage, into the hall and with the door closed, although the amplitude of $T_A(t)$ is much smaller than that inside the cage, it exhibits an almost identical frequency spectrum to that for $T_A(t)$ inside the cage. Thus, the spatial coherence length for these $T_A(t)$ oscillations is at least 10 feet. Figure 5.3c shows that $T_W(t)$ and pH(t) also exhibit the same spectral distribution for their oscillatory waveforms. Thus, we see that there is global entrainment of all of these measurement oscillations, T_A, T_W and pH to the same thermodynamic driving force, whatever that is. Table 5.1 indicates some general findings for these Minnesota-site oscillations.

We have been operating the Payson laboratory in an IIED-conditioned state since spring, 2001, and have observed temporal T_A, T_W and pH-oscillations in the same frequency range as found for the Minnesota experiments. In addition, we have observed oscillations of (1) oxidation-reduction potential of water (ORP), (2) dissolved oxygen content of water (DO) and (3) dissolved cupric ion content of water (DCu^{+2}). Figures 5.4 and 5.5 show examples of this data. In IIED-conditioned spaces, pH oscillations are either in-phase or 180 degrees out-of-phase with T_A (and not T_W as it is for the U(1) state). In Figure 5.4a, the pH-oscillations are 180° out-of-phase with T_A (not T_W), have a maximum oscillation amplitude at the beginning of measurement and this amplitude fades with time for pure water. In Figure 5.4b, the dissolved oxygen (DO) oscillation amplitude (the largest we have ever measured, ~20%-25%) are in-phase with T_A and should not be oscillating at all since DO levels are, for the U(1) state, determined by the amount of oxygen in the air and T_W (which is fairly flat here). ORP relates to the thermodynamic activity of electrons in the aqueous solution just as pH does for protons. In Figure 5.4c, one finds that the ORP oscillations are frequency-locked to T_A, as are the DO oscillations. However, the dependence of oscillation amplitude on frequency is quite different for the two. Generally, DO oscillation amplitudes are weakly but inversely related to frequency while ORP oscillation amplitude is more directly related to frequency. Also, there appear to be frequency threshold values above which the DO oscillations do not occur and below which ORP oscillations do not occur.

Figure 5.5a illustrates simultaneous measurement of DO and ORP in an IIED-conditioned space over a 5-day period. A strong diurnal variation is exhibited by both measurements but, except for the strong correlations for their minima, the overall correlation is weak (subsidiary minima for DO but not ORP and the major maxima are

Table 5.1

Some Oscillation Characteristics for the M* Experiments

1. A variety of simultaneous, correlated oscillations in material properties occur only in strongly coupled conditioned spaces.

2. Oscillations have very well defined and easily characterized frequency, amplitude and waveform behavior.

3. Oscillations exhibit a well-defined triggering signature usually related to the sign of dT/dt.

4. Frequency modulation is commonly observed and, if present, well defined.

5. Oscillations are affected by:
  a. Water composition (both ionic and solid particulate components).
  b. Experimental-setup and position and composition of parts of the experimental apparatus in the near-field (strong-coupling) region.
  c. Temperature of immediate environment (near field) and sometimes direction of temperature change (sign of dT/dt).

6. Oscillations are unaffected by:
  a. The presence of objects and people just outside strong-coupling region (far field).
  b. Motion of objects or people just outside strong-coupling region (far field).
  c. Opening/closing of doors and windows outside strongly coupled region (far field, except as it affects 5c).
  d. Running of heaters, air conditioners or fans except as they affect 5c.
  e. Experiments operating in far field.

7. Summary findings for the site-conditioning experiment
  a. Oscillations in air temperature develop that are always larger than pH oscillations.
  b. pH oscillations tend to fade out during a measurement sequence whereas this never occurs with air temperature oscillations.
  c. Temperature and pH oscillation frequencies are always the same.
  d. Temperature and pH oscillations are in-phase for much of an individual wavetrain.
  e. Temperature and pH oscillations increase in amplitude the longer the exposure to operating IIEDs.
  f. Temperature and pH oscillations increase in continuity the longer the exposure to operating IIEDs.
  g. Air temperature oscillations correlate in frequency and are in-phase for periods of time across a distance of 25 feet in two rooms closed with respect to each other.

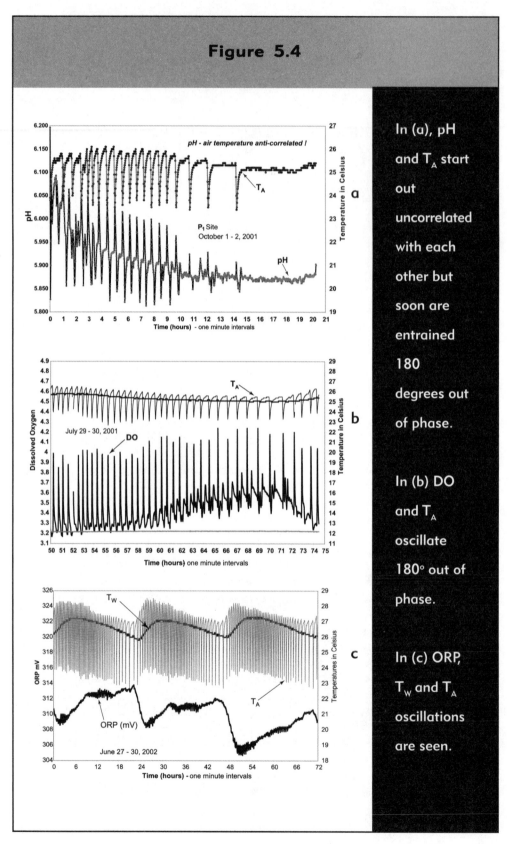

Figure 5.4

In (a), pH and T_A start out uncorrelated with each other but soon are entrained 180 degrees out of phase.

In (b) DO and T_A oscillate 180° out of phase.

In (c) ORP, T_W and T_A oscillations are seen.

Figure 5.5

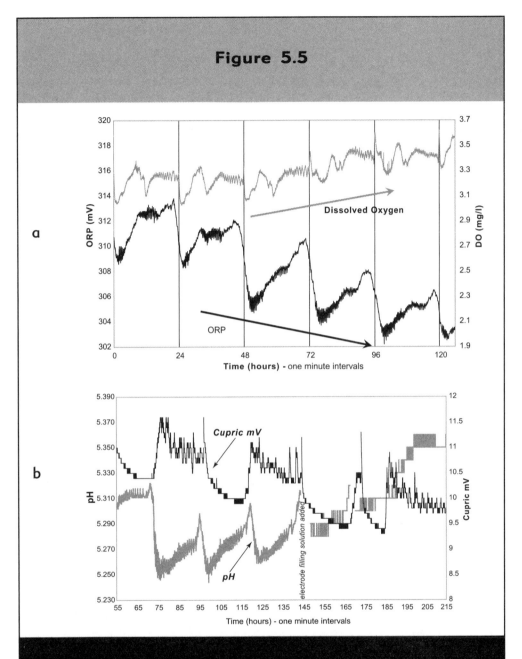

We have been operating the Payson laboratory in an IIED-conditioned state since spring, 2001, and have observed temporal T_A, T_W and pH-oscillations in the same frequency range as found for the Minnesota experiments. In addition, we have observed oscillations of (1) oxidation-reduction potential of water (ORP), (2) dissolved oxygen content of water (DO) and (3) dissolved cupric ion content of water (DCu^{+2}) with some entrainment between all of these oscillations.

poorly correlated). Overall, this indicates that both the diurnal and short-period oscillations are being driven by some factor other than temperature, although temperature modulates the variation to some degree. Since these two measurements should be directly related thermodynamically for the U(1) state, variations in the IIED-conditioned space patterns for the two measurements (that look to be essentially independent of each other) suggest that some quite different mechanism is controlling them.

In Figure 5.5b, pH and cupric ion oscillation data are provided. In a U(1) EM gauge symmetry space, one does not expect the cupric ion concentration to change significantly. However, in an IIED-conditioned space, the cupric ion electrode measurements show a drift to lower voltages at long time for both the diurnal and short-period oscillations. This suggests (1) the long-term tendency for dilute solutions of the Cu^{+2} ion to be reduced to the Cu^{+1} state, (2) the formation of the cupric hydroxide species or (3) the presence of an electrode drift problem.

The property oscillations exhibited in Figures 5.4 and 5.5 are all from simple physical chemistry measurements and, by some would be considered somewhat prosaic. However, consider the oscillation examples shown in Figures 5.6 to 5.8. In Figure 5.6a, the measurement of mass in an IIED-conditioned space was an early goal of our research. The electronic balance we used[3] has a maximum resolution of 10 microgram and this figure involves use of only the balance pan whose mass was first set to zero. One notes that diurnal oscillations in mass can range from ~3,000 to ~25,000 micrograms with superposed short period oscillations of ~100 micrograms. In Figure 5.6b, mass oscillations are compared with radiation (α, β, γ) monitor reading oscillations. In the middle of the time interval, the laboratory windows were opened allowing the room temperature diurnal oscillation amplitude to increase from ~4°C (closed) to ~8°C (open). This had only a slight lowering effect on the radiation counts (out of doors and well-removed from the laboratory the count level was ~30 μR/hr on average) but a huge effect on the measured mass oscillation amplitude (from ~5 mg to ~45 mg). This is very anomalous behavior.

In Figure 5.7a, one sees T_A-oscillatory behavior when one has a 12 hour morning period with the laboratory windows open (lowers T_A because it is winter) followed by a 12 hour period with the laboratory windows closed (higher T_A). One also sees periodic, semi-diurnal, radiation monitor behavior with the radiation count readings dropping by ~25% when the average temperature drops by only ~6°C. Since such devices are designed to

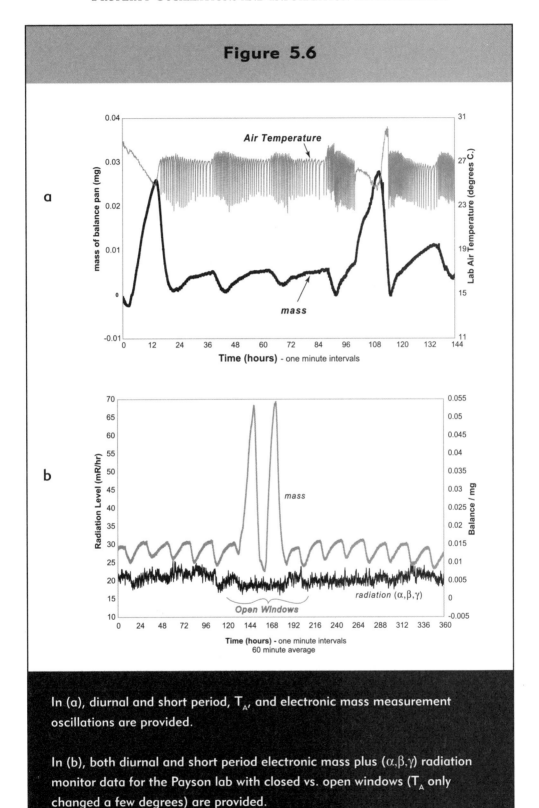

Figure 5.6

In (a), diurnal and short period, T_A, and electronic mass measurement oscillations are provided.

In (b), both diurnal and short period electronic mass plus (α,β,γ) radiation monitor data for the Payson lab with closed vs. open windows (T_A only changed a few degrees) are provided.

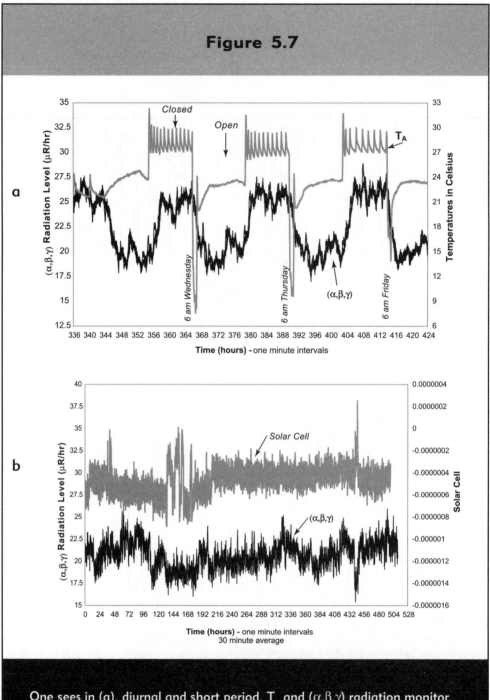

Figure 5.7

One sees in (a), diurnal and short period, T_A and (α,β,γ) radiation monitor oscillations as influenced by opening or closing the Payson lab windows.

One sees in (b), a comparison of oscillations between a solar cell monitor and an (α,β,γ) monitor (with **30** minute averaging) all at site P_1.

function in all temperature ranges without significant changes in counting rate, this is very anomalous behavior that would not have occurred in a U(1) gauge space. In Figure 5.7b, simultaneous measurements of solar cell[4] voltage oscillations and radiation monitor[5] oscillations inside the Payson laboratory are presented. In Figures 5.8a and 5.8b, respectively, simultaneous measurement of T_A (room air conditioning off in the central region and *on* in the two outer regions), solar cell[4] voltage oscillations (5.8a) and standard electrochemical cell[6] voltage oscillations (5.8b) are given. The important point for the reader to notice from Figures 5.6 to 5.8 is that all of these measurement systems are free from any connection with the wall electrical power system of the laboratory. They are either a passive response system or they have internal batteries powering them and regulating them.

A closer look at air temperature, T_A(t), oscillations

During the Minnesota experimental period (1997-2000), a wide variety of transient T_A oscillations were observed riding on the envelope of the diurnal waveform. Four variants of the basic T_A waveform are illustrated in Figure 5.9, with a reflection (in a vertical plane) mirror image of the upper right variant also being regularly seen. For this mirror image variant, Figure 5.10 shows a complete, transient wave train wherein the oscillation period increases almost exponentially as the oscillation cycle number in this wave train increases. Converting this cycle period information to frequency per cycle information shows an extremely good fit (99.8% to a parabolic variation with cycle number), from 40 cycles per day for cycle number one to 4 cycles per day for cycle number nine. Extrapolating this parabolic curve would have required the tenth oscillation in this wave train to have a negative frequency and, since this is without meaning, a new and discontinuous variation of T_A(t) must occur (which can be seen on the far right of Figure 5.10).

It is useful to compare these T_A results with results obtained from chemical reaction-driven oscillation studies.[1] Concentration oscillations have been observed by chemical engineers for decades when their complex chemical solutions are strongly departed from thermodynamic equilibrium (means a large driving force for change and multiple path processes for chemical reaction come into play).

The simplest theoretical model used to explain this chemical oscillation phenomenon is one whereby a reactant chemical is converted to a product chemical via

Figure 5.8

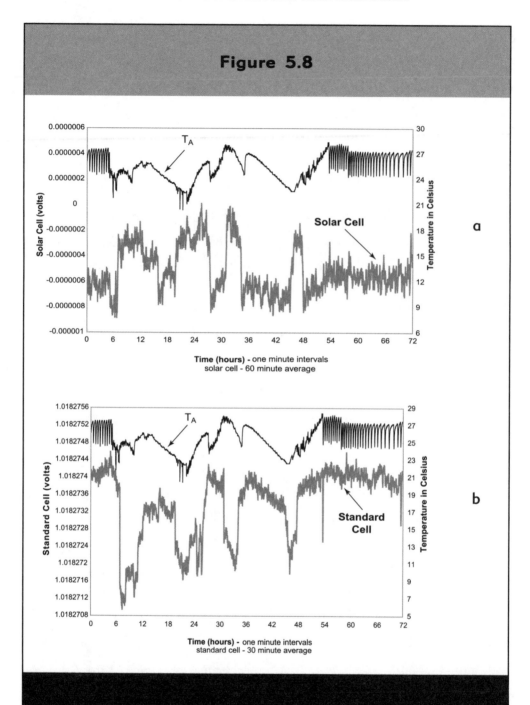

For site P_2, (a) gives an oscillation comparison between air temperature, T_A, and a solar cell monitor (with 60 minute averaging) while (b) gives T_A and a standard, electrochemical cell comparison (with 30 minute averaging for the cell).

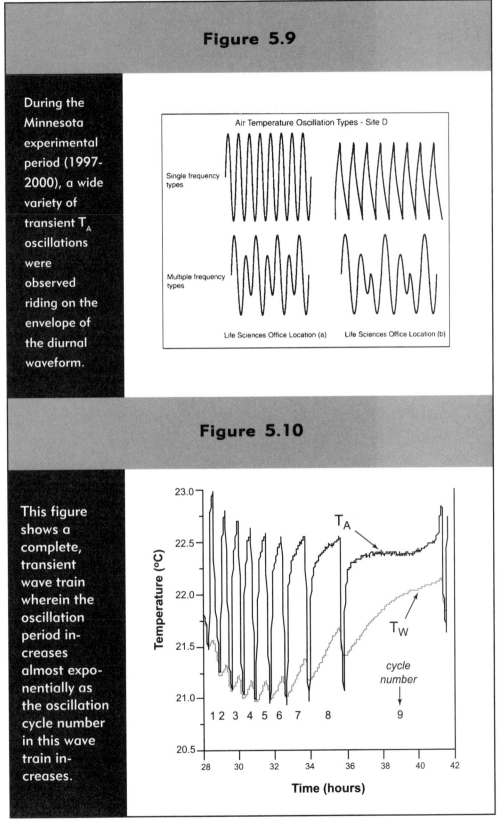

Figure 5.9

During the Minnesota experimental period (1997-2000), a wide variety of transient T_A oscillations were observed riding on the envelope of the diurnal waveform.

Air Temperature Oscillation Types - Site D

Single frequency types

Multiple frequency types

Life Sciences Office Location (a)   Life Sciences Office Location (b)

Figure 5.10

This figure shows a complete, transient wave train wherein the oscillation period increases almost exponentially as the oscillation cycle number in this wave train increases.

two intermediate chemical species A and B as illustrated at the top of Figure 5.11. The key feature in this series of reactions that leads to oscillations is the step wherein A is converted to B. The double arrow in this equation means that there are *two* process paths for producing B from A: (1) direct conversion of A to B and (2) another simultaneous reaction ultimately converting A to B but which involves feedback from an intermediate process. This means that there are four simultaneous reactions involved, one of which is a feedback reaction: (1) reactant to A, (2 & 3) A to B via *two* paths and (4) B to product. Figure 5.11 shows the computed oscillations in the concentrations of A for a selected set of chemical rate constants designed to give a fair match to the wavetrain for T_A in Figure 5.10. It is also interesting to note that a frequency to cycle number plot of the Figure 5.11 data yields a good parabolic relationship (99.82% fit).

In *closed* thermodynamic systems of this sort (the reactant concentration decays naturally with time as product is created) that involves an approach to equilibrium, the oscillation frequency *always* declines with cycle number, usually along with the amplitude, until the end of the wavetrain. In chemical systems where the reactant concentration can be held constant at its initial level (by feeding fresh reactant chemical into the system at a controlled rate), we have what is called an *open* thermodynamic system. In this case, the oscillation frequency and amplitude remain constant as time progresses (because the thermodynamic driving force remains constant with time).

In conventional *open system* chemical oscillation experimental data, one finds that, when the oscillating chemical reactions are driven very fast, one common observational feature is the appearance of oscillation period-doubling (see Figure 5.12). This is remarkably similar to such oscillation behavior demonstrated for $T_A(t)$ in Figure 5.9.

The main things to be learned about this chemical oscillation example are (1) that four, simultaneous, first order, differential equations is the *minimum* number needed for oscillations to appear and (2) the third step above is the critical one, and is called the "autocatalytic" step, because the more of B that is produced the faster does that particular step proceed (it is essentially a nonlinear contribution). This nonlinear aspect is a property of all systems involving feedback.

In our homes, thermostats are one of the most common pieces of technology that utilize feedback for the control of temperature. We set the desired temperature state, T_A', mechanically, a sensor measures the actual state, T_A, the difference between these two,

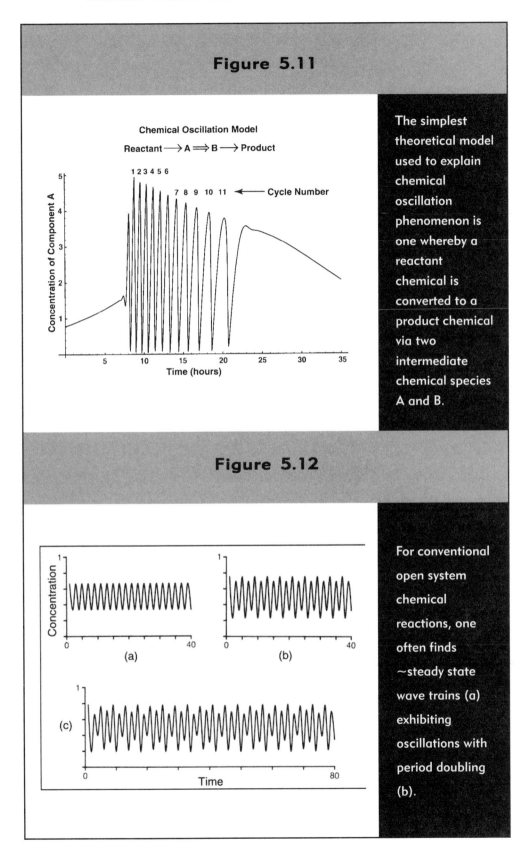

Figure 5.11

Chemical Oscillation Model

Reactant ⟶ A ⟹ B ⟶ Product

1 2 3 4 5 6

7 8 9 10 11 ⟵ Cycle Number

Concentration of Component A

Time (hours)

The simplest theoretical model used to explain chemical oscillation phenomenon is one whereby a reactant chemical is converted to a product chemical via two intermediate chemical species A and B.

Figure 5.12

Concentration

(a)

(b)

(c)

Time

For conventional open system chemical reactions, one often finds ~steady state wave trains (a) exhibiting oscillations with period doubling (b).

$T_A' - T_A$, is the error signal and this error signal is continuously fed into a servomechanism (to turn a knob) to adjust the rate of heating or cooling input to the room. This eventually causes the error signal, $T_A' - T_A$, to shrink to zero. Figure 5.13a schematically illustrates this process.

A more sophisticated application of feedback occurs in a missile defense system as illustrated in Figure 5.13b. Let us suppose that a missile, M, is tracking down another missile or enemy aircraft, E. If, at time t_1, E turns through some angle, $\Psi(t)$, then M must also turn through this angle if it is to catch up with E and destroy it. Such turning control must be accomplished automatically. Here, the sensor is usually a radar beam which will indicate the direction that must be taken by M to overtake and intercept E. If we denote $\theta(t)$ as the actual angular change delivered by the internal servomechanism to M because things are happening so fast, we will have a discrepancy or error signal, $\theta(t) - \Psi(t)$, fed back to the servomechanism so that a compensating turning effect will be created in M. If the error is large, this compensating effect must be large. If the error is small, the compensation need only be small. Without feedback, there is almost no possibility for M to intersect the course of E and destroy it.

A closer look at mass oscillations

To start, it should be pointed out that the experimental data presented in Figure 5.6a was recorded using a one-minute sampling interval over a period of many days and a weighing event for a particular weight on the scale pan usually occurs in less than one minute. The mass variation with temperature in Figure 5.6a was the first indication to us of anomalies present in mass determination as a result of IIED-conditioning of the laboratory space. The possibility should have occurred to us but it didn't (and the electronic mass-balance sat unused in the lab space for ~2 years before we began our initial study). In Figure 5.6a, the rapid variation in temperature is the result of the laboratory air conditioning (A/C) system dropping $T_A(t)$ rapidly (at least on the time-scale of this figure). When this occurred, there was always a small perturbation in the measured mass. The more significant effect was the difference in mass variation between the A/C system being in the *on* state vs. in the *off* state (and it must always be remembered that, if this had

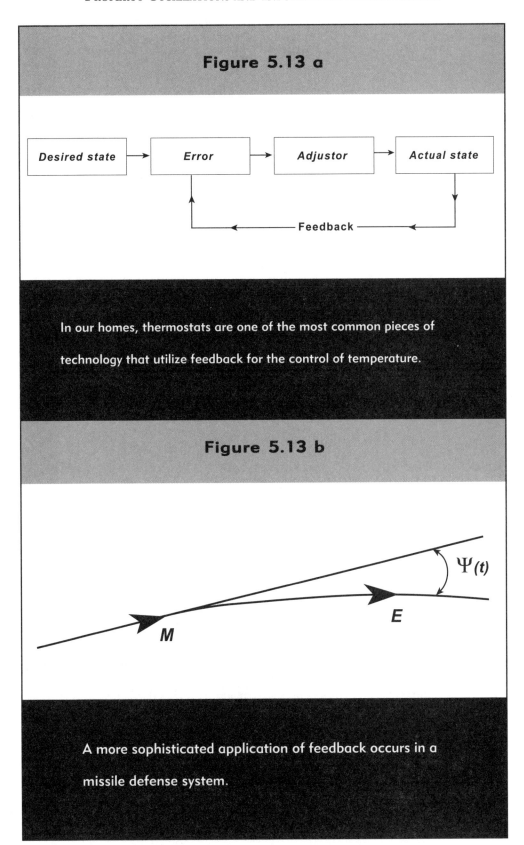

Figure 5.13 a

In our homes, thermostats are one of the most common pieces of technology that utilize feedback for the control of temperature.

Figure 5.13 b

A more sophisticated application of feedback occurs in a missile defense system.

been a U(1) gauge state space, even with the same temperature variations there would have been negligible mass variations registered by this electronic balance).

Since in an IIED-conditioned space, measured mass varies strongly with measured room temperature, diurnal mass variations are directly correlated with diurnal temperature variations. This is particularly evident in Figure 5.14a where the mass of the balance pan is observed to vary by as much as 50 mg. (5,000 times larger than the normal instrument sensitivity). This is significant since the mass of a 20 mg calibrated weight was next to be evaluated.

The data shown in Figure 5.14b reveals how the measured mass of a calibrated 20 mg weight varies with time. From simultaneously recorded pH-data, the Nernst parameter, N, is also provided (see Chapter 4). The calculated correlation coefficient between the two data sets is about 90%. As indicated in Chapter 4, N is used in the calculation for the departure of thermodynamic free energy per unit volume of the IIED-conditioned space from that for a U(1) gauge space. As can be seen from Figure 5.14b, the measured mass variation must be related to this same departure. One should also note in Figure 5.6a, for the 22-90 hour time period, the similarity in mass variation to that shown in Figure 5.14b; evidently, the A/C system maintaining a more even average T_A is partly responsible for this behavior. This mass-behavior pattern changes radically when the A/C is turned off (see Figures 5.6a and 5.14a).

The detailed driving mechanism for measuring mass of the scale pan may be somewhat seen in Figure 5.14c for the Payson laboratory with the A/C on. The oscillating temperature waveforms are highly correlated with the mass oscillations and, one finds that the sharp drop in mass measurement always begins as the slope of the temperature change rolls over near the top of a T_A wave envelope. Likewise, the mass waveform's sharp rise mostly occurs during the sharp fall in T_A for each wave cycle. There is a somewhat inverse relationship between the two. For a 20 mg mass on the scale pan and the A/C on throughout, various average temperatures were held for extended periods in order to see how the mass measurement responded to the constant average temperatures. This data comparison is shown in Figure 5.15a with a plot of measured mass vs. measured average temperature being provided in Figure 5.15b.

From Figure 5.15b, one sees that $\overline{T}_A \approx 23.8°C$ yields the true weight of 20 mg for the mass on the scale pan. In the temperature range ~22.5°C to ~28°C, this measured

Figure 5.14

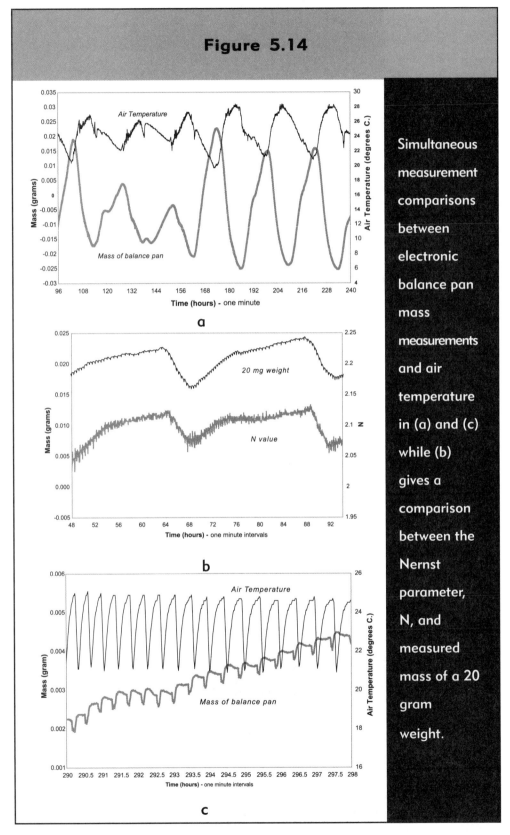

a

b

c

Simultaneous measurement comparisons between electronic balance pan mass measurements and air temperature in (a) and (c) while (b) gives a comparison between the Nernst parameter, N, and measured mass of a 20 gram weight.

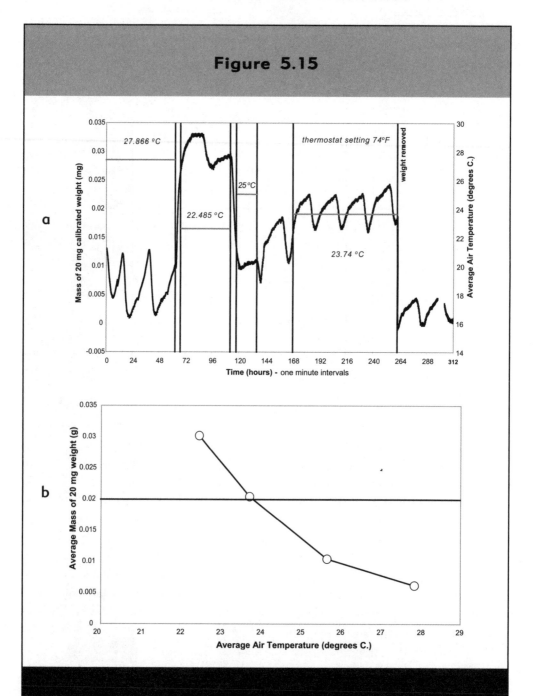

Figure 5.15

In an IIED-conditioned space measured mass varies strongly with measured room temperature. Diurnal mass variations are directly correlated with diurnal temperature variations.

mass falls nonlinearly from about 30 mg to about 6 mg, respectively, for a total reduction of ~24 mg. Once again, none of this variation would have occurred if the space had been at the U(1) level; thus, from the theoretical discussion of Chapter 3, where any experimental measurement consists of a D-space part plus an R-space part, 20 mg is the D-space part while the 24 mg is the deltron coupling- coefficient, γ, times the R-space part. It is the R-space part that appears to be strongly D-space temperature sensitive.

In addition to the foregoing, Figure 5.6b shows an anomalously large mass variation when the laboratory space windows were opened. The magnitude of this effect goes well beyond a D-space temperature change effect. Rather, it is thought to be an R-space effect associated with a significant change in D-space geometry for the laboratory (open windows vs. closed windows).

The caveat that needs to be added to the discussion of measured mass oscillations is that the inner workings of the electronic measurement system involves balancing the downward gravitational force of the mass with an upward magnetic force that is exquisitely sensitive. In an IIED-conditioned space, the effect leading to balance pan oscillations might have been really caused by oscillations in the magnetic force system in the instrument rather than physical mass oscillations as implied in the earlier discussion.

Why property oscillations occur in IIED-conditioned spaces

In an earlier section, we showed that a wide variety of chemical reactions can lead to oscillatory behavior in the populations of different chemical species with time-dependent results that were remarkably similar to those found for air temperature, $T_A(t)$ oscillations during our Minnesota (M*) experiments. Thus, let us use air temperature as the vehicle to explore why this vast array of different property measurements carried out in IIED-conditioned spaces all exhibit, at one time or another, similar types of oscillatory behavior.

Perhaps the key factor is that, in an IIED-conditioned space, the deltron coupling-coefficient, γ, between D-space substance and R-space substance can be of appreciable magnitude $\left(0.01 \lesssim \gamma \lesssim 1.0\right)$ so that the conservation laws governing the flow of heat as well as of different chemical species must now be expanded beyond their conventional form for the U(1) EM gauge symmetry state ($\gamma \sim 0$). Thus, these laws and their governing equations now require the mathematical solution to *two*, simultaneous, *second order*, partial differential equations, one for D-space and one for R-space. Further, because γ is greater than zero, an exchange between these two subspaces of appreciable magnitude can occur. This exchange is called feedback and this is, or course, the essential ingredient needed for time-dependent oscillations to appear in the data streams of our D-space measuring instruments. In word-form, the two basic equations for heat conservation that must be simultaneously solved are

Net in-flow of D-space heat content to any unit cube of D-space	+	Created heat content rate within this cube via transfer from R-space	=	Time-rate of heat content change in this D-space cube

and (5.1)

net in-flow of R-space heat content to any unit cube of R-space	+	annihilated heat content within this cube via transfer to D-space	=	temporal frequency rate of heat content change in this R-space cube

Further, the created heat content rate in a typical D-space cube via transfer from R-space is proportional to the difference between the D-space equilibrium temperature, T_D^{Eq}, and its actual temperature, T_D^A. We will call this proportionality constant, β_D. Likewise, the heat content loss rate from the typical R-space cube to D-space is proportional to the difference between the actual R-space temperature, T_R^A, of the cube and its R-space equilibrium temperature, T_R^{Eq}. We will call this proportionality constant β_R. For overall conservation of heat, the total created heat content in D-space must equal the total annihilated heat content from R-space.

In addition to the foregoing, T_C^{Eq} and T_R^{Eq} are related to T_R^A and T_D^A, respectively, via the deltron-empowered Fourier transform pair relationships.[1,2] Thus, with some effort, this set of equations appears to be mathematically solvable. Figure 5.16 is an attempt to pictorially represent this D-space plus R-space temperature equilibrium with heat content transfer between the two subspaces.

Expanding this mathematical type of picture to other types of property oscillations requires the introduction of new and detailed creation/annihilation considerations in the two subspaces. This, of course, is very important for the mass oscillation picture. If we can get to a place of mathematically solving the set of equations for mass and showing

Figure 5.16

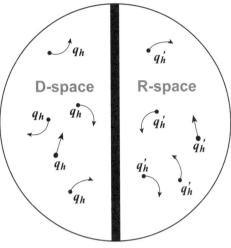

(a) U(1) EM gauge symmetry state

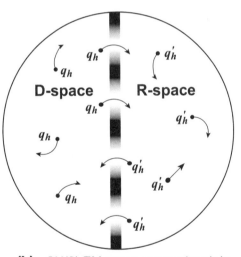

(b) SU(2) EM gauge symmetry state

Representing D-space plus R-space temperature equilibrium with no heat exchange for (a) but with heat content transfer between the two subspaces for (b).

what kinds of duplex material properties lead to oscillations, one might then be able to show that a unique range of conditions exists wherein stable duplex space solutions are obtained whereby the total mass is appreciably less than the D-space mass. This would be of profound significance for science but even moreso for transportation technologies of all types.

Information Entanglement

In Chapter 2 a number of experimental examples were given to demonstrate that the IIED-space conditioning process could not only be transferred from the IIED to the space in which it rests and is turned on but also to all other spaces in the experimental system, even over distances of ~6,000 miles (to date). We learned from observation 4 in Table 1.2 of Chapter 1 that just placing an IIED and a UED ~100 meters apart and, in the electrically switched-off state, allowed the transfer of the imprinted intention to the UED so that our "control" device was lost to us. From this we learned that an energy type other than electromagnetism (EM) was the carrier wave for the essential information contained in the imprint statement.

Our present-day technologies of radio and television allow us to transfer sound information and image plus sound information, respectively, using EM carrier waves. The transmitting stations have antennas for projecting this information over a large area, shaped somewhat like an ellipse at ground level, with the EM power level decreasing with distance from the transmitter. If no one has their radio or TV sets turned on and tuned to the particular station frequency, the audio and video information is not absorbed from the beam and the EM information just dissipates via natural processes. Using this picture as a type of guide to gain understanding of how the IIED-information imprint might be transferred to a particular site at a well-defined D-space location, we at least need to consider the following: the site must have present in its space (1) suitable receptors for receiving the carrier wave, (2) suitable extractors of the imprint information from the carrier, (3) suitable converters of this information so as to (a) lift the EM inner symmetry state of that space and (b) tune that space to specifically manifest the details of the intention imprint statement and (4) not do the same at neighboring D-space sites. The fact that, although we are consciously aware of *most* of the remote site locations in our experimental system but not for all of them (the U.K. site specifics and the Italy site specifics were not known to us in the early days of the European investigators involvement), suggests that we may have some unspecified collaborators, involved in this overall experiment from higher dimensional realms who did know these specific site locations and, with advanced R-space technologies at their disposal, arranged for the beams to activate these additional sites. At this stage of our understanding, this is a very speculative postulate on our part but we are unable to answer Item 4 above using any other rationale.

Before pursuing these difficult macroscopic information entanglement conjectures, let us say something about quantum entanglement, a very different phenomenon. In quantum information science, groups of two or more quantum objects can have energetic states that are entangled and these states can have properties unlike anything in classical physics. In classical information science, a familiar example is a string of bits, encoded via real physical objects like the spin of an atomic nucleus or the polarization of a photon of light, but abstractly by 0s (down state) and 1s (up state). A qubit, the quantum version of a bit, has many more possible states which entail both of these primary states but to varying degrees.[7] In the theoretical model of Chapter 3 that we use to account for macroscopic, room temperature, information entanglement, quantum considerations are not necessary.

Entanglement, as explained by Aczel,[8] is an application of the superposition principle to a system comprised of two or more subsystems. In his case, he lets each of the subsystems be a single particle and asks what it means to say that the two particles are entangled. He postulates that particle 1, has equal probability of being in states A or C, which have different physical locations, while particle 2 has equal probability of being in states B or D which have two additional different locations. When the overall system is in the product state, AB, particle 1 is known to be in state A while particle 2 is known to be in state B. Similarly, the product state, CD, has particles 1 and 2 in states C and D, respectively.

Since the superposition principle allows the system to also be in a combination of product states, the state AB + CD is also an allowed state and, for the entire system, this is called an "entangled state". This entangled state says that there are now possibilities concerning particles 1 and 2 that are strongly correlated. Thus, if experimental measurement finds particle 1 in state A, then particle 2 *must* be in state B and cannot be in state C or D.

This means that, when particles 1 and 2 are entangled, there is no way to characterize either one of them by itself, as if it were isolated from the other. In the superposition state they are strongly linked and do not have independence of action.

Erwin Schrödinger, Nobel prize winner for his formulation of the wave function equation for QM, was the first to predict the existence of entanglement for fundamental particles and photons, which Einstein labeled "spooky action at a distance". In 2003, Ghosh and his collaborators[9] at the University of Chicago analyzed ten year old experimental data on the very low temperature magnetic susceptibility and heat capacity of a magnetic salt containing holmium atoms and compared them to QM theory. There were significant discrepancies when one neglects QM entanglement but satisfactory agreement when entanglement is included. Such an effect was predicted by Vedral two years earlier.[10] This theory and experimental confirmation indicates that QM entanglement can occur on the more macroscopic scale of ~1 cubic centimeter for materials at very low temperature (less than 1 degree Kelvin) and perhaps even at room temperature if the theoretical idea of Reznik[11] is found to be true. He proposed that all of empty space, the physical vacuum, is filled with pairs of entangled particles. Brukner, Vedral and two others showed that time can become entangled too[12] and this puts space and time on an equal footing in QM, an absolute "no-no" for the present-day formulation of QM. We are a long way from a final answer but one thing is clear, information entanglement is a very important process that will be center stage in any major reformulation of QM.

Returning now to our duplex space model discussed in Chapter 3, the particles are in D-space while the waves are in R-space and some deltron coupling-coefficient, γ, links the actions of the particles and waves (the De Broglie particle/pilot wave concept) so any experimental measurement of a particular quality, Q, is comprised of two parts, $Q_D + Q_R$, with one part coming from each subspace. Because Q_R comes from the wave domain, its magnitude is given by the integral (summation) of the wave amplitude squared, $R^2(k)$, over the entire domain of k. The next important point to recognize is that, if one's overall experimental system contains just two subsystem parts (for example, an IIED-conditioned laboratory space and a "control" laboratory space located several to many miles away), one must first superpose the wave amplitude spectrum, $R_I(k)$, for the one space with the wave amplitude spectrum, $R_C(k)$, for the other space before mathematically squaring their resultant and integrating over the entire k-domain. This boils down to integrating the quantity $[R_I^2(k) + R_C^2(k) + 2R_I R_C \cos(\theta_I - \theta_C)]$ over the entire wave domain. Here, θ_I and θ_C are the phase angles (functions of k) for the I and C amplitude spectra respectively and cos is the mathematical cosine function. Now, R_I^2 and R_C^2 are what one would have if I and C are completely isolated from each other (totally unconnected); however, because they are always connected to some degree via γ, the additional term, $2R_I R_C \cos(\theta_I - \theta_C)$, always gives us information entanglement between separated parts of the overall system.

Types of information entanglement observations to date

Local Instruments: One clear observation of local information entanglement is illustrated in Figure 5.6b wherein the electronic balance scale pan weight increases anomalously to very large values when the windows of the Payson laboratory were opened. This was not a D-space temperature effect on the R-space mass measurement (which also exists but is substantially smaller). Rather, open windows, rather than closed windows in the laboratory appears to appreciably affect the R-space geometry of the room, especially as it relates to mass measurements. To check this point, it would be useful for someone to redo the experiment where the room air conditioning can be automatically adjusted so that the room value of T_A stays close to constant when the windows are opened or closed. Figure 5.17 illustrates that both pH and N-values at three different stations, P_3, P_4 and P_8, in the Payson laboratory do not appear to change significantly with temperature, T_A, but do change when all the laboratory windows are closed (see Figure 5.17a).

An excellent example of information entanglement between different Payson laboratory measurement stations is shown in Figure 5.18. At stations P_1, P_3 and P_4, 0.01 molar borax solutions were being studied while, at stations P_7 and P_8, pure water was being studied. In Figure 5.18a, N-values for sites P_7 and P_8 were determined continuously from pH, etc., measurements. In early June, the P_1, P_3 and P_4 stations were changed from a borax solution to purified water. Note the almost abrupt change in N-value slope at station P_7 but not as abrupt a change for the P_8 station. In Figure 5.18b, $\Delta\Psi_H$+-values are provided based on this N-value data and, here, we note that both slopes change abruptly at this June 9 date. Later (August 26), the pH-electrode at site P_1 was recalibrated and this is reflected in an N-value change at site P_7 (Figure 5.18a) but not at site P_8 nor in a $\Delta\Psi_H$+slope change at either of the P_7 or P_8 sites. On September 20 a pH-electrode change

Figure 5.17

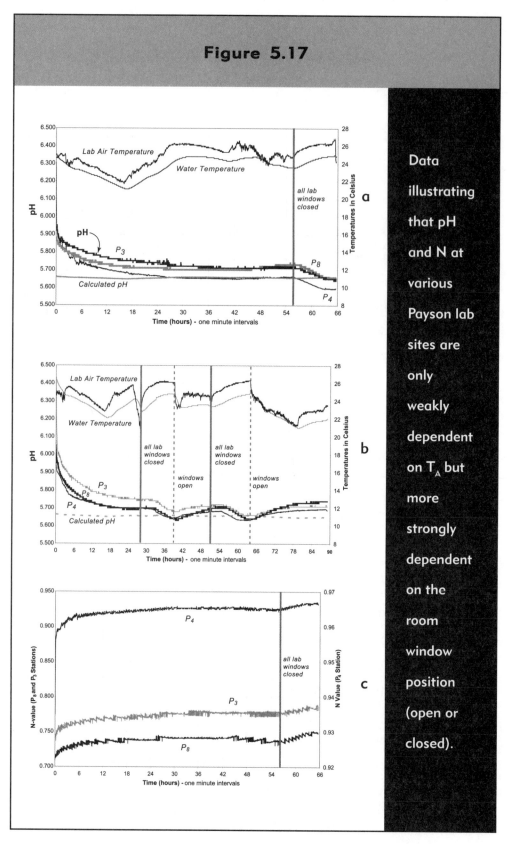

Data illustrating that pH and N at various Payson lab sites are only weakly dependent on T_A but more strongly dependent on the room window position (open or closed).

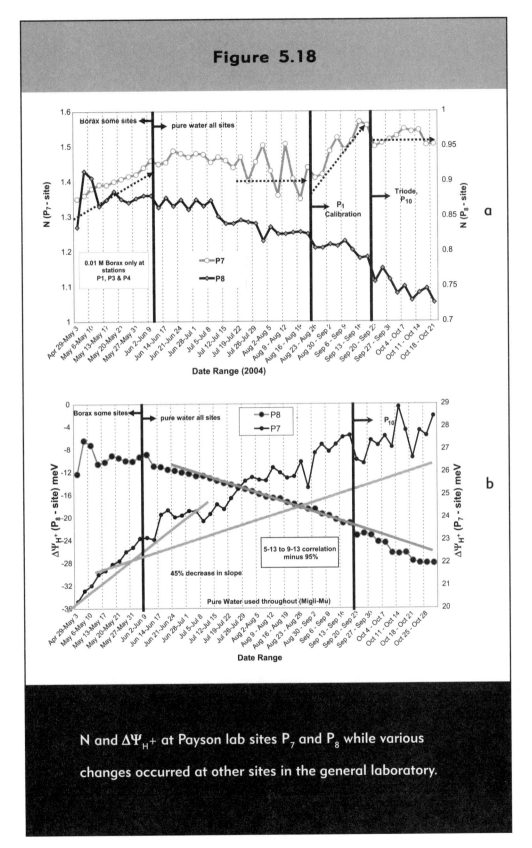

Figure 5.18

N and $\Delta\Psi_{H^+}$ at Payson lab sites P_7 and P_8 while various changes occurred at other sites in the general laboratory.

(Triode) occurred at site P_{10} and immediate responses developed at sites P_7 and P_8. All of these events are examples of information entanglement between different measurement stations in the Payson laboratory.

In Figures 5.19, significant correlations are illustrated between measurements at two sites in each case while various changes were measured at different or the same sites. Once again, these changes in degree of correlation associated with the various intervention events would not have occurred unless information entanglement existed between the sites.

Non-local instruments: The first sign of non-local information entanglement in our research occurred with Observation 4 in Table 1.2 of Chapter 1, when we placed an IIED and a UED ~100 meters apart in the electrically *off* state. Within ~3-5 days, the information intention was transferred from this IIED to this UED.

The second sign of non-local information entanglement occurred during the Minnesota (M*) experiments via Observation 9 in Table 1.2 of Chapter 1. Here the entanglement was between a pH-measurement system with an adjacent pH-changing IIED in an unconditioned space and non-IIED pH-measurement stations ~150 to 900 meters away. One of these distant sites was a highly "conditioned" space while the other was an unconditioned space. When pH-oscillations were induced at the IIED-site, highly correlated pH-oscillations occurred at the distant "conditioned" site but no correlated pH changes occurred at the distant unconditioned site.

The third sign of non-local information entanglement occurred in 2001 during an experiment by Dr. C. Norman Shealy and WAT in Springfield, Missouri.[13] Here, we were looking at the actual effect of a supposed commercial "EM de-stressor" device called the QLink[14] on the outcomes of intentional EM stressing of human subjects. Both a true QLink and a dummy QLink were used in a double-blind fashion. The experimental outcomes of the test were (1) that the true QLink had some statistically significant benefit as an EM de-stressor and (2) that the dummy QLink also had a smaller but still statistically significant effect as a de-stressor. One of us (WAT) interpreted this odd result as a sign of information entanglement between the unshielded real and dummy QLinks in the experiments (we didn't know, then, to look out for such a possibility).

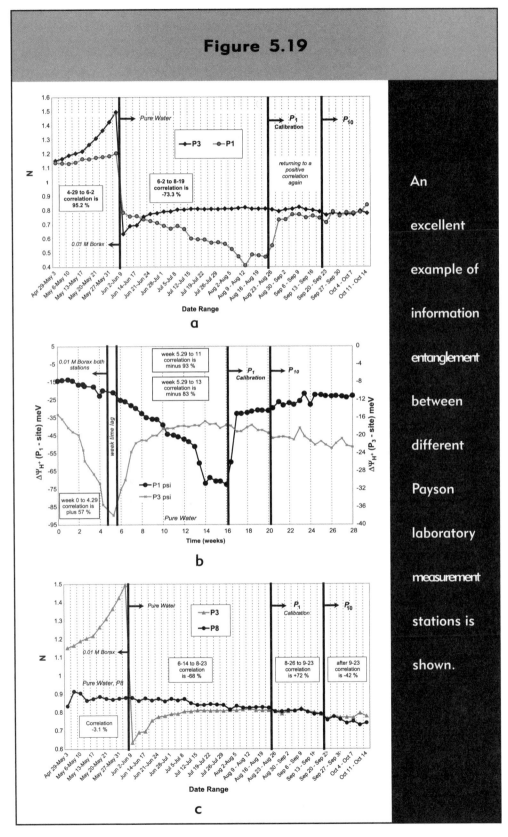

An excellent example of information entanglement between different Payson laboratory measurement stations is shown.

The fourth sign, and our "wake-up" sign regarding serious information entanglement, occurred during the early stages of our replicability at remote-sites experiment.[15] This is Observation 3 in Table 2.3 of Chapter 2. Here, although IIED-conditioning of a site in Missouri (M) and another in Kansas (K) exhibited ΔpH increases of $+1.0$ pH units, consistent with the intention statement for these two devices, at control sites (no IIED ever present) $\sim$2-20 miles away, ΔpH increases of $\sim$1.0 pH units also developed.

The fifth sign, and the first real test of the macroscopic room temperature information entanglement concept, was Observation 4 in Table 2.3 of Chapter 2. The Bethesda (B_1) and Baltimore (B_2) sites came on line initially as control sites for the (P), (M) and (K) sites and ΔpH increases of $\sim$0.8 pH units (they were both above ground at the third floor level) developed within $\sim$one month.[16] So now the basic information entanglement physics had a range of at least $\sim$1,500 miles.

The sixth sign of long range, macroscopic, room temperature information entanglement occurred with the coming on-line of the U.K. and Italy sites (Observations 4 of Table 2.3 in Chapter 2).[17] The U.K.-site was at ground level and a ΔpH of 1.0 pH units developed in three weeks. The Italy site was in the basement of a home and $\Delta pH = 1.7$ pH units developed in one week. Now the basic information entanglement process had an effective range of at least 6,000 miles.

The seventh sign of long range, macroscopic, room temperature information entanglement occurred at the M* location in early June, 2004, at the old "conditioned" space site of the second sign above. We left that site in 2000 and it was converted to a storage room for various records associated with that overall site. In the between time, we had discovered how to measure $\Delta\Psi_H$+for any site. In June, 2004, we were allowed to go back to that site and measure the present $\Delta\Psi_H$+-value for that site. Our expectations were that the site-"conditioning" state would have decayed over the ensuing four years (a typical U(1) gauge state perpective). Imagine our surprise to find that the site not only still exhibited conditioning but that the site now showed $\Delta\Psi_H$+$\sim$80 millielectron volts above the U(1) EM gauge symmetry state. This is an average hydrated H^+ ion thermal energy value of 4.5 kT (or an effective U(1) gauge state value for a temperature of $\sim$1,000 degrees centigrade).

The final input on our long-range, macroscopic sized, room temperature information entanglement process is a theoretical one.[18] There,[18] we develop a theoretical model using the perspective of Chapter 3 to analyze some of the quantitative data from Reference 1. In doing this, we found it absolutely necessary to convert time into a fourth space coordinate, X_4, in order to be able to solve the relevant equations. We showed that, for the cyclic water change at a remote site described in Chapter 2, these water change/ electrode recalibration events in time can be most simply approximated as periodic impulse events along the X_4 coordinate as illustrated in Figure 5.20. The corresponding R-space impulses decay, via the phantom effect process discussed in Chapter 6 of Reference 1, and grow via information entanglement from other impulses in the array. This implies interaction both with impulses at larger X_4 locations as well as at smaller X_4 locations which, in turn, means interactions both forward as well as backwards in time!

Human-local instruments entanglement: The concept of intentional psychokinesis and poltergeist phenomena[19] are definite examples of human biofield entanglement (interaction) with physical objects. In Chapter 2 (see Figures 2.17), we provided experimental data showing that human subtle energy field releases associated with a healing session, utilizing advanced kinesiological techniques, were simultaneously detected at five different measurement stations in the Payson laboratory. This occurred even though these instruments were ~10 - 15 feet away from the human with no kind of physical connection between the instruments and the human.

Human-non-local instruments entanglement: There is abundant experimental evidence available[20] to show that Qigong masters can influence experimental equipment in a particular laboratory (specific space) at a particular time from hundreds to thousands of miles away. One illustration should be sufficient to demonstrate that point. On December 27, 1986, the Qigong Master, Yan Xin, emitted Qi from his residence, 7 km away from a Raman spectroscopy laboratory where two tap water samples had been prepared and set up for a remote Qi experiment.[20] After the end of the Qi emission, the samples were sent to the laser Raman spectrometer for analysis. The results are shown in Figure 5.21. There are normally two peaks in the Raman spectrum of water; one peak is at 3430 cm^{-1} corresponding to the stretching vibration of OH while the other peak (weak) is at 1635 cm^{-1} corresponding to the bending vibration of HOH (see Fig. 5.21a). However, after the Qi projection, there was a single large peak in the range of ~1,000 cm^{-1} to ~3,000 cm^{-1}

Figure 5.20

The corresponding R-space impulses decay, via the phantom effect process, and growth via information entanglement from other impulses in the array. This implies interaction both with impulses at larger X_4 locations as well as at smaller X_4 locations which, in turn, means interactions both forward as well as backwards in time!

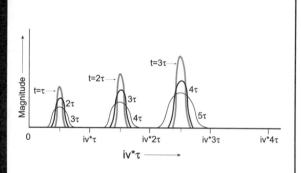

Figure 5.21

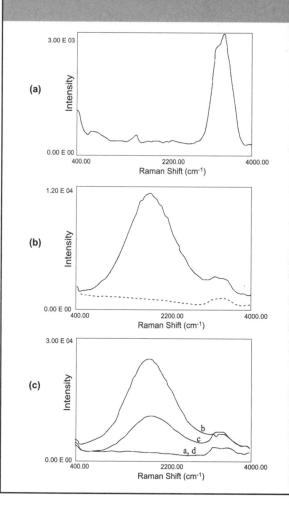

Human non-local Instruments Entanglement

(a) Raman spectrum of tap water.

(b) Raman spectra of tap water before and after external Qi treatment from Yan Xin 7 km away. Dashed line before Qi-treatment; solid line after Qi-treatment.

(c) Raman spectra of tap water in follow-up measurements after external Qi treatment from Yan Xin 7 km away,
a - before Qi-treatment.
b - 30 minutes after Qi-treatemnt.
c - 75 minutes after Qi-treatment.
d - 2 hours after Qi-treatment.

(see Figure 5.21b) with an intensity ~18 times larger than the normal 3430 cm^{-1} peak. Similar results occurred for the other tap water sample. Figure 5.21c illustrates that subsequent Raman measurements on this sample at 30 minutes, 75 minutes and 120 minutes revealed a decay of this Qi effect back to baseline in ~2 hours.

Human-human entanglement: As discussed in Chapter 2, the acupuncture meridian/chakra system of all humans functions in the fine information wave substance layer (the R-space layer) of the personality self (see Figure 1.3). This layer has been experimentally shown to operate at an inner symmetry state level approximating the SU(2) level (appreciably above our normal U(1) level). Thus, these R-space information waves can drive useful work of all kinds in this outer D-space layer, providing what amounts to *physical life* for all types of biological processes functioning in this outer U(1)-state layer. It is the *deltron coupling-coefficient*, γ, to the magnetic types of substance flowing in this inner layer, via the irrigation networks of the meridians, which nourishes these bioelectromagnetic processes. The greater the level of deltron activation, the larger is γ and thus the greater is the degree of enervation of the various biological processes. In addition, the greater the level of deltron activation, the higher does the EM gauge symmetry state of this inner layer rise above the U(1) state and the more effective is a human's intention for broadcasting both ME and EM radiations via their biofield to influence the world around them.

This ME/deltron/EM photonic soup is thought to form what has been called Qi by the Asian community and we have labeled the overall flow system as a "Qi/Prana pump". Thus, within each individual human, there is some capacity to direct the flow characteristics of this Qi/Prana pump. The more they discipline themselves via inner self-management practices, the more they advance towards Qigong mastery and various enhanced levels of output performance. The details of this overall process, in terms of the physics and chemistry involved, is something that humanity needs to learn much more about.

Figure 2.21, which is reproduced here as Figure 5.22 is presently thought to represent the five essential items that must be considered in any communication event between two or more humans[21] and, in particular, any treatment event between a practitioner and a client. In Figure 5.22, for the practitioner box, one could also substitute the words spouse, parent, minister, human performer, etc., and correspondingly, for the

Figure 5.22

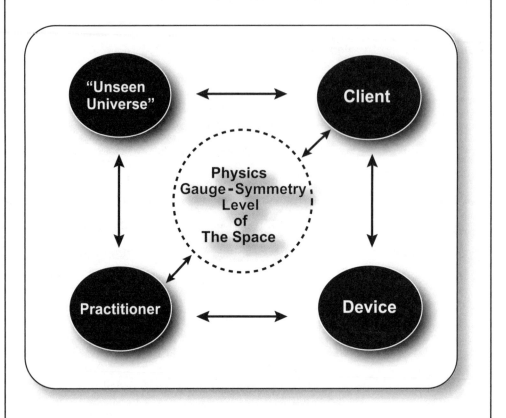

Presently thought to represent the five essential items that must be considered in any communication event between two or more humans[21] and, in particular, any treatment event between a practitioner and a client. For the practitioner box, one could also substitute the words spouse, parent, minister, human performer, etc., and correspondingly, for the client box, could substitute the words spouse, child, congregation, audience, etc., respectively.

client box, could substitute the words spouse, child, congregation, audience, etc., respectively. Here, for the client, it must also be realized that they may be strongly R-space connected (via ME radiation fields) to others at distant sites so that the actual experimental system may be larger than it appears on the surface. We are *always* R-space connected to others to some small degree but certain relationships and practices can greatly enhance that coupling.

As an example to illustrate enhancement of energy/information coupling between humans,[22] consider the situation where two humans (A and B) are wired up for EEG (electroencephalogram) monitoring and placed in separate rooms a short distance apart. Light stimulation is projected on the closed eyelids of A and this produces a readily distinguishable signature in A's brain waves. Such a signature was also looked for in the brainwaves of B but it was not found. However, when subjects A and B were first asked to sit side-by-side and meditate together for ~10 minutes before the EEG experiment was repeated, this time the special EEG signature was observed to also be present in B's brain waves when A's eyelids were light-stimulated. Here, we propose that an enhanced value of γ momentarily occurred via the joint meditation process and it was of sufficient magnitude that A-B entanglement could be instrumentally observed.

As we consider the simplest R-space entanglement case for Figure 5.22, one might think that the device part is not relevant, but perhaps an IIED or special healer has been previously utilized to raise the EM gauge symmetry state of the office space, so it is perhaps best to acknowledge it as a distinguishable part of the experimental system. Likewise, as all the great healers tell us, they try to set their personality selves aside so that they can act as a more pure channel for the "unseen universe" to act energetically/ informationally through them and do the actual healing; thus, this factor must be uniquely distinguishable as well. This means that the minimal but inclusive case is an experimental system of five interacting parts.

As mentioned earlier, since the R-space domain is a wave domain, it is primarily the square of the spectral amplitude $R_S^2(k)$ of this 4-part plus γ system which interests us. For this system, because R_j (j = 1, 2, 3, 4) is a vector and γ defines the space elevation state and there are phase angle differences, $\Delta\theta(\underline{k})$, between any two distinguishable parts of the system at each frequency, $\underline{k}$, that must be included in order to obtain $R_S^2(\underline{k})$. Thus, following the simple example on page 197, we have six information entanglement contributions of the form

Information Entanglement Form = $2R_i(\underline{k})\ R_j(\underline{k})\ \cos(\theta_i - \theta_j)$ (5.2)

Where $i \neq j$ and $(j = 1, 2, 3, 4,\ i = 1, 2, 3, 4)$ plus cos = the cosine function. Further, the greater is the deltron activation level of the space, the larger is γ so the larger would be any D-space materialization of this (ij) information entanglement because more ME photons are being broadcast by the biofields of i and j. The more coherent is the relationship between the practitioner, i, and the client, j, the smaller is the phase difference $\theta i - \theta j$, between them so the cosine term approaches unity and the largest possible information entanglement occurs between them (for these values of R_i, R_j and γ). If, instead, the relationship is an incoherent one, perhaps even an antagonistic one, then cosine $(\theta i - \theta j)$ might go from zero to minus one so any beneficial treatment of j by i is completely lost. An even deeper perspective exists in this (ij) relationship if one discriminates the three parts of the whole self described in Figure 1.3.

References

1.   W.A. Tiller, W.E. Dibble, Jr., and M.J. Kohane, *Conscious Acts of Creation* (Pavior Publishing, Walnut Creek, CA, 2001).

2.   W.A. Tiller and W.E. Dibble, Jr., "New Experimental Evidence Revealing an Unexpected Dimension to Materials Science and Engineering", Mat. Res. Innov. 5 (2001) 21-34.

3.   Denver Instruments, Acculab M-220D LA-Series Analytical Balance.

4.   Calibrated ½ Volt Silicon Solar Cell, Colorado Instruments Inc.

5.   Aware Electronics Model RM-60.

6.   Guideline Instruments, Ltd. Type 9152 Standard Cell.

7.   M.A. Nielsen, "Rules for a complex quantum world", Scientific American, 287 (5) (2002) 67.

8.   A.D. Aczel, *Entanglement* (A Plume Book, Penguin Group, London, 2003).

9.   S. Ghosh , Nature 425 (2003) 48.

10.   M.C. Arnesen, S. Bose and V. Vedral, "Thermal Entanglement in 1D Heisenberg Model", Phys. Rev. Lett. 87, 017901 (2001).

11.   B. Reznik, "Entanglement from the Vacuum", Foundations of Physics, 33 (1) 167-176, January 2003.

12.   C. Brukner, S. Taylor, S. Cheung and V. Vedral, "Quantum entanglement in time", <arXir:quant-ph/0402127 v 1> 18 Feb 2004.

13.   C.N. Shealy and W.A. Tiller, "A Double-Blind EEG-Response Test for a Supposed Electromagnetic Field-Neutralizing Device, Part I: Via the Clinician Expertise Procedure", Subtle En. & En. Med. 9 (2000) 231.

14.   QLink, Clarus Products International, LLC, 1330 Lincoln Avenue, Suite 210, San Rafael, California 94901.

15.   W.A. Tiller, W.E. Dibble Jr., R. Nunley and C.N. Shealy, "Towards General Experimentation and Discovery in "Conditioned" Laboratory Spaces, Part I: Experimental pH-Change Findings at Some Remote Sites", Special Energy Issue of The Journal of Alternative and Complementary Medicine, 10 (1) (2004) 145-157.

16.   W.A. Tiller, W.E. Dibble Jr., C.N. Shealy and R. Nunley, "Part II: pH-Change Experience at Four Remote Sites, One Year Later", Ibid, The Journal of Alternative and Complementary Medicine, 10 (2) (2004) pp 301-306.

17.   W.A. Tiller, W.E. Dibble Jr., Orlando, A. Migli, G. Raiteri and J. Oca, "Towards General Experimentation and Discovery in 'Conditioned' Laboratory Spaces, Part IV: Macroscopic Information Entanglement Between Sites ~6000 Miles Apart", submitted to The Journal of Alternative and Complementary Medicine (2004).

18.   W.A. Tiller and W.E. Dibble Jr., "Part III: A Theoretical Interpretation of Non-Local Information Entanglement", Ibid, www.tiller.org.

19.   L. Zuyin, "Scientific Qigong Exploration" (Amber Leaf Press, Malvern PA, 1997).

20.   W.A. Tiller, W.E. Dibble Jr. and C.T. Krebs, "Instrumental Response to Advanced Kinesiology Treatments in a 'Conditioned' Space", Subtle En. & En. Med. 13 (2004) 91-108.

21.   J. Grindberg-Zylerbaum, M. Delafor, L. Attie and A. Goswami, Physics Essays, 7 (1994) 422.

Chapter 6

How We Can Qualitatively Explain Various Psychoenergetic Phenomena

MASS $\rightleftarrows$ ENERGY $\rightleftarrows$ CONSCIOUSNESS

Perhaps one's growth in consciousness is strongly correlated with what one consciously thinks of as being meaningful. Perhaps when one broadens one's perspective on what is meaningful, the unconscious will edit and prepare an expanded spectrum of information kernels to send to the conscious brain. The richness and quality of these individual kernels will depend upon the character and detailed nature of the infrastructure that has been built into the various layers of the human biobodysuit.

Putting our duplex space understanding to work

I n this chapter, we attempt to put *to work* our understanding of the duplex space, D-space//Deltron//R-space, model in order to provide a qualitative explanation of various psychoenergetic phenomena such as (1) remote viewing of distant objects, (2) psychokinesis or the movement of objects at a distance, (3) healing of lifeforms both locally and non-locally, (4) precognition, (5) auric sight, clairvoyance, clairaudience, (6) telepathy, (7) levitation and (8) dematerialization/materialization. This should be a sufficiently large sampling of psychoenergetic phenomena to illustrate the various principles involved.

Before starting on an explanation for these various phenomena, let us review some of the "building blocks" discussed in the previous chapters. This will help us to see the common threads that weave these various phenomena together. These are:

(1) In our duplex RF, everything is connected to everything else and the degree of that connectivity depends upon the level of deltron activation that exists; that is, upon the magnitude of the deltron coupling-coefficient, γ. This determines the level of information entanglement between any two points in D-space.

(2) At the atom and molecule level of D-space, electromagnetic interactions give rise to *local forces* and EM waves can carry information. At the vacuum level of R-space, magnetoelectric interactions give rise to *non-local* forces and ME waves can carry higher dimensional information. Further, the larger is γ, the more can ME information excite EM phenomena and the more can EM information excite ME phenomena.

(3) Moving electric charges in D-space generate propagating EM waves while conjugate magnetic charges in R-space are correlated with propagating ME waves. Thus, the personality self body contains duplex antenna systems for radiating a biofield consisting of information-rippled EM radiation and information-rippled ME radiation. This information will be of EM, ME and higher dimensional types.

(4) The D-space aspect of the personality self body has great antenna-like capacities in its autonomic nervous system (ANS) via both its sympathetic and parasympathetic branches. These influence secretions, smooth muscle responses, blood vessel responses and electrocardiogram, heart rate variability, respiration, electroencephalogram, etc., responses. Likewise, the R-space aspect of the personality self body has exquisite antenna-like capacities in its acupuncture meridian/chakra system which is coupled to the ANS via the fourteen known acupuncture meridians. Thus, the R-space body has thousands of acupuncture points on the surface of the skin to act as sophisticated antenna elements for interfacing with the "outside" world. Such a vast antenna array[1] has information exchange capabilities that greatly exceed the most advanced radar systems existing in the world today.

(5) The overall RF which includes both the duplex four-dimensional subspaces imbedded in three higher dimensional spaces indicates that the following reaction equation is an operational reality

$$\textbf{MASS} \rightleftarrows \textbf{ENERGY} \rightleftarrows \textbf{CONSCIOUSNESS} \qquad (6.1)$$

This underscores the importance of (1) focused intention, (2) the conversion of the D-space coordinate time, t, into a fourth spatial distance, $x_4 = ict$, where c is the velocity of EM light and $i = \sqrt{-1}$ is the imaginary number equivalent to a counterclockwise 90 degree rotation and (3) the mirror principle which acts like an inversion mirror between D-space behavior and conjugate R-space behavior. In equation 6.1, consciousness is differentiated as a unique system of stuff present in the universe, different than, but convertible to, either energy or mass. At this point in human development, we don't have a clear picture of what consciousness is as distinct from awake awareness. As a starting point, or working hypothesis, suppose we think of consciousness as a biproduct of, or emergent property of, spirit entering dense matter.

How conscious are we?

It is important for all of us to be aware of just how much we process information at unconscious vs. at conscious levels of our whole person. In 1948, the engineer, Claude Shannon, founded modern information theory, which might be most simply expressed *for any worded message* that each symbol of a message is a macrostate that can correspond to 26 different microstates - the individual letters of the English alphabet. One of Shannon's main conclusions was that you can always transmit a message error-free if you have sufficient bandwidth (range of possible EM frequencies) in your EM communication channel.[2]

The bandwidth expresses the ability of a communications channel to transmit information in terms of bits per second. For example, a telephone can transfer ~4,000 bits per second, a good radio transfers ~16,000 bits per second and a television transfers ~4,000,000 bits per second.[2] Information is a measure of everything one *could have said* rather than *what was actually said*. Shannon's definition of information precludes any notion of *meaning* and concerns itself with *all possible meanings* that could have been present with the specific array of symbols in the text. Meaning, on the other hand, arises out of winnowing a large body of information to claim a few bits that we deem relevant and important to us. Thus, *meaning* is a residue or summary from the information that has been mostly discarded.

For a human, one can readily measure how much information enters our bodies via the five physical senses and these numbers are huge ~50 million bits per second. This huge number of bits are condensed again and again to provide a *conscious* experience that contains practically no information at all. The information channel capacity of the conscious brain is found to be *less than 50 bits per second*. Thus, the bottom line here is that more than a million times as much raw information enters just the outer layer of our personality-self in Figure 1.3 than that which evokes a conscious experience.[2]

Our unconscious appears to process, manipulate and edit this abundance of raw neural information and then directs *synthesized kernels of structured information* to the conscious centers of the brain *but only in areas that the conscious brain recognizes as being meaningful to it.* All the rest of the information, that which is not recognized as being meaningful to self, *is dumped!*[2]

Perhaps one's growth in consciousness is strongly correlated with what one consciously thinks of as being *meaningful.* Perhaps when one *broadens one's perspective* on what is meaningful, the unconscious will edit and prepare an expanded spectrum of information kernels to send to the conscious brain. The richness and quality of these individual kernels will depend upon the character and detailed nature of the infrastructure that has been built into the various layers of the human biobodysuit.

The bottom line, here, is that we are *mostly unconscious* and this part of our self senses all aspects of the world without as well as the world within. This part has great information processing capabilities and great access to information sources in the universe beyond our conscious imagining. On the other hand, our conscious self may or may not have developed significant information processing capabilities and may be extremely self-limiting because of the limited menu of concepts and experiences to which it gives the label "meaningful".

For the authors of this present book, our current working hypothesis is that it is our subconscious that accesses all of the essential psychoenergetic phenomena-related information that flows abundantly through R-space via, at least, ME carrier waves traveling much faster than c, the EM light velocity. Only those who give conscious meaning to such processes in nature have a significant chance of gaining useful kernels of such processed information. Those who have, over lifetimes, developed the appropriately detailed R-space and soul-self infrastructure can utilize this capability in their day-to-day personality experiences. Those who have not developed such necessary infrastructure (a necessary condition), or who do not consider such information to be meaningful (also a necessary condition) to their conscious personality self, are unable to utilize these inherent capabilities in this particular personality self lifetime.

Towards conscious understanding of psychoenergetics phenomena

Remote Viewing: Because the two subspaces in our duplex RF are reciprocal to each other as pointed out in Chapter 3, a particular quality in D-space has a conjugate equilibrium quality in R-space which is given by a deltron-empowered Fourier transform of the D-space quality magnitude. This is a complex mathematical function which is much simplified when approximated by the deltron coupling-coefficient, γ, times the standard expression for the Fourier Transform, $F(\underline{k}_4)$, where $\underline{k}_4$ represents the four-dimensional vector in terms of the R-space coordinates (k_x, k_y, k_z, k_t). The Fourier transform has several very important mathematical properties. Here, the most important one for us is that, if one takes a D-space object of any complex shape located at Position 1 and simply translates it to Position 2, some distance away, the Fourier transform (FT) for the object at Position 2 is just the FT at Position 1 times a relatively simple function of the translation distance (as a vector) times $\underline{k}_4$. For example, if the object at Position 2 is at the D-space coordinates, $\underline{s}_4 = (x_2, y_2, z_2, t_2)$ say with origin at Greenwich, England, and Position 1 is at the D-space coordinate position, $\underline{s}'_4 = (x_1, y_1, z_1, t_2)$, then

$$\mathbf{FT}_1 = \mathbf{FT}_2 \times \boldsymbol{\theta}^*(\Delta\underline{\mathbf{s}}_3 \times \underline{\mathbf{k}}_3) \qquad (6.2)$$

Where, since time is unchanged, $\Delta \underline{s}_4 = s'_4 - s_4 = \Delta s_3$, $\underline{k}_3$ takes on all possible values and θ^* is our simple phase factor function.

What this means for the phenomenon of remote viewing is the following: First, let us suppose that the object at Position 2 is the Taj Mahal. This is a well known structure whose three-dimensional shape can be Fourier decomposed into a very specific amplitude spectrum as a function of spatial frequencies in the x, y and z directions. In fact, using only the first two or three lowest frequencies in each of these directions to construct a three-dimensional picture, most people would recognize the picture as a crude version of the Taj Mahal. The higher frequency components just fill in the fine details of the scene. Our working hypothesis is that the subconscious mind could readily take *visual sensory information* from the Taj Mahal and construct its Fourier amplitude spectrum. From the Pribram studies[3] mentioned in Chapter 3 associated with Figures 3.10 and 3.11, the human brain appears to first detect optical information in this frequency spectrum format before processing it in various ways and then converting it to the inverse FT format as kernels which are then sent to the awake awareness centers of the brain and we *see* the Taj Mahal. Thus, FT_2 in Equation 6.1 could be readily accessed from the optical EM information by the human consciousness.

Next, the phase factor θ^* is a fairly simple mathematical function which the subconscious would readily know and, given the two spatial coordinates, (x_1-x_2), (y_1-y_2) and (z_1-z_2) are readily determined by the subconscious and $\Delta \underline{s}_3$ therefore readily determined. Thus, given the coordinates of Positions 1 and 2, $\theta^*(\Delta \underline{s}_3 \cdot \underline{k}_3)$ should be very easy for the human subconscious to evaluate and know.

Next, our working hypothesis is that a trained human can go within and access the information patterns present in R-space (like the middle column of Figure 3.7), one of which is FT_1. The unconscious can then transform these raw R-space information patterns by dividing them by the phase factor $\theta^*(\Delta \underline{s}_3 \times \underline{k}_3)$ and suddenly FT_2 stands out from the background as a unique R-space pattern which can be Fourier superposed via the brain's inverse FT algorithm and the conscious brain now discriminates this picture as that for the Taj Mahal.

For the foregoing to be a correct assessment of the remote viewing phenomenon, the following is required of the human subconscious:

1. The ability to calculate $\Delta \underline{s}_3$ given the coordinate $\underline{s}_4$ and knowing one's present position, $\underline{s}'_4$,

2. The ability to calculate θ^* and its inverse $1/\theta^*$,

3. The ability to access optical sensory information in one's environment of both the EM-type and the ME-type, etc., and to discriminate FT_1, and

4. The ability to multiply FT_1 by $1/\theta^*$ and take its inverse Fourier transform.

It is our postulate that the human subconscious has the ability to do this so, if the human conscious brain gives *significant meaning* to remote viewing and is willing to practice the procedures diligently, the unconscious aspect of the brain is probably willing to do the heavy work of providing the processed information kernels to the conscious brain so that the "ah ha" state is attained.

Here, we have restricted ourselves to the optical data stream, the other D-space sensory data streams can be treated in the same way so that a more rich picture is formed.

Before leaving this topic, a magnitude assessment of $\theta^*(\Delta \underline{s}_3 \cdot \underline{k}_3)$ should be considered for both EM and ME information carriers. As described in Chapter 5, the observed temporal oscillations are always in the frequency range, f $\sim 10^{-2}$ - 10^{-3} Hertz (with periods ~ 1 - 10 hours). The EM spatial wavelength $(\lambda \sim c/k_r)$ for such oscillations would be ~ 20 - 200 million miles, thus, for Position 2 being any place on the earth ($\Delta \underline{s}_{max} \sim 25{,}000$ miles), $\Delta \underline{s}_{max}$ is a very small fraction of this wavelength so that the phase factor θ^*, for such a frequency range would be extremely close to unity. However, from a conventional viewpoint, we could not transfer much information via such an EM carrier wave because the bandwidth is so small. It is thus likely that the important carrier wave for remote viewing type of information exchange is ME radiation where, via use of the mirror principle phenomenon discussed in Chapter 3, one expects the R-space bandwidth for information exchange to go up as the frequency goes down - just the inverse of D-space expectations.

Psychokinesis: Here, we are considering the movement of nearby objects as a consequence of a directed and shaped human biofield radiation pattern. From many earlier discussions in this book one can readily come to appreciate that the flow of electric charges at the D-space atom/molecule level of the body plus the flow of magnetic charges at the R-space, physical vacuum level of the body plus the deltron coupling-coefficient, γ, will lead to a spectrum of both EM emissions and ME emissions as well as higher dimensional emissions from the body. This is what we call the biofield. At present, most of science is only capable of measuring the EM portion of this biofield.

For the U(1) EM gauge symmetry state, both dielectrophoretic (from the electric-field components, $\underline{E}$) and diamagnetophoretic forces (from the magnetic-field component $\underline{H}$) are present in the human biofield[4] of strengths sufficient to move some atoms and molecules around in the surrounding air. The dielectrophoretic force is proportional to the spatial gradient of E^2 while the diamagnetophoretic force is proportional to the spatial gradient of H^2. In the conventional physics community, shaped magnetic fields using electric coils made from superconducting materials, have been utilized to levitate various materials, including live frogs. Likewise, using electric induction, cone-shaped coils have been used to levitate spheres of various metals. Here, the frequencies involved have been in the kilohertz to megahertz range. Likewise, for homogeneous EM fields (~zero gradients) in the megahertz to gigahertz range, our microwave ovens regularly heat up and cook our frozen foods. Thus, overall, heating, movement and levitation of smallish objects is an easily accomplished feat with today's EM technology.

As discussed earlier in other chapters, the acupuncture meridian/chakra (AM/C) system is at a higher EM inner symmetry state than the U(1) level and thus is at a higher thermodynamic free energy per unit volume level than the atom/molecule level of the physical body. Thus, the AM/C system can do various types of work on processes functioning at the U(1) level. Focused intent, from higher dimensional levels of self, in turn, drive the output behavior of the AM/C system. The human body acupuncture points have been shown to have different electrical characteristics than the surrounding skin even though no striking histological difference has been detected.[1] Variations in mental alertness is known to cause significant changes in the electrical characteristics of these skin points.[1] Several decades ago, Russian researchers found that mental concentration techniques can be utilized to increase the "effective" voltage difference between similar acupuncture points on the left and right sides of the body (see Figure 6.1). By connecting an electrical meter between such points on the hands, the voltage difference can be changed from ~50 millivolts to ~500 millivolts by such mental concentration. More general biofeedback techniques[5,6] show us that directed intention can not only control various autonomic body functions like skin temperature, pain, etc., but they can repair the body.

For individuals who have practiced Qigong for some time, it is a fairly common practice to hold the two ends of a functional fluorescent tube and have it light up. This

Figure 6.1

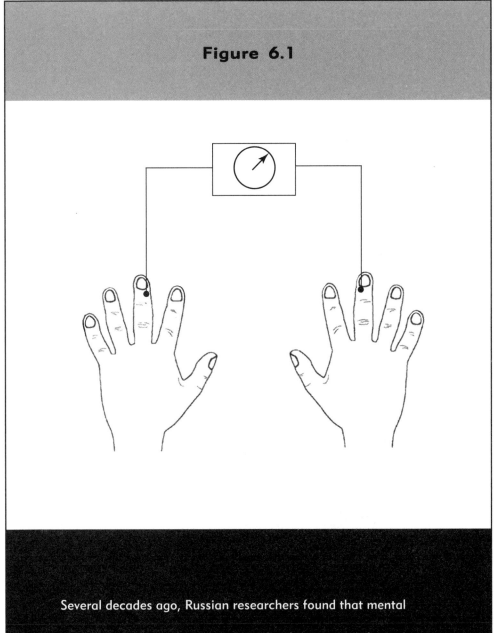

Several decades ago, Russian researchers found that mental concentration techniques can be utilized to increase the "effective" voltage difference between similar acupuncture points on the left and right sides of the body.

indicates that the EM energy stream through such a developed body is at a fairly high frequency (the electric voltage needed to produce a gas discharge decreases significantly as the frequency increases into the megahertz range) so it was not too much of a surprise to read in the newspaper that a favorite demonstration of Qigong ability is to take a frozen fish and hold it at each end as it quickly cooks between the hands.

All of the foregoing information is relevant to our working hypothesis of how human psychokinesis works. The linchpin of our hypothesis is that the ~1,000 point array of acupuncture points on the skin acts as a multi-element antenna array. With internally developed control and constructed infrastructure, this system could be taught to act as a phased- array with directional beam-forming and beam-scanning capabilities to, in principle, generate a strong gradient of E^2 at the location of the object to be moved. If, as in the aforementioned Russian work, one can increase the developed voltage at each acupuncture point in the array to be in the ~0.5 volt range, and relatively coherent one with another, then the manifested voltage in the beam might attain ~500 volts with EM intensities, E^2, in the range of 100,000 (volts per centimeter) squared. This could provide appreciable lift and directional movement dielectrophoretic forces on small objects. When one extends this picture to include ME effects, then non-local R-space forces can become even more significant.

Auras, clairvoyance and clairaudience: It is the antenna systems of the whole person (see Chapter 1) that generates a person's total biofield. Some of that biofield can be discriminated by today's instrumentation (the EM part) but most of it cannot. On the other hand, some humans have the developed internal infrastructure and the intent to perceive higher dimensional radiation patterns in the biofields (auras) of others. Thus, this capacity is a natural human capability which can be acquired by other members of the human family by diligent attempts to acquire such skills. The intellectual key to understanding the topics of this section is to begin to understand the properties of EM antennas and how the EM radiation flows from and into a human antenna system and into and from the environment.[1]

In Figure 6.2, the EM energy emission from a short dipole antenna is illustrated for both the region very close to the antenna (the near-field) and the region very far from the antenna (the far-field).[7] In the far-field, the energy flow is mathematically real and is always radially outwards. This EM energy is radiated outwards, it doesn't come back to the

Figure 6.2

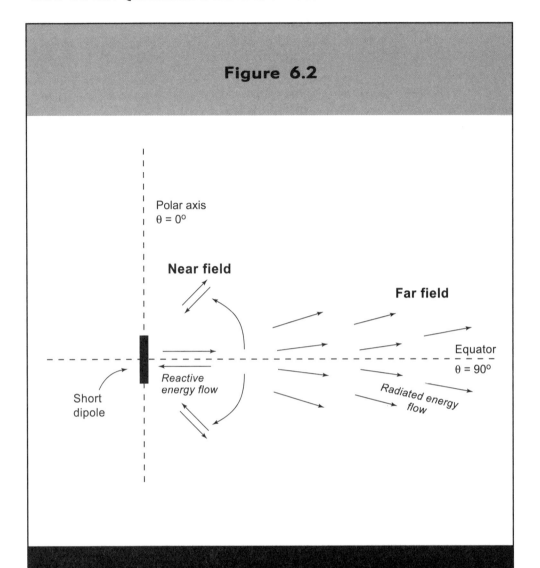

The key to understanding the topics of this section is to begin to understand the properties of EM antennas and how the EM radiation flows from and into a human antenna system and into and from the environment. In the above figure, the EM energy emission from a short dipole antenna is illustrated for both the region very close to the antenna (the near-field) and the region very far from the antenna (the far-field)

Figure 6.3

Subtle levels of substance exist in the whole person body; e.g., vacuum level magnetic monopole substances, deltron substance; general emotion domain substances, mind domain substances and spirit domain substances, and each is expected to give rise to the emission of unique radiations in a metaphorically similar manner as electric atom/molecule substance generates EM emissions. Thus, for each, we can expect to find a D-space standing wave or *auric field* representation such as qualitatively illustrated here.

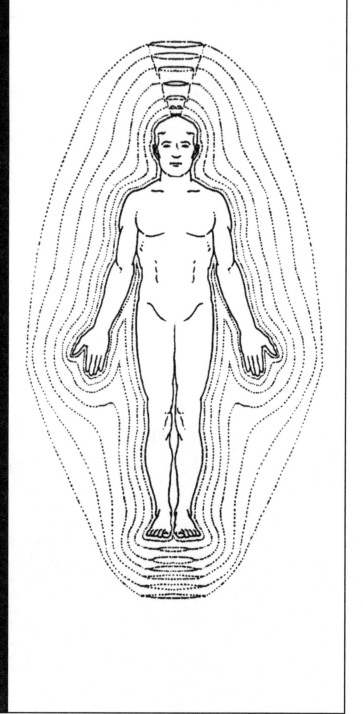

antenna and it has a maximum intensity in a direction perpendicular to the dipole axis. In the near-field, the energy is mathematically imaginary and it is called largely reactive in nature. This means that the energy flows out and back twice per cycle without being radiated (and is thus a standing field). In Figure 6.2, the arrows represent the direction of energy flow at successive instants.

Our working hypothesis is that, what is called the near-field region of this EM antenna, is the EM *aura* from this structure. If the antenna is moving, this aura would move with it (with some minor variations due to its local environment). Thus, we can consider it to be part of the antenna. If we insert a sizable metallic or dielectric material object into this EM aura region of the antenna, the electric and magnetic wave patterns will be altered and the overall effect would manifest as a power fluctuation on the meters monitoring the electric voltage, electric current and electric power delivered to the antenna from the electric power source. Conversely, via the use of small electric and magnetic field probes inserted at various locations in this near-field region, one could run a diagnostic study on the functional state of this dipole antenna.

As discussed throughout this book, subtle levels of substance exist in the whole person body; e.g., vacuum level magnetic monopole substances, deltron substance; general emotion domain substances, mind domain substances and spirit domain substances, and each is expected to give rise to the emission of unique radiations in a metaphorically similar manner as electric atom/molecule substance generates EM emissions. Thus, for each, we can expect to find a D-space standing wave or *auric field* representation such as qualitatively illustrated in Figure 6.3.

Some humans appear to have the natural ability to optically perceive distinct colors and patterns of these proposed auric sheaths beyond the EM aura and this is called clairvoyance. Many are born with the ability and train it somewhat during childhood, only to lose it when peers and parents ridicule them about it as early teenagers.[1] Others maintain the capability into adulthood and still others teach themselves the skill as a seriously interested adult. Once again, it is the subconscious levels of the brain and its subtle counterparts that process the optical information data streams from the various sensing elements in the whole person and convert it into meaningful kernels for delivery to the conscious awareness centers of the brain. In a similar fashion, clairaudience is the ability to perceive and understand sounds from an unseen source.

Precognition: This involves the perception of a D-space event by someone before it is actually observed to occur as an event in spacetime. So this individual is actually seeing an aspect of the future. How can that be possible? First, consider that to solve the equations of relativity theory, time is converted to a fourth imaginary distance coordinate, $x_4 = ict$, so that spacetime is actually a four-space. In Chapter 5, we indicated that, to solve our equations re information entanglement between distant sites in our duplex RF,[8] it was also found necessary to convert D-space time to x_4, a fourth distance coordinate. Our procedures indicated that sequential events occurring in time could entangle with each other as illustrated in Figure 5.20, both in the direction of smaller x_4-values and also larger x_4-values.

If we must look at our duplex, four-dimensional subspaces as (a) a distance space and (b) a frequency space in order to solve key equations, then the concept of time acts as a kind of traveling cursor, x_4^*, moving along the x_4 coordinate in D-space at some velocity, v, separating the past (x_4 less than x_4^*) from the future (x_4 greater than x_4^*). Likewise, the conjugate cursor, k_4^*, moves along the k_4 axis in R-space at a corresponding velocity, v', discriminating the high frequency region, k_4 greater than k_4^* from the low frequency region, k_4 less than k_4^*. Thus, as time increases in D-space, k_4^* decreases in R-space.

As stated in Chapter 3, connectivity between any two points in D-space exists in the duplex space RF via the integral over the totality of R-space and the degree of that connectivity increases as the deltron coupling-coefficient, γ, increases. Further, our experiments on humans have shown that their acupuncture meridian/chakra system is at a higher EM gauge symmetry state (approaching the SU(2) state) than our normal outside environmental U(1) gauge state. Thus, within each of us is a source of deltrons, wherein fluctuations in γ can occur, and short duration connectivity and information entanglement between separated D-space spatial points can occur. This means that everyone has the sometime probability of unity to connect, via serious information entanglement, their x_4^* point with an x_4 point that is greater than x_4^*. This generates a precognitive event. For those who strengthen their ability to intentionally move Qi (ME energy), these types of fluctuation events that we label precognition should occur with increasing frequency. And there will be some with sufficiently strong powers of intentionality as to be able to access the x_4 greater than x_4^* domain at will.

Telepathy: This is one that many people use unconsciously; communication between two or more separate minds by some means other than our normal sensory channels. Just as we have internal antennae for automatically broadcasting our biofields, we have an antenna in the head that is capable of transmitting/receiving information much as a radio is capable of receiving audio information via EM carrier wave reception. However, in telepathy, it is not an EM carrier that is involved. In this case, it is an ME carrier that is utilized and it is rippled with thoughts-type of information. Once again, it is the deltron coupling-coefficient, γ, that needs to be of significant magnitude for the information transfer process to be efficient and reliable. It is a latent human capacity that can be developed to a high degree of effectiveness in future human cultures.

Levitation: The "mirror principle", associated with our duplex RF, acts between the two subspaces so that a type of property inversion relationship acts between the two. This is illustrated via Table 3.2 where one sees that the D-space property of gravitation is counter balanced by the R-space property of levitation. Thus, it is the level of deltron activation present in the space, as manifested in the deltron coupling-coefficient, γ, that determines which force dominates in our measuring instrument. This means that, at the very least, the duplex space theoretical model *allows* the presence of a levitational force to be experimentally observed in physical reality (a necessary but not sufficient condition). Sufficiently focused intention, acting through the acupuncture meridian/chakra system of the developed human is needed to turn the possibility into reality. Perhaps the scale-pan experimental observations of Chapter 5 for an IIED-conditioned space is a step in this direction.

Materialization/dematerialization: As mentioned on Page 108 of Chapter 3, the basic concept utilized today to account for the presence of D-space particles of matter in our universe is the conversion, in the physical vacuum stuff, of a high energy EM photon from outer space into a particle/anti-particle pair. This could also be looked at as a direct transformation of R-space stuff to D-space stuff (materialization). Likewise, the basic concept mentioned above operates in the reverse direction where a D-space particle/anti-particle pair can collide and disappear into the physical vacuum (R-space stuff) with the subsequent appearance of a high energy EM photon. An alternate process path mentioned in earlier books,[1,8] is that a quality fluctuation occurs in 9-space or 10-space to produce a D-space particle plus an R-space wave with balanced opposite sign energies (see Figure 3.4 and page 124) and no net photon emission (of either EM or ME types). This is probably why we observe such a D-space particle/D-space anti-particle disparity in nature via our conventional scientific instruments. This second, and probably more important, process path for matter creation has been completely neglected by conventional science because such science is stuck in a single four-space RF (spacetime).

The previous paragraph shows that there are at least two viable process paths available whereby materialization and dematerialization events for D-space particles can occur. Now we consider Equation 3.4, reintroduced here as Equation 6.1 because it is so important to this chapter.

Thus, (1) since we already use the convertibility relationship between energy and mass in conventional science and (2) the experimental data of this book has shown convertibility between consciousness (intention) and energy, it is a very small step to take to accept the concept that a highly developed human, like Sai Baba for example, can drive the reaction Equation, 6.1, from the right to the left in order to materialize or dematerialize D-space matter. And, if one human can do it, all humans can ultimately do it. It is a natural law of nature!

Local and non-local healing: From the discussion of earlier chapters, when one wants to evaluate a whole human's state of body function from a wellness/pathology ratio perspective, one must deal with the following reaction equation in its entirety

Human Body Function

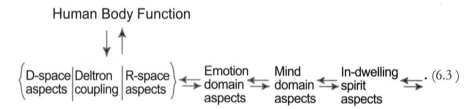

Here, for a high state of wellness, a wholesome balance between the various energies present within each aspect, and for the coupling energies between the different aspects, must exist. An expansion of certain features present in Figure 3.2b is given in Figure 6.4 to illustrate the energy scale, EM and ME photon energetics as well as zero-point energy levels for both D-space and R-space.

Except for the D-space aspects one is dealing with some spectral distribution (amplitude vs. frequency) that is ideal for a particular energy and significant departures from this ideal profile is an indication that a defect state exists from which some type of visible pathology will eventually emerge. One can expect that errors in a particular infrastructure circuit for that particular layer of the whole person (see Figure 1.3) is what generates a significant departure in the ideal spectral distribution for that layer. Thus, the healer needs to be at least loosely aware of such an overall picture.

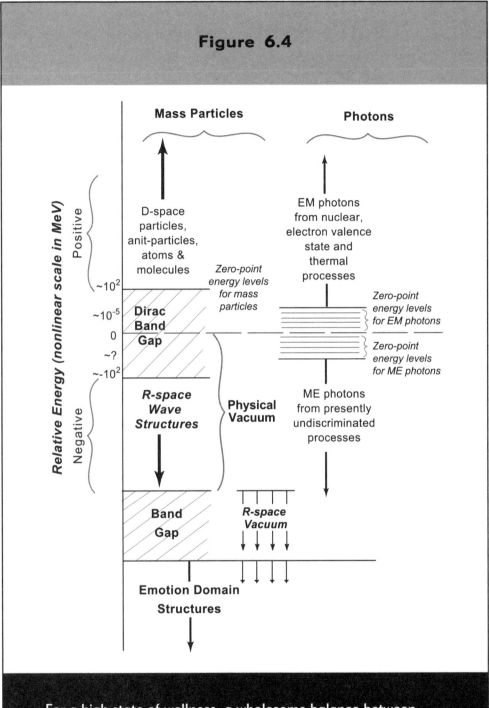

Figure 6.4

For a high state of wellness, a wholesome balance between the various Equation 6.3 energies present within each aspect, and for the coupling energies between the different aspects, must exist.

Healers also need to be at least loosely aware that any interactions between themselves and patients occur within a general framework like that illustrated via Figure 2.21. Their intention to facilitate healing in the patient will be more successful when they open a channel within themselves to allow abundant healing energies to flow from the "unseen universe" to the patient via the presence of a raised EM gauge symmetry space linking the healer to the patient. The general intention of the healer would be to facilitate energetic and infrastructure change via the following reaction equation

$$\text{Mass} \rightleftharpoons \text{Energy} \rightleftharpoons \text{Consciousness} \rightleftharpoons \text{Love.} \qquad (6.4)$$

Here, Einstein provided us with the quantitative relationship connecting the first two terms on the left. We will probably discover the quantitative relationship between the second and third terms sometime in this or the next century. The last term on the right is the force of all creation and we can't even guess how long it will take us to awaken to the quantitative connection between the last two terms. However, centering one's consciousness within a framework of unconditional love, nurturing, caring, etc., can allow the healing process to unfold from right to left in the above equation even though we do not consciously know the quantitative connections.

From all of the foregoing, a partial list of necessary requirements for one to be an effective local healer would seem to be the following:

(1) To have a compassionate and loving heart;

(2) To have developed suitable biobodysuit infrastructure for the generation of specific field spectral patterns that can be entangled with a carrier wave and delivered to the nearby patient;

(3) To have developed sufficient robustness to this particular system that the broadcast power level can be high and controllable; and

(4) To have developed the capacity to be an effective channel or conduit for higher dimensional energy to flow into the healer as well as out of the healer.

An example to illustrate the importance of item (4) above comes from some old Russian data.[9] It has been known for a long time that, for a healthy person, the electrical resistance of a particular acupuncture meridian on the left side of the body, R_L, is equal to that for the identical point on the right side of the body, R_R, so that $\Delta R = R_L - R_R \approx 0$. For an unhealthy individual, $\Delta R \neq 0$ and, as the magnitude of ΔR increases, the level of pathology increases.[1] The Russian experiment took a patient with pathology and measured the pattern of $|\Delta R|$-values for several meridian points before and after treatment by a healer. They also measured the $|\Delta R|$-values for the identical points on the healer before and after treatment of the healee. What they discovered was that (a) before the healing session, the $|\Delta R|$-profile for the patient consisted of large values but for the healer consisted of almost zero-values, and (b) immediately after the healing session, all the $|\Delta R|$-values for the patient were reduced, but for the healer they were all increased.[8] Thus, if the relaxation times for the healer's $|\Delta R|$-values to return to zero are not small, the inflow of the transferred energy spectrum from the unseen universe will be insufficient to keep the healer from not developing the patient's pathology. Thus, the picture to be generated from this example is that of a transmitter/receiver system with interconnecting conduits of sufficient conductivity that large power levels of the particular energy involved can readily flow through the system. The electromagnetic analogy forms a most useful metaphor for this process and it is illustrated in Figure 6.5.

Most local and non-local healers perceive an abundance of color around and within the patient and especially during a healing procedure. These colors are observationally important so let us mention some of the contributions in this area provided by others.

Turning to observational information on the chakras, Leadbeater and the Theosophical society[10] report extensively on this and provide the colors and distinguishing patterns shown in Table 6.1

Table 6.1; Chakra colors and patterns		
1	Root	(4 petals, 2-orange, two red in alternate sequence)
2	Navel	(10 petals, alternating red/white and white/green/yellow/pink)
3a	Spleen	(6 petals, whole spectrum, yellow and rose to red predominate)
3b	Solar Plexus	(10 petals, multicolored with light red & green predominate) - here there is an emotion field connection.
4	Heart	(12 petals, golden to yellow)
5	Throat	(16 petals, alternately bladed blue-white and white-blue tinge)
6	Brow	(2 segments, one half rose & yellow, the other half blue & purple)
7	Crown	(12 central, gold petals, 960 secondary background petals that are all colors of the rainbow with violet predominating)

Figure 6.5

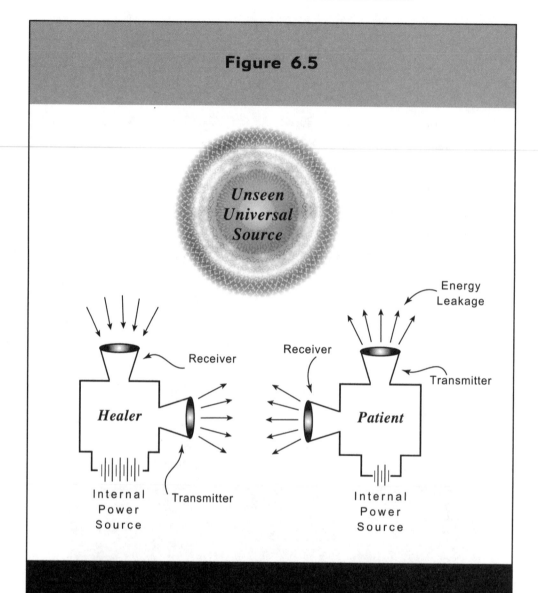

To be an effective channel or conduit for higher dimensional energy to flow into the healer as well as out of the healer, the picture is that of a transmitter/receiver system with interconnecting conduits of sufficient conductivity that large power levels of the particular energy involved can readily flow through the system. The electromagnetic analogy forms a most useful metaphor for this process.

Leadbeater's explanation of prana, which he terms the "vitality globule", is as follows. The vitality globule originates in the sun, and radiates in all directions to permeate everything; in man, it is absorbed through the spleen chakra, where it is subdivided into streams of seven different colors: violet, blue, green, yellow, orange, dark red, and rose. These different colored streams flow to one or more chakras, whence they vivify the organs and other systems of the body. The following table, taken from Leadbeater's book,[12] shows the correspondence between the five types of prana within the traditional Indian system, and his own "rays of vitality".

Table 6.2; Prana/Vitality Rays Correspondence

Prana and Region Affected	Ray of Vitality	Chakra Chiefly Affected
Prana; heart	Yellow	Cardiac; Anahata
Apana; anus	Orange-red	Basic; Muladhara
Samana; navel	Green	Umbilical; Manipuraka
Udana; throat	Violet-blue	Laryngeal; Vishuddha
Vyana; the entire body	Rose	Splenic

In Dr. Motoyama's own research using the AMI device for measuring the acupuncture meridians, he found that persons with ESP and *other psychic abilities consistently show an abnormal yin state (the state of absorbing too much energy) in the spleen meridian.* This would seem to correspond with Leadbeater, who states that the vitality globule is absorbed through the spleen chakra.

Leadbeater describes the seven individual rays of the primary force as follows (see Figure 6.6):

The violet-blue ray: The violet-blue ray naturally flows to the throat, dividing into two shades: a light blue, which remains to vitalize the throat center, and a dark blue and violet which passes on to the brain. In the brain, the dark blue submerges into the lower and central parts of the brain, while the violet goes further up, invigorating the force centers at the top of the head.

Figure 6.6

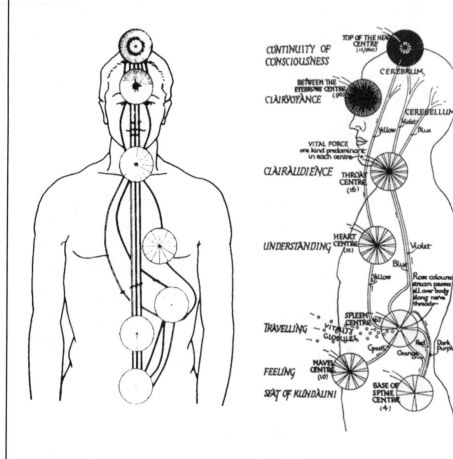

(a) Schematic illustration of the different morphological character associated with the different chakras.

(b) Main types of psychoenergetic phenomena associated with each other.

The green ray: Enters especially into the solar plexus, filling the abdomen and vivifying the liver, kidneys, intestines, and the digestive system.

The yellow (golden) ray: Originally follows a pathway to the head and after depositing substantial energy there, takes a route into the brain, directing itself mainly to the twelve-petalled flower which is situated at the midst of the highest force-center.

The rose-colored ray: Known as the nucleus or life-source of the nervous system. It is spread throughout the body in the entire nervous system. The unique characteristic of this ray is its ability to permeate and to radiate energy to other individuals. For example, a man of robust health constantly radiates these rose-colored atoms to the people around him, especially to those who are in need of this energy. Thus, certain people sometimes find themselves exhausted after spending time in close proximity to weak persons.

This phenomenon is found even among flora and fauna. For example, pine and eucalyptus trees radiate an intrinsic amount of energy, thus facilitating higher meditative powers.

The orange-red ray: Also containing shades of dark purple, this ray flows into the base of the spine and activates the urogenital organs; generally, it acts as a stimulant to the desires of the flesh and also helps to maintain body heat. However, when an individual develops an unyielding defense system, this ray can be directed towards the brain where all three shades of the ray (orange, red and purple) undergo remarkable modification. The orange changes into a golden yellow which activates the intellect; the dark-red becomes crimson, engendering an altruistic state; while the third shade of dark purple is transformed into a pale violet, enhancing spirituality. Once these higher transformations have been realized, impeccable powers are developed which enable a person to transcend mundane sensual desires. Thus, when the serpent fire is stimulated, the severe dangers inherent in the awakening process can be avoided.

In Leadbeater's view, the centers exist in both the etheric (R-space) and astral (emotion domain) dimensions. The descriptions presented up to this point depict the centers as they exist and function in the etheric body. The vortices are located on the surface of the etheric body, and they are active in the average person to some extent, regulating physiological functions and helping him/her to lead a normal life.

Although the astral centers often resemble the etheric centers in appearance and location, they are fundamentally different entities. Existing with the astral body, they control sensory, mental and spiritual functions in the astral dimension. The awakening of these astral centers can only begin with the activation of kundalini - the serpent fire - located in the root chakra. In normal persons, this serpent fire is an unconscious, inert mass, devoid of any initiating or substantiating power of its own. However, when fully awakened it reaches unspeakable heights, enlightening the soul and enabling man to obtain the highest knowledge of the universe.

When the kundalini reaches the second (spleen) chakra, a person is able to travel in the astral world with a vague sense of consciousness. When it reaches the third (manipura) chakra, feeling in the astral body is gradually awakened. At the level of the anahata chakra, the awakening of kundalini enables a man/woman to comprehend and reciprocate with other astral entities. As the power rises to the fifth center, the vishuddhi chakra, one acquires the power to hear on the astral plane. With the awakening of the sixth chakra, the ajna, the power of full astral vision appears. As kundalini rises to the sahasrara, the seventh center, the adept acquires complete knowledge of astral life, endowing him/her with the perfection of all astral powers.

It is sometimes noted that the pituitary gland controls both the sixth and seventh chakras, acting as a converging point between the physical and higher dimensions. However, in certain exceptional cases, the centers are divided - the sixth is connected with the pituitary gland, while the seventh connects with the pineal gland - thus making possible direct communication from the higher planes to the lower mental states. In these instances, the intermediary astral planes are bypassed.

According to Leadbeater, the astral centers act almost like sense organs for the astral body. However, it should be remembered that these centers differ considerably from the physical sense organs. First of all, the content of astral perception naturally differs considerably from that of physical perception; it is information from the astral dimension which is received. Furthermore, the astral organs of reception are not clearly differentiated in the way that the eyes, nose, ears, etc., are. Rather, the centers respond to vibrational information, which can be received from all directions. Therefore, a person functioning in the astral body has the power to see objects in any direction without turning his head. Leadbeater would like to add that, judging from his own experience, visual astral information can also be received through chakras other than the ajna. Thus, it seems that a given astral sense is not necessarily restricted to one astral center.

Leadbeater states that when the centers are awakened at only the astral level, the physical consciousness remains ignorant of this process. Information can be conveyed from the astral to the physical only through the etheric centers (R-space centers); thus, the etheric centers must be fully awakened for man to acquire consciousness of the astral dimension. Each of the major schools of Indian yoga has its own methods to awaken these centers. Raja yoga emphasizes concentration and meditation on the chakras; in Karma yoga, the emphasis is on the dissolution of karma; in Jnana yoga, one attempts to develop prajna, or wisdom; in Laya yoga, one endeavors to acquire paranormal abilities and develop the interaction with divine beings; in Bhakti yoga, the practice is centered on self-redemption, love, and devotion to God; and in Mantra yoga, the chanting of mantra is practiced.

Since these colors appear to circumscribe all those observed in the healing experience, are they the same as Leadbeater's or are they different (something else entirely)? If they are the same, then we have a useful framework or information skeleton via which one can map all of the healing color data. If they are different, then how are they different? Once again, we can use the Leadbeater/Theosophical model as a type of target picture *against which* one can integrate all the healing data by contrast. Either way, it would be a useful exercise because it leads to a type of integration of all the seemingly disparate healing information.

Let us also remember, as we proceed along this path, that it is our *unconscious* mind that is gathering all this information, packaging useful kernels to send to our cerebral cortex so that we might experience conscious awareness of some data. The unconscious must use symbols with which we have some awareness so, for colors, it mainly uses those from the visible part of the EM spectrum with which we have had abundant experience. In any healing experience, the colors one experiences are most likely to be from either the fine information wave substance of R-space or the substances of the higher dimensional domains above that. Ultimately, we must learn to discriminate which domain the various colors represent and the purpose for why they appear. In this fashion, one not only serves but one grows.

Everything stated above for local healers also applies to non-local healing. The phenomenon of distant healing is enhanced by incorporation of the phenomenon of remote viewing. However, instead of just operating in the R-space receiver mode, one must also add the R-space transmitter mode. Because of this, the channel of signal propagation (ME not EM) and the basic energy/information field (mind and ME rather than EM) are different.

In non-local healing, there appear to be three relevant groupings of energies involved:

(1) Higher dimensional energies from "unseen" beings in the hierarchy of life; the energies/information come from the domains of spirit, mind and emotion and can be simply designated by $\{v_E, v_M, v_S\}_{U^*}$, where v means frequency and U^* means "unseen". These are received by the chakras of the healers.

(2) The healer's chakras act as kinds of transducers or converters of these higher dimensional energies into magnetoelectric (ME) and deltron energies that also carry the key information. These converted energies can be simply designated as $\{v_R, v_\delta\}_{H^*}$, where H^* designates "healer". These radiated energies/information are quickly propagated to the healee, designated by H, via R-space.

(3) In the local environment of the healee, H, the $\{v_R, v_\delta\}_{H^*}$, do two things, (a) they act directly on the *subtle* atoms and molecules of the healee's R-space layer in the personality self (physical vacuum level) and (b) react with the local electromagnetic (EM) photon spectrum to entangle these photons with information. In turn, these *enhanced* EM photons interact directly with the D-space level of the healee's personality self body.

In an attempt to underscore these process paths, we will discriminate these steps via a set of symbolic reaction equations followed by a set of pictures. These are:

(a) $\{v_E, v_M, v_S\}_{U^*} \xrightarrow[\text{conversion}]{\text{H}^*, \text{R-space layer}} \{v_R, v_\delta\}_{H^*}$

(b) $\{v_R, v_\delta\}_{H^*} \xrightarrow[\text{through R-space}]{\text{Radiation propagation}} \{v_R, v_\delta\}_H^{\text{ENV}}$

(ci) $\{v_R, v_\delta\}_H^{\text{ENV}} \xrightarrow[\text{cross-section}]{\text{Direct absorption}} \{v_R, v_\delta\}_H^{\text{R-Level}}$

(cii) $\{v_R, v_\delta\}_H^{\text{ENV}} \xrightarrow[\text{cross-section}]{\text{EM photon entanglement}} \{v_{em}^{**}\}_H^{\text{ENV}}$

(ciii) $\{v_{em}^{**}\}_H^{\text{ENV}} \xrightarrow[\text{cross-section}]{\text{Direct absorption}} \{v_{em}^{**}\}_H^{\text{D-Level}}$

Figure 6.7

Non-local healing:

(1)   Higher dimensional energies from "unseen" beings in the hierarchy of life; the energies/information come from the domains of spirit, mind and emotion and can be simply designated by $\{\nu_E, \nu_M, \nu_S\}_{U^*}$, where ν means frequency and U^* means "unseen". These are received by the chakras of the healers.

(2)   The healer's chakras act as kinds of transducers or converters of these higher dimensional energies into magnetoelectric (ME) and deltron energies that also carry the key information. These converted energies can be simply designated as $\{\nu_R, \nu_\delta\}_{H^*}$, where H^* designated "healer". These radiated energies/information are quickly propagated to the healee, designated by H, via R-space.

(3)   In the local environment of the healee, H, the $\{\nu_R, \nu_\delta\}_{H^*}$, do two things, (a) they act directly on the subtle atoms and molecules of the healee's R-space layer in the personality self (physical vacuum level) and (b) react with the local electromagnetic (EM) photon spectrum to entangle these photons with information. In turn, these *enhanced* EM photons interact directly with the D-space level of the healee's personality self body.

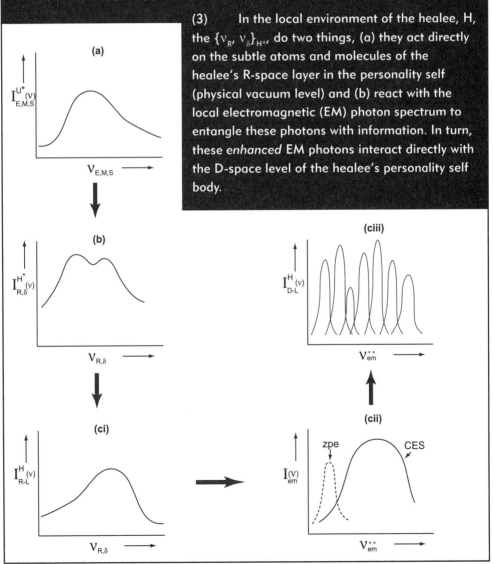

Representing $I(\nu)$ as the radiation intensity as a function of the designated frequencies, νj, Figure 6.7 reflects this same basic information in a set of schematic pictures. In part cii, we have attempted to discriminate the EM zero-point energy (zpe) spectrum from the total spectrum of EM photons (zpe + the Casimer energy spectrum (CES)) that are available in the healee's environment. Many writers, today, mistakenly lump all the physical vacuum level energies (which includes all the R-space vacuum levels of energies (ν_E, ν_M, ν_S)) with the EM zpe. For the future unfoldment of this new science, it is not a good idea to follow such a practice.

References

1.   W.A. Tiller, *Science and Human Transformation: Subtle Energies, Intentionality and Consciousness* (Pavior Publishing, Walnut Creek, CA, 1997).

2.   T. Norretranders, *The User Illusion: Cutting Consciousness Down to Size* (Penguin Books, Penguin Putnam Inc., New York, 1998).

3.   K. Pribram, *Brain and Perception. Holonomy and Structure in Figural Processing* (Lawrence Erlbaum Associates, Hillsdale, New Jersey, 1991).

4.   H.A. Pohl, *Dielectrophoresis: The Behavior of Neutral Matter in Non-uniform Electric Fields* (Cambridge University Press, London, 1978).

5.   B.B. Brown, *New Mind, New Body-Biofeedback: New Directions for the Mind* (Harper and Row, New York, 1975).

6.   E. Green and A. Green, *Beyond Biofeedback*, (Delacorte Press/Seymour Lawrence, New York, 1977).

7.   J.D. Kraus and K.R. Carver, *Electromagnetics* (McGraw-Hill Book Company, New York, 1973).

8.   W.A. Tiller, W.E. Dibble, Jr., and M.J. Kohane, *Conscious Acts of Creation* (Pavior Publishing, Walnut Creek, CA, 2001).

9.   W.A. Tiller, "Some Energy Field Observations of Man and Nature", in *Galaxies of Life: The Human Aura in Acupuncture and Kirlian Photography*, eds., S. Krippner and D. Rubin (An Interface Book, New York, 1973) p 70; Fig. 69.

10.   S. Karagulla and D. van Gelder Kunz, *The Chakras and Human Energy Fields* (Quest Books, The Theosophical Publishing House, Wheaton, IL, 1989).

11.   H. Motoyama, *Theories of the Chakras: Bridge to Higher Consciousness* (Quest Books, The Theosophical Publishing House, Wheaton, IL, 1981) pp 199-201.

Chapter 7

The Philosophical
Perspective

Extensive use of this general IIED-technology will slowly but surely transform the entire earth to a higher EM gauge symmetry state and we humans along with it. The new technologies created will allow us to heal much of the damage we have already done.

Main goals

The main goals of our research work for the last 3 to 4 decades has been (1) to design and conduct careful laboratory experiments in the psychoenergetics area in order to reveal, in quantitative detail, how human consciousness interacts with the various energies and materials of physical reality, as well as with the higher dimensional aspects of the larger reality and (2) to construct and test a satisfactory theoretical model of nature that quantitatively explains the experimental data that we and others gather via such psychoenergetics studies. We encapsulate the fruits of this effort into the following reaction equation metaphor

$$\text{MASS} \rightleftharpoons \text{ENERGY} \rightleftharpoons \text{CONSCIOUSNESS} \qquad (7.1)$$

The larger goal of this work has been to build a reliable bridge of understanding for nature's manifold expressions that (a) seamlessly joins with today's conventional scientific understanding of our outer spacetime world, on one end, (b) passes progressively through the various subtle domains of inner reality in the middle and (c) is strongly anchored in the bedrock of spirit at the other end. In service to these goals, we have attempted to communicate this new understanding to the world in all possible formats so as to inspire and uplift our entire human family to a deeper awareness of, and the great potential of, their own inner resources as well as the vast inner resources of global nature.

It is our intention to apply these new understandings in all possible ways to (1) enrich the lives of all living things on this planet, (2) create a new science and new technologies that solve problems and difficulties present in today's world so that all of humanity can evolve to a higher level of beingness in the larger reality and (3) create organizations in the world, needed for the conduct of and dissemination of the fruits of this understanding, that are based only on win/win principles and fairness in profit sharing.

Only in this way can we move away from the selfishness, greed plus material entrapments and practices that characterize today's world.

In this chapter, we try to extract the essence of the philosophical implications brought forth in this book as being relevant to the three categories of (a) humanity, (b) science and (c) technology.

For Humanity

Perhaps the three key things about humans that makes them so special is that (1) their acupuncture meridian/chakra system is at ~the SU(2) EM gauge symmetry level so that, via their sustained, disciplined, acts of intention, they can transform themselves into higher and higher states of both consciousness and beingness, (2) their innate ability to express unconditional love allows them to nurture and lift the world around them and (3) their innate ability to re-embody allows them to make many, many learning mistakes, lifetime after lifetime, and yet eventually graduate with full honors from the spacetime classroom.

We all have the internal tools for self-transformation and it is time for the general public to awaken to the realization that we are all spirits having a physical experience as we ride the "river of life" together. It is time to recognize that we can become much, much more than we presently think we are by going *within* to experience and know our "source" via our disciplined progress in inner self-management. It is time to recognize that all humans matter; that they can beneficially change themselves, their environment and our collective world. It is time for us to recognize that we are intimately connected one to the other and, collectively, we form a whole wherein "the God in me beholds the God in you" and wherein, via helping to lift another to greater personal capabilities, we are ourselves lifted.

We all share in and personally experience the collective future that we all co-create via our thoughts, attitudes and actions, thus, it is not only necessary to have *worthy* goals but we must use *worthy* means (right actions) for achieving these goals. It is the multiplicity of event amplitudes in the x_4 domain less than x^*_4 (the current now) that information entangle and superpose to create the event spectrum in the x_4 domain greater than x^*_4 (our most probable future). Now is the time for each of us to be courageous, allowing our inner light to shine into our outer world and become what we were always intended to become - and that is, loving co-creators with our spiritual "source" within.

This inner light from the general public is badly needed in the world today on many fronts and a goodly number of this readership are hearing the call. However, we would like to draw attention and address a serious problem that most never think of as a serious problem. This problem is with our current scientific establishment - they are *stuck* and need the general public's help to become *unstuck*.

When WAT first began his psychoenergetic experiments, in parallel with his conventional science work as an avocational pursuit at Stanford in ~1970 (see Chapter 1) he made a serious, but naïve assumption. He assumed that, if he continued his highly expert conventional science studies (for which he was internationally recognized and respected) and, in parallel, performed careful psychoenergetics investigations, his scientific peers would look at and read this second stream of papers with some degree of thoughtfulness and interest. Unfortunately, this initial assumption proved to be quite wrong! Just as in Galileo's time, the respected scientific establishment was not willing "to look through the telescope" at the data with a clear and discerning eye.

This is a human sociological problem involving many causative factors. Let's consider some of them.

First, scientists are mostly just like normal folks but with much more specialized education and training. Thus, they also operate somewhat on a herd instinct, want security and are not particularly courageous except in areas where they have a great deal of knowledge. Most of them are followers rather than leaders, are quite subject to peer pressure and very protective of their hard-won professional reputations. That is their personal-power base! Most work very hard, are very busy keeping up with digesting all the important literature in their particular field of expertise, carrying out their personal research, finding the necessary funding to continue and expand this research, writing scientific papers and books, trying to get these published, making presentations at scientific meetings to their peers in order to sustain and enhance their professional reputations and serving on professional, governmental and university committees. All these things, plus being a spouse and parent, are necessary activities in the life of a successful scientist in today's world. Most have no time left over for inner self-management activities unless prodded in this direction by their spouse or have had some definitive personal inner-life experiences. Most would feel tainted and reputation-threatened to be in any way connected to psychoenergetic research.

Second, top-ranked universities have a reputation to protect so they vie for the best scholars, researchers, teachers and staff that their money and reputation and local environmental quality can buy. Sadly, in today's world most have become very sophisticated high tech training schools for industry and government. Their reputations attract high quality students, foundation, philanthropist and government money plus financial donations from a wide variety of alumni. They must afford to present a collective image to the world as a successful, leading-edge, establishment-type, creative organization in order to continue to attract such students and moneys. Maverick professors in the organization are tolerated so long as they "push the envelope" along fairly conventionally accepted paths. At present, most would feel reputation-threatened and tainted by having psychoenergetics type of research occurring within the confines of their organization. Hopefully, this attitude will change in the not too distant future.

Third, the major funding source for research in a nation is its government. In the U.S., after WWII, the government planted a great deal of "seed corn" types of research during the 50's and 60's investment. Political demands for practical payoffs from such research began in the mid to late 60's and, in the 1970's, government funding shifted more to practical applications of this seed corn research. By the 1980's, almost all university research was directed towards exploiting the new understandings of the 50's and 60's. This mode of research continued through the 90's and is still so today. No new seed-corn type of research has been funded since the early 60's, except for those few that appear to have advanced military use possibilities. The psychoenergetics research of the "remote viewing" type, funded by various U.S. intelligence-gathering agencies in the 70's and 80's at Stanford Research International, is one of the few exceptions.

Fourth, most of the theological organizations in the U.S., who profess to promoting "inner-work" with their congregations, actually preach secular religious dogmas designed to entrain their clientele to a fairly narrow view of theology and its role in the spiritual development of humanity. Although some types of biofeedback tools and inner self-management processes for human self-development have been available since the 1960's, the various religious organizations have not pushed to proceed along these lines of personal empowerment seemingly because they know that, just like the U.S. government, when the public becomes awake to the power within each of them they are not so easily controlled.

With discrimination of, at the very least, these four causative factors, one can begin to see that there is no simple "fix" for this problem; however, with the present availability to publish one's data on the internet and to self-publish one's books, editors of establishment journals and publishing companies can no longer completely block the dissemination of psychoenergetic science experimental and theoretical findings to the general public and also to interested scientists.

Today, the general public of all countries pay, via their taxes, for almost all scientific research carried out in their nation. Therefore, in democratic societies, the general public are ultimately responsible for the sustaining of outdated paradigms by their scientific sector. When human consciousness has been experimentally shown to significantly influence the properties of, and processes in, organic, inorganic and living materials[1,2], it is time for the general public to require (demand) that their scientific establishment develop a new reference frame for viewing nature that has the capability of quantitatively connecting *both* the seeming outer world aspects of nature and our seeming inner world aspects of nature.

Several decades ago, the general public unconsciously birthed a significant change in the medical sector of our society when they reached out to buy, with their own, unreimbursed, out-of-pocket funds, alternative and complementary medical services to the tune of billions of dollars per year (in the U.S.) because the conventional U.S. medical community was not adequately serving their needs. This time, the stakes are even higher because the scientific establishment worldview is taken very seriously by a great many of the general public so they get "stuck" as well. This means that the children and their educational system also get "stuck". The lost potential is a tragedy!

Before closing this section, let us consider one speculative thought concerning the whole person concept of Chapter 1. Let us hypothesize that both the God self and the soul self are holograms with the latter having a lower dimensionality and a much narrower frequency bandwidth than the former. Our God self, in turn, is a small piece of the total hologram we refer to as *God*. Thus, it faithfully represents the total hologram but with much-reduced fidelity. As the soul self grows through the experiences of many, many personality selves, its power spectrum becomes richer and richer in both amplitude and bandwidth so its hologram grows likewise in greater and greater fidelity to the original image set for it by the Divine. When graduation day comes for the soul self and it is absorbed into the God self, the God self, in turn, grows in fidelity to the original *source* so it is in essence "a larger piece" of the total God hologram. It is in this manner that God grows during reconstruction. This is the *in-breathing phase of the All!*

The new contributions to science

This book has revealed the functioning existence of a device (Type I) that acts as a "source" to (1) lift the EM gauge symmetry state (inner symmetry state) of a macroscopic space significantly above our normal U(1) level, where the standard Maxwell equations of electromagnetism apply, and (2) tune or program that space to be highly responsive towards the fulfillment of the specific intention statement programmed into the Type I device from a deep meditative state by two, four or six well-qualified meditators. This book has also revealed the functioning existence of a procedure and a potential device (Type II) that acts as a "detector" of a thermodynamic free energy change for the hydrated proton, above that for the U(1) level, so that one can experimentally track the raising of the EM gauge symmetry state of the macroscopic space due to such a Type I device. In addition, experimentation has been carried out to show that humans have their acupuncture meridian/chakra system at such a higher EM gauge symmetry level (above the U(1) level) and thus, their internally or externally directed intentions can appreciably influence properties, processes and behaviors existing at the U(1) level in their own bodies, in their external environment and in the bodies of others located either locally or non-locally from them. Such capabilities are associated with the presence of a new type of information carrier wave, modulatable by human intention, which appears to function at the vacuum level of physical reality. Here, the governing variables are such as to allow effective propagation of such carrier waves to be seemingly independent of distance and perhaps also of time. This leads to information entanglement between all sites of the overall experimental system. What do these new facts mean for future science?

During the past several centuries, humanity has learned what is required to do good quality science in the simple case where objects and humans are relatively unconnected to each other, macroscopic forces are all localized and interconvertability between mass and energy has been both theoretically proved ($E=mc^2$) to hold by Albert Einstein and practically utilized via nuclear reactors. Now, we must move on to perform equal quality science in the more complex case that (1) objects are to some degree energy/information entangled with other objects, (2) humans are energy/information entangled with other humans and (3) humans are energy/information entangled with objects. Here, the sum of all parts in a system are energy/information entangled and the output performance of the overall system is intimately related to this connectivity between all of its parts. The reaction equation metaphor that applies to this kind of system is given by

$$\text{MASS} \rightleftarrows \text{ENERGY} \rightleftarrows \text{CONSCIOUSNESS} \qquad (7.1)$$

with interconvertability between one term and any other. At this point in time, we have no idea of the quantitative relationship between energy and consciousness (nor do we really have a good definition of consciousness) other than our working hypothesis from Chapter 1 that it is an emergent property associated with spirit entering dense matter which, in turn, occurs as we build various types of infrastructures into our biobodysuit at the personality self and soul self levels.

249

To view nature, we use a duplex RF consisting of two reciprocal, four-dimensional subspaces, one of which is spacetime for the atom/molecule level of physical reality and the other is a frequency domain for the physical vacuum level of reality. These two domains are coupled together via a deltron-coupling coefficient, γ_{eff} (and all of this is imbedded in the three higher dimensional domains of emotion, mind and spirit). Because of this, simultaneous solutions of second-order, partial differential equations in each subspace are required for overall conservation of energy and chemical species. Exactly how consciousness enters these equations is not presently clear. It is perhaps possible that this factor enters via the deltron activation function with its approximate coefficient, γ_{eff}.

As we entertain such novel considerations, we must ask ourselves what is involved in raising the EM gauge symmetry state, what is involved in tuning it to fulfill a specific intention statement and how does this all relate to information entanglement.

The raising of the EM gauge symmetry state is an absolute wonder of thermodynamics because, here, for the very first time in history, we encounter a process in nature wherein the opposite of normal atom/molecule level processes occurs. Instead of thermodynamic potential degrading and entropy increasing as a consequence of a reaction event, we observe that the thermodynamic potential increases (and presume that the entropy decreases) during the IIED-space conditioning process with a precursor of the following type

$$\text{UED} \xrightarrow[\text{intent}]{\text{conscious}} \text{IIED} \qquad (7.2a)$$

with perhaps the following being a clearer picture of this important process path

$$\text{UED} \xrightarrow[\text{intent}]{\substack{\text{focused} \\ \text{conscious}}} \substack{\text{key level of} \\ \text{deltron} \\ \text{activation}} \longrightarrow \text{IIED} . \qquad (7.2b)$$

In Equation 7.2b, the key level of deltron activation is that which raises the IIED to the SU(2) EM gauge symmetry state level. At this inner symmetry level, ME-photons are sufficiently deltron-potentized (γ_{eff} sufficiently large) that they can readily information entangle with EM-photons and thus other materials at the atom/molecule level of physical reality.

For the U(1) EM gauge symmetry state, the EM potentials and fields are mostly vectors given in terms of their amplitudes and phase angles. This phase angle can take on all possible values in a plane so that these phase values can be interpreted as an angular coordinate in a two-dimensional space having two perpendicular coordinates (x,y). The internal space of the U(1) EM gauge symmetry state thus looks like the interior of a flat ring where the coordinate of any point in the ring is just the phase value itself. Mathematicians call this internal space a "fiber".

Figure 7.1a shows a unique space that combines an internal space (ordinate) with spacetime (abscissa). In this unique space, the spatial location of a particle is represented by a dot at a coordinate point in the horizontal, spacetime plane while the phase value for the field in the internal space is specified by angular coordinates in the unique space. As the particle moves through spacetime (sequence of dots), it also traces out a path in the internal space (dashed line) above the spacetime trajectory. When there is no external gauge potential acting on the particle, the internal space path is completely arbitrary. When the particle interacts with an external gauge field, the dashed path in the internal space is a continuous curve determined by the gauge potential. In mathematical jargon, the unique space formed by the union of our four-dimensional spacetime with an internal space is called a "fiber bundle" space.[3]

Several decades ago, it was discovered that the nuclear force is independent of electrical charges.[4] That is, the strength of the nuclear interaction between a proton and a neutron, or between two protons or two neutrons is exactly the same. This electric charge independence was formulated as a new symmetry principle via introduction of the new concept of "isotopic spin" which was defined as the invariance of the nuclear force under a new isotopic-spin rotation group (called the SU(2) group) in analogy to the accepted law for the conservation of angular momentum. For example, the proton and neutron can be considered as the "up" and "down" states, respectively, of an abstract isotopic spin, similar to the ordinary spin states of an electron. In analogy to the EM potential, Yang and Mills[3] postulated a new potential for the isotopic spin. However, the greater complexity (tensorial) of the SU(2) isotopic-spin rotation group, compared to the U(1) phase group (vectorial), means that the Yang-Mills potential is quite different than the EM potential.

In this book, we have a different example that requires the use of the more complex SU(2) gauge symmetry state. This is also needed for the situation where both electric and magnetic monopoles, and thus both electric and magnetic currents, naturally

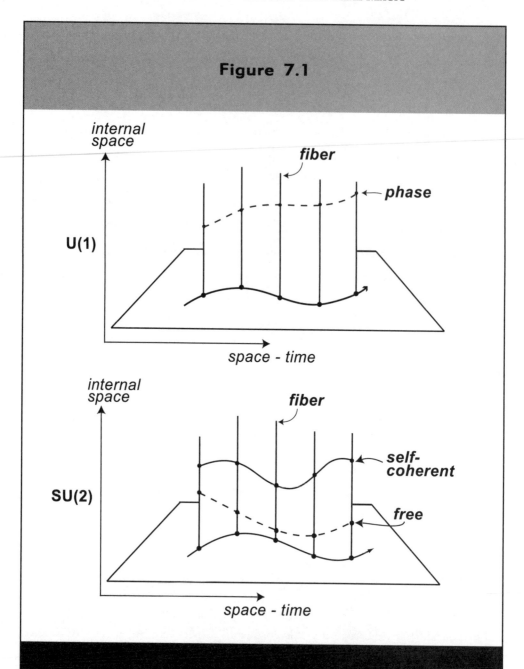

Figure 7.1

If indeed the substance of the vacuum level of reality behaves as if it were traveling at velocities appreciably greater than c, then it requires a certain level of deltron activation to ensure that ME photons can meaning fully interact with the EM gauge potential and lift the EM gauge symmetry state.

coexist and can interact with each other.[5] In order to move from the higher degrees of freedom state of the SU(2) EM gauge symmetry level to the lower degrees of freedom state of the U(1) EM gauge symmetry level, a symmetry breaking transformation is required to occur.

The internal space defined for the SU(2) gauge symmetry state is more complicated than that for the U(1) gauge symmetry state because it describes rotation in a three-dimensional space (think of two, independent phase-angle (vectors) rotations in perpendicular planes and, from Chapter 3, a vector times a vector produces a tensor which characterizes the SU(2) state). For the SU(2) gauge symmetry state, values of three angles (two are independent) which specify the rotation can be considered as the coordinates of a point inside an abstract three-dimensional space. Thus, the internal symmetry of the SU(2) gauge symmetry state looks like the interior of a sphere so that, for the SU(2) state, one would need to attach a sphere at each spacetime point of Figure 7.1a. Symmetry breaking, in group theory terms, means that the initial symmetry group (SU(2) say) is broken down to one of its subgroups (U(1) say).

As shown in Figure 7.1a, for a particle, any changes in the internal space direction (dashed line) between different spacetime points is completely determined by the minimal coupling to the gauge potential. The internal space direction is free to rotate in any way required by the gauge field so no additional constraints exist on such an internal space direction. In order to break the symmetry imposed by the particle's interaction with the gauge field; the particle must somehow determine its own direction in the internal space independent from the requirement of the external gauge field. At the same time, the particle must still be minimally coupled to the gauge field in order to preserve the invariance of its free energy state.[3] This means that the wave function for the particle must have an intrinsic relative phase factor that is different from that illustrated in Figure 7.1a. In turn, this means that a new type of physical system that interacts with the gauge field, labeled self-coherent in Figure 7.1b, must be introduced. Here, the phase of the self-coherent system traces out a different path (solid line) in the internal space that is different than that for the free particle (dashed line) in the same gauge field. The gauge field, itself, must undergo certain changes in order to adjust its phase requirements to that of the self-coherent system. This is the actual meaning of gauge symmetry breaking. The gauge field is "broken" from the free particle form to the self-coherent form.

In our case, the new type of physical system is the deltron-coupled, vacuum level physics that begins to seriously interact with the U(1) EM gauge symmetry state and lift it to a level of complexity requiring the SU(2) EM gauge symmetry state designation because the new inner symmetry phase angle also starts to become important in determining the invariance of the thermodynamic free energy state. Thus, if indeed the substance of the vacuum level of reality behaves as if it were traveling at velocities appreciably greater than c, then it requires a certain level of deltron activation to ensure that ME photons can meaningfully interact with the EM gauge potential and lift the EM gauge symmetry state to the upper curve in Figure 7.1b. As indicated in Equation 7.2, it is the deltron activation that is crucial here. Without that, the electrons in the atom/molecule level of physical reality would not be able to access signals from their magnetic counterpart at the physical vacuum level of reality.

Now that we begin to understand how the experimental space is IIED-conditioned to higher EM gauge symmetry levels, we need to address the question "how does the spaces tuning or programming to a specific intention statement work?"

What one sees for the $\Delta pH = +1$ units IIED in the remote sites experiment is that (1) the litmus paper test yields $pH(t) = pH_{U(1)}$ and $\Delta pH(t) = 0$ while (2) the two digital measuring systems yielded $pH(t) = \Delta pH_{U(1)} + \Delta pH(t)$ with ΔpH growing from zero to ~one pH unit over cycle number. The implications of these findings is that digital systems either detect a *real* thermodynamic measurement, in which only $pH_{U(1)}$ comes from the atom/molecule level of physical reality and $\Delta pH(t)$ comes from the γ_{eff}-coupled physical vacuum level of reality, or all digital measurement instruments are subject to huge errors. Consideration of the side-by-side, treatment and control experiments with the liver enzyme and the fruit flies[2] appears to confirm that the digital measurement systems are all behaving consistently. At a philosophical level, this seems to mean that digital measuring systems are primarily information registering systems and that the thermodynamic free energy change associated with a ΔpH change correlates 1:1 with an information change. In conventional information theory[6-8] initiated by Shannon[9], the quantity of information, in terms of bits for a process or information transfer event, is quantitatively connected to negentropy (reduction in entropy) which is fully consistent with an increase of thermodynamic potential. And this is what our experiments show for an IIED-conditioned space - the EM gauge symmetry state is increased and thus the thermodynamic free energy per unit volume is also increased. *This means that the γ_{eff}- coupling of our measurement instruments to the physical vacuum level of reality is reducing the rate of entropy production occurring in our atom/molecule level world!*

Extension of this line of thought indicates that aspiring humans, through their conscious intent acting on and through their acupuncture meridian/chakra system into the U(1) level world, can slow down and perhaps reverse the degradation of that world via lifting themselves and their surroundings to ever higher EM gauge symmetry states! The experimental evidence concerning long-range, room temperature, macroscopic sized space, information entanglement between remote sites confirms that the ME carrier wave is intimately connected with this "uplift" process. However, exactly how this important process works is an important goal for science to discover.

The key issue, here, is exactly what is the mechanism for this information transfer? Which of the following mechanisms is closest to the truth?

$$\left\{\begin{array}{l}\text{R-space}\\\text{information}\\\text{at }\underline{k}_4\end{array}\right\} \xrightarrow{\gamma_{eff}} \left\{\begin{array}{l}\text{D-space}\\\text{information}\\\text{at }\underline{s}_4\end{array}\right\} \xrightarrow[\text{through D-space}]{\text{Propogation}} \left\{\begin{array}{l}\text{D-space}\\\text{information}\\\text{at }\underline{s}_4{}'\end{array}\right\}, \quad (7.3a)$$

or

$$\left\{\begin{array}{l}\text{R-space}\\\text{information}\\\text{at }\underline{k}_4\end{array}\right\} \xrightarrow[\text{through R-space}]{\text{Propogation}} \left\{\begin{array}{l}\text{R-space}\\\text{information}\\\text{at }\underline{k}_4{}'\end{array}\right\} \xrightarrow{\gamma_{eff}} \left\{\begin{array}{l}\text{D-space}\\\text{information}\\\text{at }\underline{s}_4{}'\end{array}\right\}, \quad (7.3b)$$

or both. Since R-space is a deltron-empowered frequency domain, it is relatively independent of distance and time, so information transfer from $\underline{k}_4$ to $\underline{k}'_4$ in R-space allows γ_{eff}- coupling to provide the information at both S_4 and S'_4 in D-space and it therefore looks like non-local information entanglement from a D-space-only perspective.

A new door has been opened in physical reality with this experimental work. Magnetic monopoles and the physical vacuum have become more accessible for exploration. The effects of human consciousness, via IIEDs or other techniques, on the various chemical or radiation processes presently known to materials science can begin to be explored. Many behavioral qualities of materials, heretofore thought to be an exclusive property of a quantum mechanical description of nature, can begin to be explored as a simple, classical expansion of our basic reference frame for viewing nature. Almost all properties of materials have heretofore been shown to depend exclusively on electromagnetism via

Maxwell's four beautiful equations and this field has been ploughed extensively for the past century. Now, we see a way to expand that picture, to incorporate the dynamics of the magnetic monopole and lift the whole electric/magnetic interactions processes to an entirely new level. On such a path, we will learn to understand and harness ME energy as a new communications vehicle and to step confidently across the boundary separating slower than EM light processes (v = c) from faster than EM light processes. We will also learn to understand and harness information entanglement processes for the benefit of humanity. Most importantly, we will learn more about the fundamental nature of consciousness, how it connects to various energies and how it should be expressed in our equations, both classical and quantum mechanical, to enhance their predictive power as we bootstrap our way towards a more realistic T.O.E. (theory of everything). Figure 7.2 shows the various stages one must go through in the development of a possible T.O.E. using the postulates outlined in Chapter 3. The door has been opened, we invite the scientists of this readership to walk through!

Impacting technology

We are at a very important transition point in our U.S. society with respect to our global society. For the past century, our technology, education and inherent creativity have led to a very high standard of living for U.S. citizens relative to the majority of the global society. Thus, at this point in time, this productive engine of commerce is based upon two categories of technology, (1) those existing prior to World War II and (2) those created post WWII. The latter are almost all based on the new "seed corn" research planted by the U.S. government in university and industrial laboratories during the 1950's and very early 1960's. No such creative investments have been made since the beginning of the 1970's.

In the past five decades, the communication between, interconnectedness of, and interdependence of all world nations within our global society has increased dramatically. The other nations of the world, following our early example, have (1) greatly strengthened their educational systems, (2) greatly enhanced their technological skills and output in primary industries to become, more than on par, competitive with us, in part because of a much cheaper human labor force and (3) greatly enhanced their sophisticated knowledge skill sets and their societal technical infrastructure to catch up to and even lead the U.S. in many areas of technology. The bottom line for all of us to realize is that, now, our world

Figure 7.2

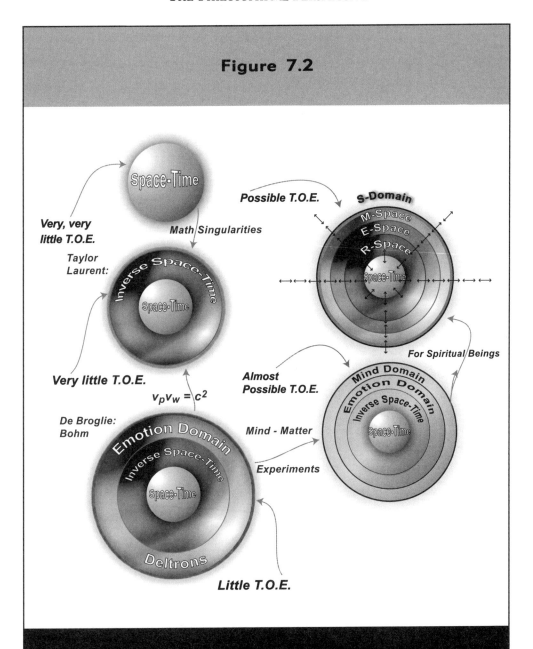

We will learn more about the fundamental nature of consciousness, how it connects to various energies and how it should be expressed in our equations, both classical and quantum mechanical, to enhance their predictive power as we bootstrap our way towards a more realistic T.O.E. (theory of everything).

is a *truly dynamic, interactive, thermodynamic system,* so large disparities in standards of living between the human populations of different nations are no longer viable. This means that, over the next decade, the present trickle of jobs that are moving off-shore will become a flood in order for our companies to maintain commercial competitiveness. This will occur in spite of what special taxation and policy measures are put in place to slow down the flux of this change, because our world has become a global thermodynamic system in all ways including transport of monies, jobs, pollution, material resources, etc.

Probably the only way that we can maintain a long-term high standard of living for the U.S. is to do the one thing that our unique culture does very well and that is *move outside the "box" and create entirely new kinds of industries.* Unfortunately, this time we will not have government planted "new seed corn" to build on. Those national resources are all being spent on military adventures. However, findings of this book and its two predecessors[1,2] show us a new pathway for both enhancing the capabilities of all our old technologies and building entirely new ones.

From what we have learned thus far, the IIED technique appears to have application to enhance the performance of every technology on the earth today and to create new ones. The essential steps are (1) condition the space that houses the key technological equipment to ~the SU(2) level, (2) tune the space, via specific intentions, to realistic performance enhancement goals, (3) continuously monitor the degree of elevation of the EM gauge symmetry state above the U(1) state and (4) develop the human team so that their collective "experimenter" effect pumps the space "up" rather than drains it "down". Not only various utilities, manufacturing and transportation applications but medical, professional, educational, correctional, etc., facilities should benefit from these techniques. Three obvious limitations to all of this will be, (1) the willingness of employees to become sufficiently inner self-managed to be "pumper uppers" rather than "drainer downers", (2) the willingness of the "unseen universe" in Figure 2.21 to cooperate in the creation of the particular IIED needed for the specific application and (3) our ability to further shield against natural imprint leakage processes in the basic IIED technology.[10,11]

If we look at present technology areas in a little more detail, we note the following:

1.   In the computer area, the artificial intelligence (A.I.) activity of the last couple of decades has not been particularly successful. One major implication of our proposed IIED technology is that the incorporation of a specifically designed IIED, with its built-in intelligence, into a computer system is expected to significantly enhance the performance

of such a system well beyond today's best examples. Computer software and hardware developers should be seriously interested in more fully understanding this class of new phenomena, even if only to develop reliable shielding procedures to protect their systems from possible intrusions of focused human consciousness. Further, they should be interested in creating hybrid systems between IIED technology and current computer software/hardware technology to lift computer performance to a whole new level.

2. A major application exists for chemical and pharmaceutical industries wherein a valuable product is produced via a chemical reaction yielding several isomers or enantiomers, only one of which is commercially valuable, and separation/extraction of the desirable product from the mix is a costly process. Using the IIED technology with a suitable imprint statement, from past experiments it seems feasible to significantly increase the yield of the desirable product and simultaneously reduce the yields of the competing process paths. In general, it seems quite feasible to significantly increase both the thermodynamic driving force plus the initiation and transformation kinetics for specific commercial chemical reactions.

3. In the medical application area, applications of the IIED technology abound. For chemical medicine, example 2 above is straightforward, enhancing specific outcomes and limiting possible side-effect reactions for a particular medicine seems perfectly feasible. For EM energy medicine, enhancement or diminishment of particular photon absorption cross-sections in patients seems quite viable. In information medicine which directly involves ME photons, once again manipulation of particular spectral absorption cross-sections appears to be viable. Beyond these various treatment modalities, the maintenance of health homeostasis of at-risk patients at various or all subtle domain levels also appears to be viable.

4. In the human area, we have already pointed out the importance of the acupuncture meridian/chakra system as being necessary body infrastructure for expanding the qualities and capabilities of humans. We have also postulated that the ME spectrum encompasses the spectrum of Qi utilized by Qigong masters to perform their remarkable feats and our $\Delta\Psi_H+$ - detector is an instrument capable of instrumental detection of some if not all of the energy consequences of Qi. Thus, it is not too large a step to presume that we will soon be able to measure the strength of Qi-flow around humans and other vertebrates and, if so, to construct a device suitable for functioning as a biofeedback device for the strengthening of an individual's Qi.

Extensive use of this general IIED-technology will slowly but surely transform the entire earth to a higher EM gauge symmetry state and we humans along with it. The properties of materials will thus change and our establishment science will pursue the study of nature and consciousness with new eyes. The new technologies created will allow us to heal much of the damage we have already done and are continuing to do to the earth. Hopefully we will expand our inner capacities to achieve a significantly higher level of wisdom than we now display before some of us emigrate to the stars in vehicles tightly engineered and powered to balance both the inner and outer capabilities needed for tapping that great resource - the vacuum.

References

1.   W.A. Tiller, *Science and Human Transformation: Subtle Energies, Intentionality and Consciousness* (Pavior Publishing, Walnut Creek, CA, 1997).

2.   W.A. Tiller, W.E. Dibble, Jr., and M.J. Kohane, *Conscious Acts of Creation* (Pavior Publishing, Walnut Creek, CA, 2001).

3.   K. Moriyasu, *An Elementary Primer for Gauge Theory* (World Scientific Publishing Co. Pte. Ltd., Singapore, 1983).

4.   G. 't Hooft, "Gauge Theories of the Forces Between Elementary Particles", Scientific American, 242, 6 (1980) 104.

5.   T.W. Barrett, "Comments on the Harmuth Ansatz: Use of a Magnetic Current Density in the Calculation of the Propagation Velocity of Signals by Amended Maxwell Theory", IEEE Transactions on Electromagnetic Compatibility, 30 (1988) 419.

6.   G. Raisbeck, *Information Theory, an Introduction for Scientists and Engineers* (Massachusetts Institute of Technology, Cambridge, MA, 1963).

7.   L. Brillouin, *Scientific Uncertainty and Information* (Academic Press, New York, 1964).

8.   L. Brillouin, *Science and Information Theory* (Academic Press, New York, Second Edition, 1962).

9.   C.E. Shannon and W. Weaver, *The Mathematical Theory of Communication* (University of Illinois Press, Urbana, IL, 1963).

10.   W.A. Tiller, "Towards a Quantitative Science and Technology that Includes Human Consciousness", Vision-In-Action (VIA) Magazine, 1 (4) (2003) 30-43.

11.   W.A. Tiller, "Towards a Society with Strong Hybrid Outer and Inner Technology", ReVision Magazine, 26 (3), 2004, 17-22.

Glossary

Biobodysuit: All the layers of uniquely different kinds of substance needed to allow our own kernel of spirit to meaningfully interface with our outer spacetime reality. What we put on when we are born into the earth plane and what we take off when we die from the earth plane.

Biofield: Proportional to the spatial gradient of the sum total of all the types of different energies radiated by a human or other living system.

Chemical potential: The partial thermodynamic free energy, on a per atom or molecule basis, for an electrically neutral species of a specific type.

Clairaudience: The ability of a human to cognitively hear information that is not accessible by our normal sound sensory system.

Clairvoyance: The ability of a human to cognitively see information patterns that are not accessible by our normal sight sensory system.

Cognition: The action or faculty of knowing. Our physical level of cognition involves the parameters of distance and time (the physical 4-space) to make sense of the phenomena in this direct space outside of ourselves. These parameters appear to be qualities associated with the intellectual brain's process-mechanism for this type of knowing. There are other types of knowing of which the most often mention is listed under the label "intuition". This book expands the parameters for cognition to higher dimensional spaces than the familiar four. In particular, it focuses especially on an 8-space consisting of two conjugate 4-spaces; one is the above-mentioned familiar 4-space while the other is its inverse. For observable phenomena, this automatically leads to wave-particle duality. For cognition, it leads to dual information maps which together form a whole. The familiar one is manifest in terms of shapes, textures, colors, etc., the other is manifest as a topography of wave crests and valleys in a coordinate frame (four orthogonal frequency directions) that is cognitively new to us. Unfortunately, at the present time, we can only visually represent this new information map on a piece of paper by using the familiar distance plots and change the labeling of the axes from (x, y) to (v_x, v_y).

Connectivity: A unique property of objects associated with a universe comprised of two reciprocal subspaces with a non-zero coupling coefficient acting between the very different types of substance inhabiting the different subspaces.

Consciousness: Thought by most to be the totality of the impressions, thoughts and feelings of an individual. Here, it is all the output expressions from the manifested in-dwelling spirit of that individual.

Constructive/destructive interference: Wave emission from multiple sources separated in spacetime, or scattered from multiple and similar objects separated in spacetime, to produce a superposed wave envelope which has a greatly increased amplitude when all the wavelets are in phase with each other, and they add constructively, but a greatly decreased amplitude when they are out of phase with each other, and add destructively.

Deltron: A type of substance from the emotion domain of reality that can travel both slower than EM light in vacuum, and thus interact with D-space substance, and faster than such EM light, and thus interact with R-space substance. This allows D-space substance to interact with R-space substance via deltron/deltron interactions without violating Einstein's relativity theory constraints.

D-space: This is what we currently call spacetime.

Deltron coupling coefficient, γ: A measure of deltron activation magnitude which, in turn, determines the degree of D-space substance interaction with R-space substance. As γ increases, the degree of connectivity between any two D-space objects increases regardless of separation distance.

Duplex or biconformal RF: A proposed new RF for a more internally self-consistent description of nature that includes all conventional science phenomena plus the main aspects of all psychoenergetic phenomena. This new RF is a special member of the general eight-dimensional space which comprises two, reciprocal four-dimensional subspaces, one of which is spacetime. Thus, the coordinates now are the four of spacetime (called D-space) and the four of reciprocal spacetime (all frequencies) which we label R-space.

Electrochemical potential: Extension of chemical potential to an electrically charged species.

Electrostatic potential (ϕ): The scalar potential driving purely electrical phenomena via its mathematical relationship to electric charge density.

EM gauge symmetry state: Relates to the inner symmetry condition of a space relative to its electromagnetic nature. At present, the normal EM environment of our world is the U(1) state where Maxwell's four equations, applied simultaneously, quantitatively define the entire range of electric/magnetic phenomena that can occur.

The SU(2) state is a higher EM gauge symmetry state wherein both single electric charges (+ and -) coexist with single magnetic charges (N and S) and Maxwell's four equations must now be modified to quantitatively define the range of electric/magnetic phenomena that can develop in a space maintained at this EM gauge symmetry state.

Ether: Sanskrit *akash*. Though not considered a factor in present scientific theory on the nature of the material universe, ether has for millennia been so referred to by India's sages. Paramahansa Yogananda spoke of ether as the background on which God projects the cosmic motion picture of creation. Space gives dimension to objects; ether separates the images. This "background", a creative force that coordinates all spatial vibrations, is a necessary factor when considering the subtler forces - thought and life energy (*prana*) - and the nature of space and the origin of material forces and matter. For this book, R-space matter is synonymous with ether.

Experimenter effect: An experimental result associated with the biofield of the experimenter interacting with the equipment and materials of the experiment to produce a change in the observed data compared to a case of perfect isolation between the experimental system and the experimenter.

Faraday Cage: A cage of some appreciable volume and constructed from fine mesh copper screen. Because of copper's high electrical conductivity, the cage when electrically grounded serves to reduce, by a significant factor, the magnitude of ambient high frequency electromagnetic waves that penetrate through the copper mesh to the cage's interior space.

Fourier transform: A unique mathematical operation acting on a mathematical function of distance or time or both to provide either a spatial or temporal or both spectrum of waves that equally describe the essential pattern of this function.

Frequency space/inverse space/k-space: In this space, waves or harmonic undulations of etheric (magnetic) substance are proposed to exist. The distribution of intensity in this space yields the topographic map for such magnetic substance. Although there may appear to be a close correspondence with the above item, k-space, there are profound differences. Here, an individual wave extends along k_x^*, k_y^*, etc., and has a k*-length analogous to a wavelength in direct space or physical space. A particular k*-value does not refer to a wave in physical space; however, an individual wave in the k*-space refers to a particle in direct space. At present, quantum mechanics empirically maps these two conjugate information domains into a single 4-space description of nature that exhibits wave-particle duality.

Gauge Theory: Represents a new synthesis of quantum mechanics and symmetry wherein gauge invariance is recognized as the physical principle governing the fundamental forces between all elementary particles. Such invariance must be satisfied for all observable quantities in order to ensure that any arbitrariness in A (magnetic vector potential) and ϕ do not affect the field strength.

Human aura: The biofield radiation pattern around the human body that can be seen by one with developed clairvoyant sight.

IIED: An intention imprinted electrical device which is an effective host for a specific intention statement. It can be transported thousands of miles from its original imprinting location and, when turned on in that distant space, lifts the EM gauge symmetry state of that space and tunes the space so as to experimentally manifest the specific intention.

Inner self-management: The gradual building of stable infrastructure within self, at non-spacetime levels of reality, through the practice of spiritual, mental and emotional discipline.

Intentionality: The Oxford dictionary gives "the quality or fact of being intentional; of or pertaining to purpose, pertaining to operation of the mind." As such, it represents the quality of one's conscious purpose, often thought of as self-directed mind. In this book, applied intentionality means placing a desire imprint from the level of spirit into the "simulator" at the mind level which then cascades through the various levels giving representative patterns at each level and materializes action at the physical distance-time level. This is, in turn, observed by the individual's physical cognition system.

Levitation: The ability of a human to cause an object to lift in space against the normal downwards gravitational force.

Macroscopic information entanglement: A long-range, D-space connectivity between remote sites of the same overall experimental system, which occurs at room temperature with macroscopic spaces ($\sim 10^2$ -10^3 cubic feet in size) so that anomalous experimental data behavior at one site is, to a significant degree, also manifest at a remote site.

Magnetic vector potential (A): In conventional electrodynamics, it is equation-connected to both the magnetic flux (or magnetic field, H) and the electric flux (or electric field, E) so it and the electrostatic potential, ϕ, define the two basic fields (E and H) involved in electromagnetism. Here, it is also used to connect the physical domain to the subtle domain.

Magnetoelectrochemical potential: Extension of electrochemical potential to a species that is both electrically charged *and* magnetically charged.

Materialization/dematerialization: The ability of a human to cause matter to appear/disappear at or from a region of space.

Maxwell's equations: Four coupled mathematical expressions created by James Clerk Maxwell in 1873 that beautifully synthesized the accepted electrical and magnetic phenomena of the 19th century.

Mirror principle: The mathematical relationship between D-space and R-space creates an inversion (not reflection) mirror type of relationship between a quality of substance in D-space and its conjugate quality in R-space.

Nodal network: A lattice of nodal points in which a key quality of the nodal species (vector direction, say) may be ordered or disordered at the various nodal site locations. These nodal points are non-linear transducers of one type of energy into another.

Paradigm: A prevailing worldview of how science interprets causal behavior of nature.

Particle-pilotwave concept: Created by De Broglie in the 1920's stating that every particle in physical reality had a pilot wave envelope which surrounded and guided the particle's motion. This concept became a cornerstone of quantum mechanics.

Phantom phenomenon: A long-lasting memory of an experimental result retained by the space wherein the original D-space cause has been removed. The magnitude of the effect decays much more slowly than expected for typical atom/molecule phenomena.

Precognition: The ability of a human to cognitively be aware of an information event that has not yet occurred in spacetime.

Psychoenergetics: All the unique energies associated with actions of the psyche - human, animal or other.

Psychokinesis: The ability of a human to move objects without physically touching them.

Quantization: The experimental observation by Planck that energy changes occur in discrete steps, as an integer multiple of some minimum size, rather than continuously. This concept has been expanded to embrace all fundamental spacetime variables such as time, mass, etc.

Quantum mechanics (QM): The mathematical formalism and paradigm that superceded classical mechanics to describe the inner working processes of nature but based on quantization rules.

Quantum perspective: A view of the very small at the sub-atomic/atomic particle size scale where energy flows in discrete packets and where most of seeming solid matter is empty space.

R-space: This is inverse spacetime.

Reference frame (RF): A coordinate system that an observer uses for both qualitatively and quantitatively describing an internally self-consistent explanation for all the manifold expressions of nature. In both the classical mechanics (CM) and present-day quantum mechanics (QM) paradigms, this has been three perpendicular coordinates of distance and one perpendicular coordinate of time to comprise a four-dimensional coordinate called spacetime.

Relativity perspective: A view of relative motions of objects where the speed of the object is sufficiently high that space and time cannot be treated as independent variables but are intimately coupled. Applies equally to things very large like planets and to things very small like electrons.

Remote viewing: The ability of a human to cognitively access detailed information concerning a very distant site that may be hundreds to thousands of miles away via other than our visual sensory system.

Renormalization: In many mathematical particle theories, one sometimes gets a number turning out to be infinite which ought to be finite, like the model of the electron as a point charge. By introducing a coupling constant or screening constant into the theory, an atmosphere of polarization collects around the bare particle so that the measurable entity is now the point particle plus atmosphere which now takes on finite values. The theory has been mathematically renormalized.

Scalar/vector/tensor property: A quality which may vary in magnitude from point to point in space but which does not vary with orientational direction about such a point (scalar) versus one which also varies with direction (vector). Tensor: a generalized vector with more than three components, each of which is a function of the coordinates of an arbitrary point in space of an appropriate number of dimensions.

Simulator: A programmable device designed to simulate the particular set of motions or events that reproduce a particular experience or result.

Space conditioning: Here, the meaning extends beyond adjustment of outer thermodynamic intensive variables of space like temperature, pressure, chemical concentration, etc., to include inner variables like electromagnetic gauge symmetry state, specific intention tuning (a matrix element) of that state, etc.

Subtle domains: Potential cognitive domains of the universe beyond the domain of physical cognition by humans or present physical instruments. Some humans presently sense these domains, most do not. Here, they have been labeled etheric, astral or emotional, mind, spirit, divine.

Subtle energies: All those energies existing in the universe beyond the four known to and accepted by present-day science. There may be more to be discovered at the physical level and there will certainly be many more to be discovered in the subtle domain levels beyond the physical band of consciousness.

Subtle radiations: The analogues to physical level radiations, which are presently classified as "mediators" and will now be reclassified as P-mediators. We will use the terms E-mediators, A-mediators, M-mediators, etc., to denote the radiations of the etheric, astral (emotional), mental, etc., types. In the text, the photon has been used to designate the P-mediator for the electromagnetic interaction; for the counterpart E-mediator due to the magnetoelectric interaction, we could provisionally use the term E-photon and, for the counterpart A-mediator, we could provisionally use the term A-photon.

Subtle substances: The analogues to physical substance at the various subtle domain levels. Until better words are chosen, we shall use a simple extension of the physical level building blocks, leptons and quarks, redefining the general building blocks as (P-leptons/P-quarks), (E-leptons/E-quarks), (A-leptons/A-quarks), (M-leptons/M-quarks), etc., for the physical, etheric, astral (emotional) and mind domains, respectively. In this text, two subtle particle discriminations beyond the foregoing have already been made; i.e., the magnon is the E-lepton counterpart to the electron, the most important P-lepton and the deltron is an A-substance counterpart of the P- and E-substances without finer discrimination at this point in time.

Superluminal state: A state wherein moieties can travel faster than EM light in physical vacuum.

Supersymmetry state: A state where both single electric charges and single magnetic charges coexist so one can anticipate the presence of electric currents inducing magnetic fields and magnetic currents inducing electric fields in such a medium.

Symmetry: An operation that one can perform (at least conceptually) on a system that leaves the system invariant.

Telepathy: The ability of a human to transmit to, or receive from another human, information via a seemingly direct brain to brain process.

Thermodynamic free energy: A quality of substance that defines its potential for doing work. This quality includes both energy and entropy contributions and their dependence on the thermodynamic intensive variables of temperature, pressure, concentration of chemical species, etc.

Tiller multidimensional RF: An eleven-dimensional RF that comprises this eight-dimensional duplex base-space imbedded in the three higher dimensional spaces of emotion (a 9-space), mind (a 10-space) and spirit (11-dimensions and above). This RF is the minimum needed to accommodate a qualitative and, one day, a quantitative internally self-consistent picture of nature (including all vertebrate life forms).

Tiller simulator/nodal network (NN) model: A nodal point is an interdimensional transducer/frequency converter device for consciousness/energy. Three unique, close-packed hexagonal arrays of nodal points are present in superlattice configurations in 10-space, the mind domain. The nodal point separation distance is $\sim 10^{-26}$ meters for M_{NN} and $\sim 10^{-16}$ meters for R_{NN}, which is for R-space and is rotated 90 degrees counterclockwise from M_{NN} and $\sim 10^{-6}$ meters for D_{NN}, which is for D-space and is rotated $90°$ counterclockwise from R_{NN}. A unique intention imprint from the domain of spirit forms a unique consciousness/energy pattern on M_{NN} which then radiates waves to diffract onto the R_{NN} for conversion in type and pattern to be, in turn, radiated onto the D_{NN} for new conversion in type and pattern to, in turn, influence physical reality in spacetime. Overall, this is a simulator type of device acting as a teaching tool for spirit to both experience and influence spacetime reality.

Wave-particle duality: Restatement of De Broglie's concept for quantum mechanics which limited its mathematical formulation to spacetime, thus, physical substance was required to have dual particle and wave behavior and, assuming this dichotomous behavior, all of QM's weird outcomes can be predicted.

Whole person: Our own three selves; (1) our personality self, (2) our soul self and (3) our high spirit or God self.

Zero point energy, zpe: Defined as the energies associated with all the modes of motion of physical atoms and molecules at absolute zero of temperature. This includes the EM photon spectrum in equilibrium with these changing modes.

Zero point field, zpf: Since the EM energy is always proportional to the square of the EM field, the zero point field is proportional to the **square root** of the zero point energy.

Index

ThermOrion (products), 155, 159, 162, 163, 165
thermostat, 186, 188, 189
Tiller reaction, 130
Tiller, Jean, 2-4, 6, 24, 26, 39, 52
time, 205
Tomanaga, 101
Toshiba computer (experiment), 164, 165
Transcendental Meditation (TM), 26

U(1) state, 91, 106, 107, 114, 120, 123, 124, 130, 144, 145, 148, 149, 142-155, 158, 160, 161, 169, 176, 180, 190, 193, 195, 204, 207, 220, 226, 248, 249, 251, 253, 255
U.K. site, 77-80, 197, 204
UED, 28, 36, 52, 140, 144, 196, 202, 250
unity, 64, 121, 129, 137, 153, 155, 158, 210, 219, 226,
unseen, 3, 4, 28, 39, 52, 53, 92, 108, 197, 208, 209, 230, 232, 237, 239
vacuum (physical), 37, 82, 104, 107-109, 113, 122, 124, 129-135, 137, 141, 170, 214, 219, 225, 227, 229, 238-240, 249, 250, 252-255, 260

Van de Walls, 148
vector (qualities), 117-122
Vedral, 198

water experiments, 28-30, 36, 37, 56-86, 104, 140-142, 155, 156, 158, 159, 199, 200, 203, 205, 206
water, 16, 28-30, 36, 37, 56, 61, 63, 68, 146-153, 155, 156, 158, 165, 170, 199, 205, 206
wave (form), 32, 33, 171, 172, 173, 176, 177, 183, 185-187, 190, 196, 198, 199, 207, 209, 214, 217, 219, 225, 227, 230, 249, 253, 255
wave/particle behavior, 9, 112, 113, 114, 116, 129
Werbos, Paul, 101
whole person, 7-9, 110, 210, 222, 224, 225, 228

Yan Xin (Qigong Master), 205, 206

Yang-Mills, 251
yoga, 14
Yogananda, Paramahamsa (S.R.F.), 25
Young's double slit, 116

zero point energy (zpe), 107, 108, 228, 229, 240
zero point field (zpf), 107, 108

Also by William A Tiller, Ph.D.

Science and Human Transformation:
Subtle Energies, Intentionality and Consciousness

Conscious Acts of Creation:
The Emergence of a New Physics

Order: 888-281-5170
International: 620-229-8979

www.tiller.org

100 GAUSS

S. POLE RAISES PH - 100 to 150 HRS
N. POLE LOWERS PH

ROLAND McCREADY HEARTMATH

S POLE STRENGTHENS MUSCLE GROUPS
N POLE WEAKENS - MUSCLE GROUPS

FISCHER SCIENTIFIC FOR WATER

DELTA pH .09
ERIC PEARL - SEDONA
WATER DOMES

$$Q_m = Q_D + \gamma_{eff} \, Q_R$$

PARA - MAG
ORTHO NON/MAG
DELTRONS $V_D \frac{Z}{Z} C$ FROM THE DOMAIN
OF EMOTION

SEC. NOAA. gov /SWN/
DIALS SHOULD BE IN THE GREEN   —
LOCAL SIDEREAL TIME 13:50
11:50
6:00 LEAST

TYCHO. USNO. NAVY. mil /SIDEREAL. HTML